OUT OF BOUNDS

Ted Russel

MINERVA PRESS
ATLANTA LONDON SYDNEY

OUT OF BOUNDS

ISBN 0 75410 575 X

First Published 1999 by
MINERVA PRESS
315–317 Regent Street
London W1R 7YB

Printed in Great Britain for Minerva Press

OUT OF BOUNDS

182 Wing
12 WOU (Wireless Observational Unit)
Chittagong
Bengal

Chittagong

December, 1943

We were a small unit of RAF personnel, consisting mainly of fitters (eng.) and wireless (mech.) – hence the name WOU.

Our transport section consisted of one Bedford Q4 three ton truck and three jeeps, all tucked away under the cover of mango trees and corrugated sheets, in an area resembling a smallholding.

Apart from our small unit, sections of the army making this place their base included Gurkhas, a JAT regiment, the Indian Pioneer Corps, and many others, all building up supplies in readiness for the three hundred mile push towards Lushai and farther on to Imphal. The first test of endurance would be negotiating the fast-flowing strength of the Karnaphuli river.

There were rumours of the Japs infiltrating through the northern stretch of the Assam–Burmese border towards Imphal. These were making the troops very jittery, and we were all wondering where our destination was and when we were due to start.

We had a small NAAFI there, which provided facilities for troops to get together in sport and recreation.

One morning, while passing the CO's office, I noticed a note displayed asking for two volunteers to travel up to the Assam–Burmese border to maintain existing observation posts, erect them where needed, and employ native labour necessary to achieve this.

All necessary equipment would be supplied, including a transmitter and portable 'jenny', together with tools and fuel. These would be securely packed into crates, and we would have enough for our everyday needs to last till we reached a trading post, where we'd restock and push farther on.

I immediately contacted the CO, to say that once a suitable wireless technician was found, I would be glad to be given the chance to take up the challenge.

He explained it would be a hazardous journey. He thanked me for coming forward and said, 'Now we must wait while I seek out another volunteer. The quicker we find one the better, as there is news of the Japs infiltrating down towards Imphal, the capital of Manipur State.'

It was on the following day, during conversation in the NAAFI, that the name of a wireless technician who would be just the chap came up.

I very soon found him out. He was about my height, 5' 10", was slightly built, with quite an intelligent face, and seemed just the right man.

He had passed all the technicians' courses, so he would be well qualified to take on the job. His name was Douglas Coombe, he was married, and his home was on the Isle of Wight.

Our next step was to report to the CO to await instructions and movement orders. The following morning, we had quite a long session with the CO, during which we were given a graphic picture of the hazardous country in front of us, together with details of the primitive people there – some were still practising headhunting!

The next step for us was to report to the medical section for inoculations against malaria and dysentery. After these we would have to take a day's rest. During this time, crates of provisions and equipment were being prepared ready to be taken down to the river's edge. Here they would be guarded till the arrival of the riverboat.

By now we were both feeling rough; our arms were swollen and aching, and we needed to take a day off, to be fit enough to start in the morning.

We were to be ready to board the boat by twelve noon. We had spent a restless night, and were both feeling weak, but as we moved about the stiffness eased. At the mess, a few colleagues gathered to wish us well, after giving us a huge breakfast that was big enough to last the day.

A jeep was waiting to take us down to the water's edge, and after putting our luggage on board, we climbed into the stern of the boat, waving as we pulled away.

Arriving at our departure spot, we discovered all our gear stacked and ready for loading. It was guarded by a sepoy, who seemed to be very pleased at our arrival.

It must have been an hour later when at last the jug-jug of a diesel could be heard rounding the bend coming towards us, escorted by numerous small fishing craft.

We had to chuckle at our first sighting; it looked the typical riverboat, with the wheelhouse in the centre, and black smoke pouring from the funnel, just clearing the upper deck.

The main deck was packed with natives, all jabbering away to their nearest companions. They were all carrying loads of merchandise and at the same time looking for a space to squat; one lucky native was in the process of making room for his Primus stove, and was mixing dough for some chapattis and rice.

The boat itself was about thirty feet in length and about twelve feet wide at the centre. The fore and after ends were rounded.

As it made anchor in the middle of the river, a figure in white could be seen waving. This had to be the skipper, so now we began to transfer our kit over. Natives were soon busy hauling our crates on to flat-bottomed boats. Then we were poled across to the riverboat, where all the crates were lifted aboard.

Immediately, tarpaulin sheets were found to cover them over, away from the prying eyes of all on board. We were the centre of attention as we were helped on to the boat.

Making our way towards the wheelhouse, by stepping over and squeezing between natives, we became aware of a few shady characters. Jap spies were everywhere. We'd have to get the captain to check.

We had to climb up a short ladder to reach the top deck, to be greeted by the 'captain' – I use that term, but to look at him, he seemed a proper grease boy, with his white jacket and trousers covered in smears of oil. His cap did show the Royal Navy badge, but I expect it was obtained illegally.

Making us both most welcome, he indicated two wicker chairs he had put out for our use, explaining that the boat would be packed until passengers disembarked at their villages en route up the river.

He seemed to go out of his way to please, making tea for us, and saying we'd start soon. In the meantime, a few natives were still coming aboard, trying to find spaces in which to sit down. This drew shouts of abuse from those already seated, who had laid out their pots and cooking utensils ready to prepare meals.

During conversation with the skipper, I inadvertently called him 'Charlie', at which he seemed highly amused, showing his appreciation by displaying a set of broken and discoloured teeth.

By this time, the decks were packed. Most of the travellers had their Primuses lit and were in the process of mixing the dough for making chapattis and rice. During this process the air was filled with the babble of screeching natives, all trying to put their point over.

There were a few suspect characters I decided to keep an eye on; they looked a little shifty and the Japs had informers everywhere. They'd pass on any intelligence that would bring in a few rupees; they would even sell their own mothers.

It was about ten when we finally moved off, the jetty receding as the black smoke from the funnel obscured the final sighting of our departure point. Now we had to take things day by day as the little riverboat chugged along, keeping to the centre of the river, making use of the deepest part.

As we held the middle of the river, I noticed the banks on either side seemed much closer, the ground covered by trees and shrubs of all colours, while exotic birds made their presence known by their full song.

We seemed to be settling into a lazy cruise, with the engine chugging away and all aboard busy making conversation or cooking a meal, when suddenly a scraping sound was heard below, and it was evident that we had run aground.

Charlie had hoped to miss this high point on the river bed, but as it was we had to wait for the water to rise before making an attempt to move the boat manually.

In the meantime cha (tea) was brewed, together with a pot full of rice, after which we lazed for a while, waiting for the water to rise.

At 4.30 we were all waist-deep in the water, clutching whatever protruding ledge there was, in our attempt to free the boat by rocking it from side to side.

Slowly and surely, it began to move. There were shouts of joy from everyone as it moved off the ridge and we all clambered back on to the deck.

The whole exercise had certainly brought all the families together; they were now jabbering away, laughing at the parts they had played.

Now that we were slowly moving again, it became evident that the boat was going against a much stronger current. The water was now clearer, and the river bed could be seen, covered with large boulders. Some looked very dangerous as the little boat steered by. Charlie managed to avoid them.

As we pushed along at a much slower pace, our main job now was to look for a suitable clearing on the river bank.

It was about six when a village was sighted far off, perched high up on the bank. Out of the bamboo huts, natives with children came running, and went down to the water's edge to await our arrival.

We sighted a small inlet offering just enough room and shelter, and we made the boat secure. By this time, dusk was falling so we sent the passengers off to prepare a camp and gather wood to make a fire in its centre.

By this time a crowd had gathered. Charlie had spoken to one of the headmen and was told the name of the village, Chowlong, and that the people would help us in any way if asked.

We had arranged that Doug and I would sleep on the boat, together with Charlie and one of the boat crew, while some of the passengers chose to make camp with the villagers on shore.

By now a large fire was crackling away, with big pots of rice and two cockerels hung over it on tripods. In the meantime, the incessant high chatter was enough to keep away any inquisitive inhabitant of the jungle.

Our meal was served up on a large leaf; so there we were, squatting around a huge fire, picking up the tasty portions of chicken and washing them down with mugs of the local rice beer or coffee.

The air was filled with buzzing mosquitoes – we were continually swatting the blasted pests. After our meal, as the darkness fell, we settled down to sleep, covering ourselves over with nets.

With the sound of weird cries from all the inhabitants of the jungle, it became impossible to sleep. As we lay there, the guttural croaking of bullfrogs seemed to be all around us.

I must have dozed off, for I felt my shoulder being shaken, and a voice was saying, 'Cha, Sahib!' I beheld the cheerful face of one of the natives holding a large mug of cha. Doug had woken up by now, and when I told him his snoring had kept me awake all night, he promised to lie on his side.

We woke up to a chorus of all the animals and birds of the jungle – shrill cries and strange sounds filled the early dawn, while high up in the trees the monkey troupes were chasing each other from bough to bough and making a hell of a din. In the meantime Doug told me he'd had a fair night and felt ready for the challenge ahead. He asked me where we were meant to wash.

'Over the bloody side,' I said. So over the side we slipped, into cold water; which, after the first shock, felt very refreshing.

By this time the boat wallahs had arrived and were busy making up the fire to prepare our breakfast of fried eggs – I thought we'd give rice a rest for one day. After eating these washed down with coffee to soften our hard ration biscuits, we both felt fit for the day. We began to make ready to battle against the fast-flowing Karnaphuli, which was by now building up to a challenge.

The boat wallahs had by this time got all provisions aboard, and it was about nine o'clock when we finally started. Both chaps stood on top with their long poles, one at the front and the other at the rear, guiding the *kisti* (as illustrated in my forces' news cuttings) between the dangerous boulders which could be seen through the clear water.

Meanwhile we made ourselves as comfortable as possible on mats of woven bamboo, peering ahead and marvelling at the way these blokes managed to guide us. We were slowly making progress against the strong current and I noticed the banks either side were getting closer, which meant the force of the water was stronger; but the chaps doing all the work were singing away as they dug the poles deep into the bed of the river.

As we slowly battled our way against the force of the river, I was amazed at the deep foliage rising to about thirty feet on either side of the river and filled with schools of monkeys. It echoed with the cries of fabulously coloured birds of all kinds. There were parrots everywhere, screeching from bough to bough, making a hell of a din, while in the background one could hear the grunts and shrill cries of larger animals.

'What the hell are we in for?' I asked Doug.

It would take us two days to reach Rangamati, and as it was midday I called out to the boat wallahs to look out for a likely spot on the bank to have a rest and brew tea.

After much grunting and pushing, we finally steered over to a clearing when we could get out of the *kisti* and stretch our legs, while the boat chaps scouted round for firewood. Soon they had a pot full of rice on the boil, and a little later we were all on our haunches scooping up the rice, and downing it with mugs of coffee.

We rested for about an hour, then cleared up the signs of our camp by dragging branches along the sand; you never know who's about.

Back on the *kisti* we had another three hours or so of battling against stronger currents before we could find another clearing to put in for the night.

There were much larger boulders to negotiate, with the chaps running up and down on the roof and using all their skill to find suitable places to propel the *kisti* clear. Just as dusk began to close in, we rounded a sharp bend and we were lucky to find a long clearing ahead: an ideal place to kip down for the night. It wasn't so overcrowded by the jungle as the last stop, and there was more room to bed down and move around.

We looked round for wood and soon we had a welcome fire ablaze, throwing light over a wide circle in which we prepared our sleeping spaces. Our boat handlers were busy cooking the meal, all the while laughing and jabbering away; so far, I believe they were enjoying the whole venture.

The meal they prepared was a chicken curry. While it amazed me how it was prepared in the time, as I didn't see the chicken being plucked, it was the best meal we'd had so far. With mugs of the local rice beer, we both felt full up and sat around making signs and agreeing with all the toothless grins of our fellow-travellers.

Again it was nearly midnight, and time to turn in and try to rest, while our friends took turns keeping the fire going, to deter any wildlife lurking around. In spite of all the queer noises, which we were getting used to by now, and having to cope with the hard ground, we did manage to get to doze off now and again; though my thoughts were always of home and how my wife was coping. As usual, I felt sure she was quite capable of meeting the conditions prevailing at the time. We would have to wait till we reached a village for news of any kind, and we hoped all was well in the meantime.

We both seemed to have had a more restful night; perhaps we were getting more used to roughing it. If only we could manage to keep away from mosquitoes and heat rash!

Dawn was breaking, with a chorus of jungle wildlife filling the air, heralding another day. I rolled out of my makeshift bed to be handed a nice mug of tea with the cheerful greeting, 'Cha, Sahib,' and the usual toothless grin. Doug had woken before me and had already had a wash down at the river's edge, so down I went to freshen myself up, and found the water bitingly cold.

After we'd had coffee and biscuits, our provisions were loaded back in the *kisti*. We then cleared up the camp with the usual procedure, disguising our traces so as to leave the place as near as possible as it was when we found it.

Down the bank we scrambled to climb into the *kisti* and arrange our living quarters until we reached Rangamati. This we hoped to make by nightfall.

Amid curses and laughter, the boat wallahs dug their poles deep into the river and we were off, to battle against the strong swirling currents and avoid the boulders once more.

The water was now much shallower and very clear, with a bed composed of different coloured pebbles, making it very bright. The vegetation on either side was getting much denser, with schools of monkeys following us all the time, chattering and making a hell of a din.

Hoping to reach Rangamati by dusk, we steadily made our way upriver, marvelling at all the different colours of the dense undergrowth. All the while we were on the lookout for hostile natives who might take a suspicious view of us, but the boat chaps told us so far we were all right. We both hoped so.

We pulled into the bank for a rest and made coffee to wash down our ration biscuits (which were like dogs'). We stopped for only about an hour before pushing on, with about a mile left to cover.

As we rounded a bend, our destination came in sight. High above the steep bank we could see the bamboo bashas, or huts, and the population beginning to gather to gaze down and to wonder who we were. Making the *kisti* safe, one of our boat wallahs climbed up to make our presence known. At this they started to wave, and we knew we were amongst friends.

We left one of the boat chaps to look after the *kisti*. Doug and I climbed up the bank to meet the people and to see the chief to explain what we wanted, with the help of a boat wallah as interpreter. We were led to a large hut in the centre of the village, built entirely of bamboo and standing on a platform four feet off the ground, supported by numerous tree trunks. A bamboo fence made the platform safe and stopped people falling off.

A ladder at the main entrance led to an open doorway, and as we climbed up we were met by the chief – a huge fellow standing about six feet. He had bamboo ornaments stuck through his nose and ears, and long black plaited hair high on his head. Round his arms and legs were bangles of bone or ivory, and the long traditional coloured skirt gave him a look of authority.

He amazed us both when he said, 'Welcome!' He explained to us that his village was frequently used as a resting place for British government officials on tours of inspection of the Lushai Hills.

Furthermore, there was a special bungalow built on the outskirts for the use of these personnel, and while his women were preparing food, he would despatch men to prepare and clean it out; he hoped it would be to our satisfaction.

In the meantime, two women were bringing in bowls of rice and portions of curried chicken, while our host offered us mugs of the local rice beer. After a couple of these we both felt quite amicable.

Squatting down, I gazed around the interior; as there were no windows, it was difficult to penetrate the gloom and see any objects at all. But then – horror of horrors – I saw a few shrunken heads resting on ledges a few feet apart. After all, the people had been headhunters until a few years ago; so we both had to get accustomed to these primitive displays.

We stayed with the chief for about an hour, trying to make conversation by waving our hands and arms about, and with his smattering of English I think we managed very well.

We both seemed to get on well with the chief, so it was about seven when we thanked him for his hospitality and said we'd have to find our way to the dāk bungalow. At this, he said one of his men would go along with us as a guide.

Following a narrow path out of the village, we picked our way through high foliage, and as the dusk was falling fast it became more difficult to keep to the path.

At last we could see lights ahead and soon came to a large grass clearing at the end of which stood the dāk bungalow. It was a large bamboo building on stout four-foot tree trunks, keeping it well away from any marauding jungle inhabitants who wanted to take a look inside. A wide ladder led up to a walkway round the entire bungalow, protected by a fence of woven bamboo.

We were met inside by one of the cleaners and shown around. We found the accommodation quite roomy, consisting of two bedrooms, a sitting room overlooking miles of hills and the forest far below, and the kitchen in a lean-to built at the rear. In the sitting room was a table and two wicker chairs, which both looked as if they were put there during Victorian times.

One of the chief's men said he would do the cooking and cleaning, if he got permission, which I told him to go and ask for. Doug and I unpacked our tea chests and found spaces along the walls against which to arrange them all.

By the time we had unpacked, our man returned to say the chief had agreed, and would we like a curry? So that was settled.

We found some whisky, two earthenware mugs from the kitchen and a little *pani* (water). We then sat down to gather our strength with two large mugs – full, of course. We found there were plenty of provisions: tins of bully beef, milk, sugar, beans, large tins of hard ration biscuits, tins of ham, tea and coffee powder, flour and salt.

There were plenty of ration cigarettes, enough to last quite a while, though the taste was bloody awful. I supposed we'd have to get used to them, but then I'd been told there were tobacco plants growing wild farther up in the Lushai Hills.

We both decided that as this was an ideal spot to have a rest and build up a little energy for our future battle against the fast-flowing river, with its dangerous falls and hazardous boulders to negotiate. We were just taking a well-earned rest. The bobijee (our man who cooked and looked after us) woke us up at dawn with mugs of cha and the usual toothless grin. He then scurried off to prepare breakfast. I noticed the room was full of mosquitoes, and was glad that I'd put my net up last night or I would have been covered in bites.

I daubed my body with insect cream, after washing outside in cold water. Later, I was joined by Doug. We both sat on the verandah to have our breakfast of eggs and beans, enjoying the marvellous panorama of the hills and valleys of the forests far below us, and wondering if there were any Japs down there.

We decided to stop there for two days, which would give us time to check our provisions and transmission gear.

On checking our stores it was apparent that a bag of flour was missing. Where the hell it was pinched was difficult to determine, so in future I'd have to keep a closer check.

Of course, nobody knew where it went; they all gave us the innocent look. So in future tighter checks would have to be made as we proceeded.

During our stay there I made two or three trips down to the village and found the inhabitants quite friendly, grinning and laughing at all and sundry.

They had a small bazaar, mostly of produce from the jungle: yams, oranges, edible roots, bananas, and all kinds of fruit that grew there in abundance.

All the women wore the traditional skirt which they wove themselves, called a *poen*. It was made from cotton, grown and picked to form lengths of hard-wearing cloth. When the housework was done, the women could be seen sitting on the ground weaving skeins in long lengths from makeshift bamboo frames, deftly creating a very durable cloth.

At the same time, *chikos* (children) ran about playing games and making a hell of a shrieking and laughter, which, I suppose, is what makes village life.

Dogs were everywhere, looking thin and scrounging for food, while the fur on their backs bore all the signs of disease.

I saw the chief at his basha, to tell him we would be moving on in the following day; I think he understood, as he did know a few English words, taught to him by previous visitors.

I forgot to mention that while exploring the rooms of our bungalow, I found a tattered and worn visitors' book which contained some very interesting addresses – those of Government and civilian officials passing through on inspection.

After a meal of rice and bully beef, the rest of the day was spent in getting all the gear and provisions ready to load on to the *kisti* in the morning.

One of the boat wallahs arrived to inform us that he had obtained another good *kisti* from a village nearby, and would I give him a chit for the owner to present to the DC for payment? So that was fixed up.

We had a final check in and around the bungalow before dusk, then we sat out on the verandah to a chicken and curried rice supper, gazing down at a panorama of all the colours of the jungle stretching far beyond our vision.

We stayed outside till midnight, before having to retreat to our rooms to escape the hordes of mosquitoes. We were to set off in the morning.

I had a fairly good night; I heard swarms of mosquitoes in the room, but hardly any managed to penetrate the fine mesh of the net.

I was awakened at dawn by the cheerful, 'Cha, Sahib,' and the toothless grin of our temporary bobijee. He was holding a large earthenware bowl of hot cha, and telling me that our stores and equipment were being loaded into the *kisti*, under the supervision of Doug. Doug had the matter well in hand, and by the time of my arrival down at the mooring, the job was nearly complete.

By ten o'clock we were ready to push off, having said goodbye to the chief and his women and all the villagers, hoping to see them all on our return journey. The river was flowing much faster and stronger. It would take all the skill of the two boat wallahs to keep the *kisti* clear of the huge boulders that protruded out of the river bed. One chap had the job of propelling the *kisti* against the strong current by means of a long pole. The steering was done by the other chap sitting at the rear using a rather primitive looking rudder.

Before setting off, Doug and I arranged the interior to give enough space amongst the tea chests and equipment to allow our two wicker chairs to be placed, giving us as much room as possible.

By about ten, the *kisti* had been manoeuvred to the centre of the river, and we began our seven hour journey towards a village called Barkal, amidst the chattering and laughter of the two boat wallahs and their curses at some of the difficult twists and bends in the river.

After two hours we decided to pull into a suitable space to have a brew-up and rest and stretch our legs. By this time it was getting very humid, and the sweat began to roll off us, causing a few rashes which in turn caused horrible itching. Since we were only wearing shorts, our first job on landing would be to search among the kitbags for our antidote cream.

At last we sighted a likely spot, set back in the shade of overhanging foliage; we hoped all the insects had taken the day off.

The boat wallahs lost no time in collecting firewood and soon a pot of rice was boiling, together with chicken joints, to make a nice curry. I suggested to Doug that we ought to open a tin of bully, but, as he pointed out, it was against their religion to eat the stuff. So as we had several 7 lb tins in our stores, we'd have to eat all the damned stuff ourselves.

We cleared enough of the undergrowth for our sleeping space, and while one of the boat chaps kept the fire blazing away, we covered ourselves with mosquito nets to get what sleep we could. I didn't get much rest – the continuous noise of all the jungle creatures made it impossible to drop off to sleep. I joined the chap by the fireside just after midnight. I believe he was glad of my company, for in spite of our language problem, we communicated in signs, by waving our arms and using a smattering of Urdu. He made coffee and two small chapattis as dawn was seen breaking through the thick foliage. Soon it would be time for Doug and the other boat chap to wake up and get ready to move on towards Barkal.

We had a snack of rice and ration biscuits washed down with hot coffee, and proceeded to go through the usual drill of obliterating all signs of an overnight camp. This we did by dragging branches over the ground and laying dead wood all around, hoping it would allay the suspicions of anybody who was nosy.

It was about ten when we were finally loaded and pushed off for Barkal, hoping to reach there before dusk. The boat wallahs were doing a marvellous job keeping the *kisti* clear of all the obstacles, while Doug and I gazed into the jungle, hearing all the different species calling out in different cries and making a hell of a din. I did notice a few wildfowl flying around and pointed them out to the tiller chap, telling him to steer to the bank in the hope of catching one or two for future meals.

After making the *kisti* safe, and leaving the steersman to enjoy a rest, Doug and I, together with the other boat wallah, pushed our way through the thick undergrowth, looking for stout bamboo branches to make into spears.

Having obtained three, we trimmed and made them serviceable; now all we had to do was wait for the birds to return.

We spaced ourselves about four yards apart and waited. It must have been after about ten minutes when we heard the loud fluttering and squawking of the birds coming towards us. Soon the magnificent birds were only a few feet away. We hurled our spears with all our strength – and lo and behold, two were downed, and quickly put out of their misery.

They were very large birds, much larger than our domestic fowls at home, so I presumed they had more meat.

The marvellous colours of the feathers would be much sought after in the markets. Returning back to the *kisti*, we decided to keep them till we reached Barkal and share them with the natives, hoping it would make us many friends. We had a rest for about an hour, and made coffee to go with a snack of bully beef and biscuits. We finally pushed off to the middle of the river, hoping to reach our next stop by dusk. On either side of the river the forest grew much more dense with packs of small monkeys shrieking as they followed each other, swinging from branch to branch.

It was about four when, on rounding a bend, we were suddenly in the midst of a mixed sex bathing party.

On seeing us, they all immediately vanished into the undergrowth, racing up the bank to hide amongst the village bashas, which were clustered around the brow of a bank, high above the river. By the time we had secured the *kisti*, a reception party had assembled and was coming down the bank to meet us. Leading the party was a huge native wearing an array of bamboo ornaments stuck through his nose and ears, with the usual bangles on his legs and arms.

It was obvious they were used to parties of the military passing by to hill stations farther up, for the leader came forward with outstretched hand to say, 'Welcome, Sahib,' and gave orders to some of his people to carry all our gear up the bank to where we were to stay.

We were quite surprised to be shown a smaller dāk bungalow set in a small clearing on the outskirts of the village with marvellous views of the range of hills and dense jungle far below. While we were unpacking our kit, the village drums could be heard, droning out a monotonous beat. On enquiring, we were told that our arrival at this village was being sent by this bush telegraph to the next – a distance of approximately ten miles. I had sent the two cockerels to be prepared for a get-together feast for that night, and was told a large fire was being built in the centre which would create a big gathering of people from the small settlements around. By dusk the village was full of natives of all types, including of proud old warriors squatting around the centre, smoking their hubble-bubble pipes and exchanging tales of the past.

By the time the fire was at its height, the younger warriors had consumed quite a quantity of the local rice beer, which I believe was named *Zophan* or a similar word. Anyway, it was very potent, for after drinking a couple of mugs I had joined the dancers, jumping about and flinging my arms around as they were doing – much to their delight!

By midnight all the food had gone, huge bowls of curry had been consumed, and most of the villagers from around had gone home, so Doug and I decided to find our way to the dāk bungalow. The chief insisted on instructing two natives to look after us, in case of tipsy revellers being about. After ten minutes of pushing our way through the undergrowth, we saw the lights from the bungalow, and our faithful guides waved goodbye to return to the village.

Our temporary bobijee was waiting up to see if there was anything else to do, but after being thanked for staying up, he retired to his space at the end of the verandah to settle down amongst his belongings.

Doug and I poured out a stiff whisky each and spent another hour making plans for an early start on our final push up the river to a trading post at Demagri.

I forgot to put the mosquito net up, and found quite a few bites on my shoulders and arms when I woke up at dawn. I immediately found the cream and rubbed it well in, hoping it would stop the swelling and itching. I went into Doug's room to find that he, of course, had remembered to use his net, and was sleeping peacefully.

The bobijee came in with coffee, waking Doug up, so it was a good moment to tell him of our plan to move up the river toward Demagri, and would he make the *kisti* ready for loading again.

While Doug collected the equipment and crated up the food, I thought I'd better go down to the village to make our farewells to the chief and his family.

On arrival at his basha, I found I was just in time, for he and three other tall warriors were all kitted out for a day's hunting, and he was pleased that I had thought of informing him before slipping off. He gave me a couple of bottles of the local beer, shook hands, and said he hoped we would meet again on my return down the river. I walked through the village on my way back and found mainly women there, sitting outside working away at their crude looms, making cloth dyed different colours. The cloth was woven very close to make into *poens*, which they wore tucked in at the waist, reaching down to their feet.

There were hardly any men around; I suppose they were down in the jungle hunting. As I made my way through the village taking note of all the friendly smiles and nods from the women and children, I envied them for their quiet way of life. What made me question our high pressured lives was the tranquillity of these people, who might be rather crude in their basic lifestyle and medicines, but at least they were free of all the bureaucracy we had to contend with.

By the time I had arrived back at the dāk bungalow, a lot of the villagers were standing around watching as our stores and tea chests were being put outside ready to be taken down to the *kisti*.

I made signs for four tough-looking natives to carry our equipment down to be loaded, and soon all was safely stored inside the *kisti*. Doug stayed on guard while I had a final check through the bungalow. We waved a final farewell to the villagers before clambering down to the *kisti*. Then, with the boat wallahs pushing against the bank to get us out to midstream, we were on our final battle against the fast-flowing Karnaphuli.

It would take more than a day to reach Demagri for our last lap. We had been told there were dangerous rapids to negotiate ahead, and to avoid them we would have to shove and hump the *kisti* high up over the boulders above the rapids. To lighten the load, it would mean making several journeys carrying all the stores and equipment to higher ground. Then we'd have to put our shoulders to the *kisti* and heave it over the boulders ourselves.

It was early afternoon when we finally steered the *kisti* to the centre of the river with the boat chaps having to use all their strength and skill to push against the strong current.

As we moved farther into the interior, the river became much narrower. This, because of the overhanging jungle foliage, diminished what daylight there was left, so our next problem was to find a clearing to put into for the night. Dusk was falling fast when we sighted a small section of the bank that was not too overgrown. This would have to do for the night.

While our boat wallahs were making the *kisti* safe, Doug and I had to move a couple of tea chests to make room to put blankets down for our sleeping quarters. The boat wallahs had collected wood and soon had a roaring fire blazing away, with a pot of rice being boiled up. I found a tin of bully; that would be our meal. As for the natives, I think it's against their religion to eat bully beef – something about the sacred cow, or that sort of thing.

Our friends sat hunched up near the fire, jabbering away, while Doug and I dug into our bully and rice. The air was filled with all the cries of the various creatures of the jungle, and of course hordes of mosquitoes swarmed in the night air. We spent most of our time swatting the blasted pests, leaving bloodstained swellings on exposed areas of our bodies.

By the time we were ready to turn in for the night, I was itching and scratching and found it impossible to sleep. I spent the night smoking heavily, hoping the smoke would clear the air. It did to a certain extent, for I dozed off now and again before the golden dawn shone through the overhanging foliage. Then the boat wallahs began stirring, and started to jabber while building up the fire to boil water for our morning cha.

We had the usual rice and biscuits as a hasty meal before clearing the camp of all traces of our stay, leaving broken branches scattered about as usual. When we finally got away in the *kisti* and looked back, we saw it was a job well done.

I had planned to reach Demagri by dusk, but I realised now that it would be quite a battle, as the force of the current of the rapids was taking all the strength and skill of the chaps on the roof. They had to use their long poles to find suitable places between the boulders on the river bed to propel the *kisti* forward, which at this stage was most difficult as the boat was being swept at all angles across the width of the strong current.

As we slowly zig-zagged forward, we could hear in front of us the sounds of a huge waterfall, and wondered how far ahead it would be, and how to negotiate it. I made signs to the chap at the stern to ask how far it was. At this he held up two fingers meaning, two hours. Steadily we pushed forward, and I noticed the foliage on either side getting much denser, with chattering monkeys swarming amongst the branches overhead.

Rounding a bend, we could see the waterfall ahead, and decided to get as near as possible to look for a clearing. It would be impossible to approach it head-on, as it was at least four foot high. Thankfully, to the left we could see a well-worn track leading into the undergrowth, obviously made by travellers bypassing the rapids. By this time, dusk was beginning to fall, and once we had secured the *kisti* I realised we'd have to move fast to carry all the stores and equipment over to the other side.

I must say the boat wallahs really put their backs into the work. It took four journeys to move all the loads to the other side.

Now came the main job – heaving and lugging the *kisti* up the bank and dragging it over the uneven track, a distance of about five hundred yards. Heaving and cursing, it took about three hours, and by this time daylight had gone; but as luck would have it, the sky was cloudless and gave us enough light to see our way.

The river bank wasn't that steep, but the torrent of water rushing to the fall looked very dangerous. It would take all our strength to hold it while we secured landing rope to a suitable bamboo.

On finding a stout bamboo trunk, I wound the rope round it while Doug and the boat wallahs lowered the *kisti* gently into the torrent.

Before loading all the kit, I decided to have a fire built, and soon a huge blaze gave us further light, and succeeded in keeping any nosy animals away. We were all exhausted on finishing the loading, and I was very grateful to one of the boat chaps for making coffee. With the *kisti* securely held, Doug and I slept by the fire while the boat wallahs took turns to keep guard.

I couldn't sleep – the cries of all the jungle creatures made sleep out of the question; I must have dozed off now and again, for soon I felt my shoulder being shaken gently and heard the voice of the guard saying, 'Cha, Sahib.' He was offering me a rather stained mug of tea.

The sun was just beginning to rise, showing through the bamboo, and looking to where Doug was lying I could see he was beginning to stir.

He hadn't got much sleep, and we agreed to make up for it later, and we both made preparations to break camp. The boat wallahs had rice and coffee ready, so we made a hasty breakfast before returning the campsite to its original state, using branches to drag over any tell-tale marks of our stay.

After checking around, we made our way down to the *kisti*, only to find it had moved away from the bank. It now was about four feet adrift, the securing rope having slipped down the trunk of the bamboo.

The only way to reach it was to wade across, and as the water was only about three feet deep, it seemed quite straightforward; but we hadn't reckoned with the rate and weight of the fast-flowing river. The two boat wallahs slid down into the water first, holding small loads of provisions on their heads, while Doug and I watched their progress. As the bed of the river consisted of boulders and pebbles, they had evident difficulty keeping upright, but at last they made it.

Now it was our turn to wade, but not before they had hauled on the rope to move the boat nearer to the bank.

As we slid into the river, all the loose rupees in my pockets tumbled into the water. I saw them slowly sinking out of sight, and hadn't the faintest idea how much there was; I would have to forget the incident, as it wasn't much money.

The water came up to my waist, and it took all my strength to stay upright. The force of the current made the short wade to the *kisti* quite an ordeal, and I felt great relief on reaching the boat to be hauled aboard by Doug and the boat chaps.

All was now ready for our last mile or so on the river, for after Demagri, the rest of our journey would be foot-slogging through the jungle. We were heading for our base at a village called Mullianphui, where there was an observer post manned by the two WOU personnel we were to relieve.

For an hour or so we made steady progress, and on sighting a clearing I told the boat wallah to pull in. As we were very near Demagri, I thought it would be a good idea to have coffee and make ourselves presentable.

Demagri

We sighted Demagri ahead. I could see the bamboo bashas built on high stilts in clusters in open areas cleared of forest, so I presumed the supply depot must be just above the river level. On approaching the depot, we came to a wide opening to our right on the river, and could see that a twelve-foot channel had been cut to allow small craft access to go into the overhanging jungle.

The boat wallahs shouted with joy, and began to call out loudly, to be greeted by a number of natives waving at us from high up on the bank. I noticed a large basha and indicated that I wanted the *kisti* brought near enough to it for us to get ashore.

As the *kisti* was being tied up, a white man appeared at the doorway of the basha, waving and beckoning us up.

Doug was the first to meet him, while I told the boat chaps to wait and guard our load, during which time they could make coffee and rice. Climbing up the bank, I was met by a chap of about my height dressed in crumpled, not very clean white dungarees. He had a round face, was slightly bald, and looked as if he liked his wallop; but then, living in that godforsaken hole would be enough to drive anyone to it.

He introduced himself as Oliver, and enquired what the devil we were doing in this out of the way hole, and asked us to come inside to have a drink and a bite to eat. To reach his basha we had to climb up a rickety bamboo ladder leading to a wide verandah with a trellis about four feet high. As we walked along the floor it sagged alarmingly, but apparently it was quite strong, as it had taken the weight of many people over the years. Oliver led the way as we entered, and indicated two bamboo chairs for us. He called out in Lushai, and a tall native girl came in dressed in a coloured blouse and *poen*. She smiled and started to prepare a meal.

We explained our mission and enquired how far away the village of Mullianphui would be. He said it would take us about three days, as the track, which wound round steep hillsides, was a test of one's ability to keep a good foothold, especially in the rainy season. As the monsoons were due about then we hoped to reach our destination before them. During our meal of curried chicken and rice, Oliver said he would show us the way through the store sheds and village to where the government dāk was situated. He told us he had sent a trustworthy bobijee to check and clean it up, and hoped by the time we arrived there that all the cobwebs would have disappeared.

While we were having the meal, he told us he had arranged for natives to transfer all our gear and provisions up to the dāk bungalow, and hoped by the time we had sorted it all out we'd find nothing had gone astray. During our conversation, he asked us to let him know how many porters we would require, so that he could muster them up ready for us when we resumed our journey. He also told us about two liaison officers resident there, who acted for and gave help to official parties passing through on their way up to the Lushai and Chin Hills. We would be meeting them in the morning.

By the time we had staggered up to the dāk bungalow at about two o'clock it was a great relief to find our beds made up ready for the night, with mosquito nets erected.

I had spells of intermittent sleep; the air was close and humid, while the cries of night-time marauders filled the air around me.

I awoke at dawn with the early sun throwing shafts of light through the bamboo walls. I could hear chatter and laughter from the kitchen and presumed the bobijee had female company. He came into the room, showing a wide grin, and put a mug of coffee by my side with the usual '*Tekai*, [All right] Sahib?' I don't think he spoke much English, but he seemed quite efficient.

Doug came into the room to have a chat and plan our day. I said we'd see. We could mooch around and meet some people, in particular the two liaison officers.

The bobijee had prepared fried eggs, and set them out on a table on the verandah. It was during the meal that two army officers came round to introduce themselves as Captain Scott and Captain Robertson. They wanted no bullshit, and with them, as with us, shorts and loose shirts were the order of the day.

They were most interested in our mission and promised all the help we required. They told us that the track through the jungle was a bit dodgy and some of the villagers were headhunters and very primitive, to which I said, 'Thank you very much!' They promised to contact Oliver and ask him to be careful to pick a trustworthy porter corps. I reckoned we would want nine stout chaps, but in any case we'd have a few days rest there, for it would take time to sort out what supplies were needed. In any case, a full list would have to be compiled.

Both officers stayed to have coffee and chat about home, and asked how people were coping. 'We seem so isolated up here, but I suppose this job has to be done,' they said. I believe they were glad to meet any white chaps, for we were invited to have an evening meal with them, which we gladly accepted. They asked us to be ready about six, when an orderly would arrive to show us the way down to their quarters.

By the time the orderly arrived, we had managed to dig out clean shirts and trousers and were waiting, so off we went down the hill led by the chattering Pathan orderly. On arrival at the depot we were shown to a bamboo hut apart from the main huts, with a porch entrance through which a dim light could be seen.

On entering, we were met by Captain Scott and were introduced to two Indian officers, whose names I'm afraid I didn't catch. They seemed quite nice chaps and made us feel at ease, and after a few tots of rum we were swapping tales of home and working conditions.

The meal consisted of lamb with vegetables – just like home – followed by a few tots of whisky; so by dusk we were well away, exchanging jokes and getting well acquainted, with the promise of any help we needed. It must have been after midnight when we staggered up to our bungalow, to find our bobijee dozing in a chair on the verandah, waiting for our return. After bundling him off to bed, we sat up and discussed when to move on up the Karnaphuli River to finally reach our main destination. This was Lunglei, where the DC (District Commissioner) had his residence and administration headquarters.

We'd decided to have the next day off in order to get together the provisions we needed for the trip. So, after a light meal and coffee, we decided to contact Oliver to discuss our needs with him. On climbing his rickety ladder, we found him sitting cross-legged on the floor checking papers, complete with the usual mug of local *Zophan* beer. He was pleased to see us, and offered us a drink of the beer; after a few gulps of this, I found it quite potent and decided to make it last.

When we'd explained our plans, it was decided that we would have to make the journey taking two canoes, as the river would be very shallow, and it would take all the skill of the boat wallahs to steer clear. We were shown the canoes, parked in a lean-to, and were quite impressed by their size. In fact Doug and I lifted one up and found it quite light, considering its length. So, taking the width into account, I thought we'd manage quite well. We had decided to leave the heavy gear – transmitter, batteries, and the 'jenny', our name for the generator, which itself weighed 90 lbs – in store with Oliver. We had to come back this way to make our trek up into the Thiga Ridge range of hills, towards our base village of Mullianphui, where I was told there were two WOU chaps waiting for us to relieve them.

The two already there had only arrived about three weeks previously, but both were in a poor way, and had signalled for reliefs to take over. Hence we two fools had volunteered. That night we were busy packing and clearing out the dāk ready to push off in the morning.

I awoke to the sun just rising above the jungle treetops far below. I marvelled at this glorious sight, thinking however that we'd soon be down there amongst all the insects. Doug came in, all cheerful, saying, 'Ready?'

We had a good breakfast of fried eggs and toast. The bobijee collected our packages and piled them on the verandah for collection by the village people. Then we were all ready to go down to where our canoes were waiting to be loaded.

On leaving the dāk bungalow, on my way down to the river, I had to glance back to memorise our stay there, and recall how tranquil life could be. On reaching the river bank, we found quite a crowd of villagers gathered there with our two friends, Captains Scott and Robinson, standing in the canoes, directing how they should be loaded! All was ready by about noon. I sat in the middle of the leading boat with two chaps with paddles at each end, while Doug brought up the rear in his boat.

With much shouting and waving of arms from everyone, we finally pushed off into the strong current to battle our way towards our next village stop, at a place called Phiragai.

It would take about three days of heavy going, as there are about four waterfalls to negotiate; but it wouldn't be as bad as lugging the *kisti*, and at our present rate I reckoned we were making steady progress.

Negotiating the protruding boulders on the river bed by skilfully manoeuvring the boats seemed quite easy to these chaps. While doing this, they were laughing and singing their native songs, and would shriek and curse when just missing a huge boulder. We had been travelling for about three hours and hadn't yet approached a waterfall. As dusk was closing in, I decided to look out for a likely clearing to spend the night. After about five minutes, the perfect place appeared to our left. As we neared the shore, troupes of small monkeys ran screeching into the undergrowth, warning us to keep a guard on our supply of food; the chaps would have to keep the fire well lit all night.

25th December, 1943

The four boat wallahs soon collected loads of wood ready for the night's needs and made a small fire to make coffee and rice. Doug and I made a clearing to lay our blankets down, but before doing so I put bundles of decayed leaves on the ground, hoping to make a soft bed. By now the coffee and rice were ready, so we sat cross-legged around the fire, eating the rice with our fingers. We had no plates, so it was served on a huge green leaf, and during the meal I suddenly remembered it was Christmas Day. I spent a restless night; at times I lay there listening to all the strange noises of the jungle creatures; while the two boat wallahs were talking in low tones and keeping the fire well alight. I suppose this was their life and they were quite used to these journeys. The other two were asleep nearby.

I was woken up by the usual, 'Cha, Sahib,' and found a mug of coffee thrust towards me. Doug was already sitting up sipping his and taking stock of our surroundings. The air was filled with screeching monkeys, darting from tree to tree and hoping there would be scraps left. After a hasty snack of bully beef and biscuits, we gave the camp the usual disguising treatment, to eliminate all signs of our overnight stay, and got settled in our canoes. I looked back and could see no traces at all. I started first, with Doug about ten yards distant, and we began the same routine of dodging the boulders and making steady progress.

As we pushed forward we could hear the rumbling of a waterfall in the distance, and the boat wallahs waved their arms and pointed farther ahead, grinning from ear to ear. It was about an hour later when we sighted it. We approached carefully, and I could see a well-beaten track had been opened by travellers avoiding the falls. Waving to Doug, I made for the bank.

After securing the canoes safely, our next job was to transfer our provisions to the other side. It was quite a climb up the bank, and we carried what we could along an uneven track, stumbling and cursing most of the time. On reaching the higher ground, we had to stack everything on the bank and leave one of the boat chaps to guard it.

Eventually the three of us lifted a boat at a time, and carried it round to the higher ground. Then we had to drop the boat into the water and load all the provisions again, after securing the canoes by driving stakes deep into ground. Soon it was midday and time for a snack. After searching around for branches we had a small fire on the go with the water pot hanging from a tripod over it. Coffee was made, and that, together with bully beef and hard ration biscuits, was our meal. We wanted to push on towards Phiragai, a small village; but as the daylight faded quickly, it meant camping on the river bank that night.

As we zig-zagged between the boulders, with the light failing, I was keeping a sharp lookout for a likely spot, and on rounding a bed, I made for a clearing to the left.

On landing, we found that the bank hid a flat area, which, when we had cleared all the scrub off, gave us quite a good space to build a fire and prepare sleeping places. While the fire was being built, Doug and I made the canoes secure and carried all our provisions to the site; by this time it was nearly dark, and the light from the fire gave a welcome glow, enough for all our needs. The boat chaps prepared a very good meal: chapattis with curried rice, followed by the usual mug of coffee; and sitting there on our haunches with the fire glowing, we all felt quite relaxed.

The four boat wallahs had made a roster of the guard duty during the night, and I reckoned Doug and I wouldn't be sleeping that soundly, what with all the cries of the night life. The usual chatter of our boat companions woke me; they had the fire still alight, giving a certain amount of warmth. This helped to get rid of the stiffness in our limbs, as the mist hung heavy before sunrise.

The fire was made up, and soon we had our coffee and biscuits, before clearing the site to make it look as we found it. It didn't take long to load the canoes; the boat wallah we had left guarding them said it was all quiet during the night, except for a few wild dogs sniffing about.

It was about eight, and the sun was just clearing the jungle, when we got into the main torrent in the middle of the river. Then the battle started all over again, with the boat wallahs putting all their strength and skill into pressing forward, looking for and finding a clear passage. I believed there was another waterfall to negotiate before reaching Phiragai. I hoped it would be smaller, as the previous one was a real gut stretch. When we had been hard at it for about three hours, I decided to pull in for a rest; only this time the banks were too steep, and it was only much later when at last a suitable spot was located.

Having secured the canoes, we collected wood and soon a small fire was going – enough to make coffee, and to rest by for half an hour. I didn't want to stop long, for we had to negotiate the next waterfall; we were hoping it was smaller and easier to get round than the last. Soon we were off again, against the swirling current, and I must say these boat wallahs were getting more proficient as we proceeded.

We came up against our next obstacle a little later, and thankfully it wasn't as high as the previous one; but we had to go through the same procedure, lugging all the gear round to higher ground and eventually the canoes as well.

Having negotiated the two waterfalls in good time, I felt we should stop for a rest and a meal, and as we were in a clearing with plenty of room, Doug and I decided to make camp. A fire was made and lit, with a crude tripod to carry the pots for hot water, and soon the rice was on the boil. Doug, in the meantime, found a tin of bully beef. The boat wallahs wouldn't touch the beef. To them, the cow was sacred; that's why in all the markets and villages cows can be seen sprawling everywhere: they are not to be harmed.

Doug and I actually had a snooze for half an hour, while the boat chaps cleared the campsite, returning the pots and pans to the canoes. It was just after midday, and we should reach Phiragai before sunset, as I reckoned it was about a mile to go. I was hoping there were no obstacles in the river to obstruct our progress.

Eventually the village came in sight, high up on the bank to our left. Natives were gathering, gesticulating and waving their arms at our approach, and by the time we had secured our canoes they were staring at us a bit suspiciously. A tall native led them down, and as he came near, my boat chap shouted out in Urdu. He leapt into the shallow water and met the headman to explain who we were.

After the introduction, it was all smiles and willing hands to help us with our gear. We were assured that the canoes would be guarded at all times, and in fact, the villagers had been warned of our approach by a runner from the previous village.

The climb up to the settlement was made much easier, as we were relieved of all our luggage by cheerful and chattering children, who by now seemed quite friendly, with all their shyness gone.

Phiragai

On reaching Phiragai, we were at once struck by its obvious poverty; the bamboo hovels were all dilapidated and in awful condition, mangy dogs and swine were running about everywhere, and it struck me then – where the hell were we to bed down for the night? Our guide led us to a hut away from the centre, which from the outside seemed quite passable – but the inside was terrible! The floor was covered with muck, and I sent the guide back to the chief to send villagers up to clean the place out and supply fresh matting. Four women arrived, and I must say they worked really hard, chattering away sending huge grins in our direction. They cleaned the floor all right, but the stink!

I detailed one of the boat chaps to make a fire in the centre to boil the rice. I thought that the smoke would at least help to smother the stink. The women had brought fresh matting, so after the usual rice and bully beef we tried to get some rest.

We didn't get much sleep. What with rats scampering and squealing, and the terrible stink, it was a relief to see the sun's rays through slits in the bamboo walls, and to get outside into the fresh air.

Fresh water was brought in a large earthenware jar. After washing and shaving, we both felt better and ready for something to eat. To our surprise, one of our boat chaps came up to cook, bringing fresh eggs from the village. We ate four each, nicely fried! During the meal we discussed our plans further, and decided to leave the canoes there and proceed on foot. This would mean asking the chief to detail a porter corps to carry our provisions on our next slog to Lunglei.

I went into the village, accompanied by one of the boat chaps to translate my request. I found the chief sitting outside his basha on the verandah, consuming a drop of the local beer, with two local girls giggling at his remarks.

When he understood, it was all smiles and a promise he would have seven porters ready for us in the morning. For this, I would give him a chit authorising payment by the DC at Lunglei.

The rest of the day was spent in preparing our loads for the morning: mainly provisions, pots and pans, blankets, mosquito nets, flour, rice, and so on.

By the evening, we had it all stacked up in nine loads, all ready for an early start. We had a wash and decided to visit the Chief to say our farewells, and that we hoped to meet him on our return to Chittagong.

Dusk was falling as we climbed up on to his verandah. We found him smoking a long hubble-bubble pipe, which made a gurgling sound as he drew the smoke through the water container. He could see I was interested and passed the pipe to me, and after much laughter I did manage to draw up some smoke, but it nearly choked me. Our boat wallah asked if the porters could be sent up early, and was assured they would be there. One of his chief's women brought in a large earthenware bowl of chicken curry, which went down very well; it was served on huge green leaves and eaten using our fingers.

After drinking a few mugs of the local *Zophan* beer, we were both well away, and I thought then, what a situation – sitting here in this godforsaken hole, away from it all! I wondered what Audrey and Nick would say!

By midnight the chief was trying to teach the Lushai language to me; but, with howls of laughter, I had to give the lesson up, as I couldn't understand what the devil he was saying. At last the time came for Doug and me to say farewell, and that we hoped to meet again on our return to Chittagong – which I hoped wouldn't be before too long. After much waving, we staggered down the rickety ladder and stumbled along the trail leading to the bungalow. Our temporary bobijee was still waiting up, half asleep, but still loyal and ready to serve drinks; I told him to go to bed. In a short while, we crept under our mosquito nets to try to get some sleep before dawn.

We were awakened at dawn by chattering natives, and sure enough, there were the porters the chief had promised, squatting just outside my window; no wonder I was woken up! The bobijee came in with coffee, which I was ready for after the night before, and I asked him to tell the porters we'd be out soon, *tora-peechee*.

We had a snack of bully beef and biscuits, and checked the rooms to see if anything was left behind. I also had one last gaze down at the wonderful panoramic view below of the jungle, which stretched as far as the eye could see, and wondered how many blasted Japs were on patrol out there.

After sorting out the loads amongst the porters, we were ready to start off again. I reckon it was about eight when I led the way down from the village on the winding trail into the jungle, with Doug bringing up the rear.

I believed Lunglei was about fifteen miles off, and as the trail was a bit rough in places, I doubted whether we could get there by the following evening. Leading the way, I always had an uneasy feeling about whom or what I might meet. As it was, for the first three to four miles we met only a few of the local natives setting out on hunting parties, and these our porters knew well. At midday, we decided to make camp for a meal and rest, and soon the water was over the fire in a large earthenware container, while the porters were busy making chapattis or pancakes.

The open space we were camping in was quite large, and surrounded by tall bamboo grass, so we had to keep a sharp lookout for snakes and other marauders that might be lurking about. Within an hour all the food was ready, and we ate sitting on our haunches round the fire.

It amazed me how quickly the meal was prepared in the time. It was curried chicken and rice, served on large chapattis, and for the next half an hour no word was spoken; all we heard was eating and burping! Afterwards we all had a short rest to digest our food; then we cleaned up the camp, hoisted the packs on and proceeded on our journey.

By late afternoon, when dusk was falling, I reckoned we had covered ten miles and it was time to halt again; so at the next clearing we made camp for the night.

The site we pulled into that night wasn't as large as the previous one, but it would have to do as we'd left it rather late in deciding. In any case, we should be at Lunglei the following day, and hoped to have a good rest there.

The usual guard duty was kept, and I managed a few hours' sleep, well covered by my mosquito net. I was awakened at dawn by the chattering and laughing of the porter corps, who were building up the fire and preparing rice. A bowl of water from the river was brought to me for shaving and washing, after which I felt much fresher, and ready for a hot bowl of rice; but I'm afraid the ration biscuits didn't go down very well, as they were very hard.

I reckoned we had covered about eight miles the previous day, so we were due to reach Lunglei before dusk, depending on the state of the trail. It was about eight by the time we had loaded all the packs again, cleaned up the site, and were ready to make the last lap. As our destination was nearly four thousand feet up, we would have to endure a hard day's slog, so it would mean more resting. I took the lead, accompanied by a tall Bengali porter, with Doug bringing up the rear. Sure enough, the trail rose gradually as we pushed through the dense undergrowth. It was very slippery at times because of dew from the overhanging branches, which made the porters curse, as they found it difficult to get sound footholds.

After about three hours we had to have a rest; as the trail ran through deep undergrowth, to emerge on a steep open hillside, offering a nasty drop of a few hundred feet on to the trees below.

Before we attempted to go into the open, a space was cleared to make a small fire to make coffee and have a rest. For this, the porters were very thankful, as the going had been very strenuous up the narrow and slippery trail. A pan of water was soon boiling and coffee was made, after which we all made ourselves a space on the ground for five minutes' rest, before emerging to tackle the open trail up the hillside.

It was just after midday when we started off on the last mile or so, hoping to reach Lunglei before dusk; we were climbing gradually all the time, and noticed the appearance of open green spaces. The air was much fresher with fewer swarms of insects to avoid.

Our first sighting of a habitation was the IOC (Indian Observation Corps) observation post towering above trees on the highest peak, and we could see the personnel waving to us. Within half an hour Doug and I were being warmly greeted by the Sergeant in charge and his men. We were told the post had received a signal from Chittagong, warning them that we were somewhere on the trail on the way up, and to keep a lookout for us.

Not far from the post, a large dāk bungalow could be seen, so it was to that we were taken. We found it all ready for our occupation, with a grinning Lushai native to look after us.

The IOC had stocked some food in preparation for our arrival. After a wash and clean up, we found the bobijee had our meal ready; curried chicken and rice, washed down with the local beer. After the meal we retired to sit on large bamboo chairs on the verandah and take in the wonderful view of the jungle and hills below.

We sat outside till long after dusk; then the mosquitoes took over, so we had to make a hasty retreat inside. The rooms were quite large; besides my charpoy there were two tables and chairs, with plenty of room to move around and arrange my personal belongings. The bobijee had put up our mosquito nets for us to crawl under when ready, but we were so fascinated by the whole set-up that we were talking till midnight. Next day, the bobijee came in with coffee to awaken us and say the sun was high in the sky, with the morning nearly gone! Then Doug came in to say it was about ten o'clock!

On going to bed, my worry had been whether I would sleep, but I must have gone out like a light. After breakfast, we decided to stroll along the level ridge, then down into Lunglei, to enquire where the DC's residence was and introduce ourselves.

Lunglei

We were about half a mile from the village, and as we started out, we were struck by the lush tall grass up there – what a change from what we'd been through!

Just off the path, clumps of pineapple were growing, while down the hillside there were banana trees full of green fruit.

As we strolled along, Doug pointed out tobacco plants everywhere, saying we should pick some on the way back, and lay them on the roof of the basha to dry out.

Descending into the village, which was fairly large, we could see the DC's residence above, overlooking the whole assembly of stores and workshops, so we made our way in that direction. As we approached and entered the main gate, a sepoy of the IOC asked for our identification, after which we were informed that the DC was up-country on inspection. We were instructed to contact the Major in command at the workshops below.

On the way we observed many Lushai Brigade fighters – tall, ferocious warriors, scantily clad, with a rifle slung over their shoulders, complete with a holder to carry their deadly poison bamboo darts. There were men of the JAT Regiment, part of the Lushai Brigade operating in the Lushai and Chin Hills, who had covered about five hundred miles over mountainous jungle country, at an average of five miles a day.

They all showed us respect; I suppose, as we wore no rank and were dressed only in shirt and shorts, it was the safest way to treat us both. We were directed to a large bamboo built building, where we were told we would find the supply officer somewhere about in the place. He was found in an office tucked away in a corner, and rose to shake hands with us and ask what the devil we were doing up there.

He seemed quite a nice chap; he was Indian – Bengali, I thought – and when we explained our mission, he promised to help with provisions and porters to our requirements when we asked him. I told him about our journey up, and said we would have a couple of days' rest. In the morning, Doug and I spent the time with the IOC up in the observation tower, checking all the equipment for worn parts, to see if any needed replacing. If so, we had to signal Chittagong.

We stopped up there for most of the day, hoping there might be a signal for our movements, but, apparently our whereabouts were still not known to them; we'd have to try to get a signal through that night.

The Sergeant and four sepoys made us most welcome, preparing a bumper meal of chicken curry and rice, followed by large chapattis, with mugs of the local beer. After this we found space in the compound and blankets, lay down and snoozed the afternoon away.

The climate up there was just about right – about 75° during daytime, with not many mosquitoes; but night-time brought them out in swarms, so we had to secure our nets properly. That night, Doug and I wanted to go up into the observation post, to try and contact Chittagong for further instructions. We would be listening for our call sign to decode among all the others being sent during the night.

Doug knew there would be difficulties, for our code was changed at different times to try to stop the Japs from pinpointing our location; but Chittagong should notify all posts beforehand. The IOC prepared a surprise meal at about seven – sausages, bacon, and eggs. The Sergeant said we ought to have a change from rice! It was a meal we thoroughly enjoyed, and we washed it down with the local rice beer.

Now for our night stint – to climb up the shaky bamboo ladder and crawl into the small but well hidden lookout amongst the trees. There, we'd settle down for the night with headphones on, to await our call sign and decode. Doug had explained to me what to listen for, and if it came to me I was to immediately pass the headphones over for him to decipher.

We also had as tea boy a sepoy, who kept chattering most of the time; this didn't help our concentration as we listened.

By about three we had had enough, and sent the sepoy down to the billets for two reliefs to take over. We had sat up listening to hundreds of different codes, most in signals which were difficult to understand, and there wasn't a blasted peep from Chittagong among them.

It seemed a long time before our two reliefs arrived. They were half awake, but they didn't seem to mind; I expect they were used to being dragged out for duty at all times of the night.

We arrived at the verandah just as dawn was breaking, and were jolly glad to crawl under our mosquito nets and have a few hours' sleep. The sun was well up by the time I awoke and found a cold mug of coffee on the table at my side; I suppose the bobijee thought it best not to wake me up. It must have been about ten when I awoke, and, wondering if Doug was up, I called out but got no reply. Slipping out of my charpoy, I looked into his room to find it empty; he must have gone for a stroll. Soon afterwards, the bobijee came in, to enquire if I wanted anything cooked; but all I had was bully beef and biscuits.

Doug came in later to say he felt much better after some fresh air and a stretch. We then discussed plans to arrange our trek down to Demagri again. We would branch from there up the Thiga Ridge range of hills towards Lushai and the Chin hills.

We decided then to move off the following morning as early as possible, so our first job was to contact our Major friend at the depot to arrange porters and provisions for first light the next morning.

We'd decided to keep to the jungle trail, rather than going halfway via the Karnaphuli River; though this way, I was told there were a few precarious bamboo bridges to cross. We'd have to meet the challenge when they were reached. We had a light lunch of bully beef and biscuits, before making our way down to the supply depot to find the Major in command and tell him of our plans to move off in the morning. He proved to be a very efficient chap, and he had both porters and provisions detailed ready when we were.

We were with the Major discussing our journey and needs for quite a while; he was very interested, and promised us porters and supplies would be ready at dawn.

Thanking him for all his help, and hoping to meet him again on our return later, we returned to the dāk bungalow to sort out and pack what we would want during the trip. The bobijee had prepared a meal of eggs and rice on our return, to be taken on the verandah; this would be our last sighting of the marvellous view of the range of Lushai and Chin Hills. I must say, it was quite pleasant to sit there smoking one of my rolled tobacco leaves; it did at least keep the mosquitoes away!

I had a fairly good night. The air was very humid, and the sweat was rolling off me all night, but I did manage to snooze off now and again. I was woken up by the chattering natives starting up the fires again to boil their rice and get the cha made. The bobijee came in with my coffee and made signs that Doug was already up and was checking the loads. Doug came in later, and while I got my belongings together, we discussed the route we would take. It appeared that we would make for a small village where there was an observation post manned by IOC named Ridge Camp; it was about four miles' trek. By eight the porters were ready to move off, with their fifty-pound loads on their backs, held there by a large sling around the crown of their heads. As we started off they bent their backs to even the load, and started to chant a tune, while the others were all chattering and laughing. I reckoned we could be heard quite a distance away.

The first half-mile consisted of tall bamboo grass, about shoulder high, leading us gradually down towards deep undergrowth and the jungle itself, with our friends the baboons shrieking out high in the treetops as they escorted us along our journey. The trouble was, they gave our position away to other travellers, both friend and foe. So at all times, we had to keep a sharp eye in all directions; no reliance could be made on the natives we met, for they might be Jap scouts, though I doubted whether they were down as far as this. Apart from our friends in the trees, there were other means of transmitting messages; for as we made our way along the trail, the continuous beat of drums from villages behind and in front were monitoring our positions. After about two hours, we decided to take a rest and have coffee. On finding a clear space, we soon had a fire going, with the water pan on the tripod and the water boiling.

The porters squatted round the fire, chattering and laughing, glad to have a rest; they all seemed to get along with each other, helping with their loads, which made me think they were a single gang of porters who were in constant use.

We rested for about an hour, then loaded up. After clearing up the camp, we plodded along the trail, aiming to make Ridge Camp before dusk.

Our progress along this trail was hampered by uneven footholds and twisted roots that were difficult to avoid; this was due, I would say, to lack of use, as most of the laden travellers went down by river, bypassing this difficult route.

Our pace slowed down, so it would be nearly dusk before reaching Ridge Camp; but the spirit of the porters still remained high, the chanting and laughing was still there. Considering the conditions, I had to admire them for their guts.

Rounding a corner, I sighted the observation post set in a clump of trees high on ridge. There was also a small basha with a verandah overlooking the valley below.

I reckoned they had sighted us, for I could see someone waving; it wouldn't be long now.

On arrival at the post we were greeted by three IOC Pathan sepoys, who seemed very pleased to meet us; they said they had received a signal from Chittagong of our whereabouts, but didn't know when we would arrive.

We were shown where to wash, after which I felt much better, and returned to the basha to find a meal of eggs and rice had been prepared, together with mugs of the local beer. Our porters were camped just outside, where we could keep an eye on them. I can see them now, building a huge fire and preparing a meal.

Our provisions and equipment were brought safely into the basha. There we could watch them, which was a good thing as these natives moved so silently at night, and it was impossible to catch them in the act.

The Sergeant in charge left his room for the night, so that Doug and I could have as much rest as possible. Then, after a few drinks of the local beer, we both were ready to hit the hay! I had a fairly good night, and was woken up by the chattering of the porters getting their fire ready to boil their rice. The dawn was just breaking, with the rays of the sun piercing through the gaps in the bamboo wall; and as I lay there, my thoughts were of home, and hoping all was well there.

In his charpoy at the other end of the room, Doug began to stir and called out, 'Morning!' He said he'd slept well, and though his legs felt stiff, he hoped it would wear off with use. One of the sepoys came in with coffee and said breakfast would be ready in half an hour. Was there anything we wanted? This I thought was very considerate and thanked him for all the attention.

We enjoyed a breakfast of eggs and rice and by eight we had the porters loaded up all ready for the trip to our next stop, which would be Phiragai. This was a distance of about nine miles; I was hoping to reach there by dusk but I doubted we'd make it.

We all shook hands and thanked Ridge Camp for their hospitality. Meanwhile the Sergeant in charge said he had sent a signal to Chittagong informing them of our whereabouts, which they acknowledged, so we had the satisfaction that they noted our position.

The trail led us through the most difficult parts of the jungle and among tall bamboo grass. We wondered all the time if we would meet anybody around the corner, but for the first two miles all was quiet.

We were making steady progress when we came face to face with a small hunting party. We could see they were as surprised as we were, since they stood along the path staring in disbelief at our party. There were five of them, tall natives wearing the traditional bamboo ornaments and holding long bamboo spears. While I stood there and tried to smile, the porter behind me stepped forward to explain who we were.

After a long babble in the local lingo, they were all smiles, touching their foreheads with hands together, and stood aside as we passed. As I did, I couldn't help glancing at one or two, and was glad to be on the right side. I called out to Doug bringing up the rear. I saw him wave and he shouted '*Tekai*!' [All right!]

By noon we had made good progress, but I doubted if we'd reach Phiragai by dusk, and glancing at the porters I could see a good rest was in order. So at the first opportunity I called a halt, which the porters gladly welcomed, and soon they had a fire going and water boiling. The rest certainly paid off, for when they hitched up the loads again, they were different men, chatting and ready for another slog.

I realised we wouldn't make Phiragai that evening, so before dusk, at a suitable clearing we came to, we camped down for the night. While preparations were being made, Doug and I discussed whether to push on through the jungle or take to the river from Phiragai, and it was decided that if we could obtain a *kisti*, we would have a go at shooting the rapids; this would make the journey to Demagri much quicker.

The porters prepared a very tasty curry of wildfowl! I asked it had come from, and it seemed it had been caught about an hour ago. To pluck it, it was dipped in boiling water, then the feathers were just wiped off!

It was the best meal we'd had for ages, and was washed down with mugs of local beer. Then we settled down gratefully for the night.

The porters had arranged between themselves to keep a constant guard during the night, and as I was half awake I noted that guard duty was maintained all night. Dawn came with the sounds of all the creatures – croaks from bull frogs, and weird cries from troupes of baboons and monkeys. These mixed with the calls of exotic birds beginning to leave their nests and stretch their wings in an early reconnoitre of their territory.

The porters were beginning to move, and the fire was being built up for making coffee and rice: amid the incessant chatter and laughter, another day had begun.

Doug woke up to complain of a painful tummy and feeling stiff all over, and I must say my legs were beginning to feel the same; but we had to push on and hope the aches would go.

The usual procedure was carried out – having breakfast, restoring the site to how we found it, and the porters loading up again. Then off we started along the trail, to reach Phiragai before dusk. As we made our way the porters began their monotonous chanting. I'd got used to it by now; each note marked a stage in their walking. I suppose it set a rhythm to help them carry their loads.

I was sweating terribly – it was pouring out, but I'd have to put up with it, hoping I wouldn't break out in a rash. On reaching our destination I'd have to cover my body with powder to stop the itching; perhaps there might be some cream.

We made good progress, covering the last mile on a widening trail, which wasn't so difficult. The air was much clearer, and soon Phiragai was in sight below us nestling on the brow of a hill. As we entered the village, natives came running out to meet us. Among them were some I had made friends with previously, and soon they were chatting away with our porters.

Doug and I made our way to the observation post, to be welcomed by a sergeant of the IOC in charge of nine Pathans. They all made us most welcome. I enquired if there were any signs of the Japs, and the answer was negative. The Sergeant said the villagers had scouts posted within a radius of thirty miles. If any sightings were made there, the village drums would signal their whereabouts to read back here.

The Sergeant had commandeered a clean basha for our overnight stay (quite different from our previous one on our outward trip), in which he had put down a clean covering of bamboo matting, and fitted in two charpoys; we also had a Pathan guard.

I explained to him that we would want a *kisti* in the morning, and asked him to make our porters comfortable for the night. I said that I would give the head porter a pay chit in the morning.

I had a restless night. The basha was full of mosquitoes, and one or two managed to find an enlarged hole through the net. Frequently I could hear the droning of their flight as they moved around. Suddenly, they would dive-bomb towards my head, and I would duck under my blanket to avoid them.

Dawn came at last, with the sun's rays piercing through slits in the walls. I heard Doug mumbling, 'Are you awake?' We could hear movement outside, and presently mugs of cha were brought in by the Sergeant's bobijee, who asked if would we like some water to wash in.

After a breakfast of bacon and eggs (what a change!), all our kit was taken down to the river to be loaded into the *kisti*, and by the time we had said farewell to the chief and his wives, the sun was well up, with the temperature rising.

There wasn't much space in the *kisti*. All our gear was neatly stacked and by the time we stretched out our legs, there wasn't enough room to move about.

It was a hair-raising experience, negotiating the boulders and the shallow bed of the river. The boat wallahs using their long poles to guide the *kisti* clear, and then we came to the first waterfall. We could hear it ahead, and pulled into the bank. One of the boat chaps went ahead to see how high the fall was.

On returning, he said, 'About that long,' and stretched his arms wide. This I took to be about four feet. He also said we could do it: '*Tekai*, Sahib.'

Doug and I decided to risk it, so before pulling away from the bank, all the gear was checked for movement, and then we set off.

We made for the centre of the river where the flow was strongest, which would help the boat to take the fall – the exhilaration we felt as the fall was cleared! It all happened so quickly, and thankfully there were no mishaps.

As the boat went over the fall, the two boat wallahs stood on either side, clinging to the woven bamboo roof covering the *kisti*. How they managed to stay on board was a miracle! The strong current then took us at a very fast rate, with the boat wallahs using all their skill in avoiding boulders; at this speed we should arrive at the remaining waterfall within the next hour.

As we had made good progress, we decided to put in at the earliest moment, to stretch our legs and have coffee. Sighting a suitable open space, we went in and secured the boat safely. While the boat chaps scouted round for firewood, Doug and I made a recce in the undergrowth to see if there was any fruit about.

We hadn't gone far when a clump of bananas presented itself, and going farther in we found pineapples among the bamboo grass. Having gathered as much as we could carry, we made our way back to the camp, where there was a mug of coffee and biscuits waiting.

After about an hour's rest the camp was cleared, and we were off again, making for the centre of the river where it was deepest, to keep clear of the huge boulders on either side. I reckoned we should make the next waterfall quite soon; at the same time I tried to recollect its height on the outward journey, but couldn't. Anyway, we would soon know.

The boat wallah at the front gave the first indication, waving his arms and pointing forward to where a faint mist could be seen. From this it would seem to be quite deep. We approached carefully so as to appreciate the height of the fall, and decided to carry the provisions and *kisti* by the trail, avoiding the danger of attempting to shoot over at that height.

The transition of provisions and *kisti* was made in under two hours, which I thought was good going, at this rate we should reach Demagri by dusk.

Getting to the centre of the river again, we made good progress, as the turbulence was much lighter, and the *kisti* consequently easier to manoeuvre. To cap it all, the boat wallahs started to sing and laugh; after all, they had done a good job so far.

The sun was fast disappearing and the light starting to diminish when Demagri came in view – what a welcome sight!

We pulled in at the small landing place, to be met by a few natives who immediately helped to carry our provisions up to the dāk bungalow. Meanwhile, we were thanking our boat wallah friends, shaking their hands and wishing them good health, hoping we would meet again. Climbing up a steady incline to the dāk bungalow, we were heartened to see the place had lights in all the rooms. On entering, we were met by a grinning villager, who had apparently been instructed to have the place prepared for the night.

He indicated a meal would be ready soon, and I made signs that we would wash and change and were glad to be there again. He had made both our charpoys up, complete with mosquito nets. After a meal of rice and chapattis we both were ready to turn in for the night, our temporary bobijee had gone home soon after dishing up the meal, so it would be up to us to get down for a good night's rest.

I must have slept like a log, for when I did come to, there was Captain Scott by my charpoy offering me a mug of coffee, and asking, 'How are you?' It was he who had arranged the bobijee to get the place set up. Word had arrived there by runner of our position on the trail, so he guessed our arrival would be last night. After I'd thanked him for the coffee and his kindness, we were chatting away, when Doug joined us. He looked fagged out and walked awkwardly, saying his legs had gone as stiff as pokers!

We decided to rest for the day, as in the evening we'd been invited for supper at the depot by the liaison staff. I expected Captains Scott and Robinson would be there, together with Oliver, plus a few IOC officers. We'd have to wear trousers and clean shirts! We had a bottle of rum sent up, which helped the day's rest pass quite nicely, together with a chicken curry. By sunset, we were both beginning to regain strength in our limbs and feel relaxed for the night's binge.

Having washed and put on clean linen, we decided to stroll down to the depot and present ourselves. We arrived at about 6.30, to be met by an orderly and shown into the main room. Besides our friends, there were four IOC officers, plus one civilian by the name of Henderson. The names of the Indian Observer Corps I couldn't quite catch, but they all discarded rank, and in no time we were all talking shop.

It appeared that Mr Henderson had a tea plantation somewhere towards the Chin Hills, and during conversation we became quite friendly. He was kind enough to say he could find a job on the plantation that would suit me, say, maintenance engineer on the power plant. Perhaps it was the rum talking, for I let it go at that, as the end of hostilities then seemed a long way off.

By the time dinner was being served, we all were well away; even Doug seemed to let his hair down, as I could hear his laughter now and again.

I must say the meal was excellent – steak, vegetables, and chips, washed down with a nice glass of whisky or rum. That evening would remain with me for quite a long time.

I couldn't recollect how we managed to stagger up to our billet that night. Next morning I felt a bit heady, and hoped it would wear off. So much for a get-together! But at least we had acquired new friends, and that might be to our advantage in our walkabout.

The bobijee came to inform me that Doug was unable to get out of bed because his legs were so stiff, and was asking if I could see him straight away.

On entering his room, I could see he was in pain, and after examining him I put it down to the fact that both knees had seized up – or were very stiff! Telling him to stop in bed, I said I was sure we had a bottle of embrocation in our store. After a long search, I found it in a first aid box and returned to Doug. I spent the next hour massaging both his knees till my arms ached, and received his sincere thanks.

At about mid-morning I looked in on Doug and found him fast asleep. I decided to go down to the depot to arrange stores for our next journey up into the hills of Thiga Ridge. I found our friend the Bengali Major in his little office, and asked him if he had got the better of the night before at the party – which he found most amusing. He said he'd found it a good get-together, and wished us the best of luck on our next trip.

I gave him a list of all the provisions we would require, and told him of Doug's knee trouble. He immediately phoned through to his medical orderly to go up to our bungalow and attend to Doug, for which I sincerely thanked him.

I also enquired as to the whereabouts of Mr Oliver, to which he replied I would very likely find him in his treetop basha entertaining one of his Lushai women!

I found his place again, and when I was halfway up the ladder, he emerged out of the main opening, all smiles, and with his hand outstretched. I wondered then whether he cursed me or not. I explained that I'd come to enquire if the jenny and other equipment were still in good storage, and to say we would pick them up in a few day's time.

I also asked him for nine stalwart porters and an interpreter for our journey up the Thiga Ridge range to a village called Mullianphui where there was a WOU post.

Oliver pointed out that the trail at times was very rough, and gave me the advice not to travel too far in one day. Three miles would be quite good, he said.

We became quite friendly and more at ease, and after a few mugs of the local *Zophan* beer, I found out why he took this out of the way job.

Apparently he was Warrant Officer in charge of stores in Chittagong and this job came up. He applied for it to get away, and to do a job on his own, at which I said I had acted in the same way.

Returning to the bungalow, I came across a small group of Gurkhas camping away from the main depot and decided to enquire about their destination, hoping it might be in our direction; if so, it would help to make our slog much safer.

The Sergeant in charge said they were making for Ijal, a busy communications centre, which would be about eighty miles south of Kohima. The journey would take them three to four weeks. They were all technicians, trying to report for duty as quickly as possible.

I explained to them about my job, and where I was making for, and hoped they would accompany us part of the way; but no luck, they were heading for far too much to our left, seeking a trail almost opposite to ours.

During my chat, I enjoyed a nice cup of coffee, and noticed how well they were dressed, and remained prepared at all times. I especially noted the ever-ready *kukri*, always kept handy.

I shook hands with the Gurkha platoon, thanking them for the chat and the coffee, and said I hoped we would meet again, perhaps at Ijal. I then continued on my way up to the bungalow.

I arrived to see Doug stretched out in his charpoy feeling much better, since the medic had spent considerable time massaging his knees. Now we could hopefully organise getting all our gear together, and set off.

I spent the rest of the day writing letters home and compiling a list of provisions and medical supplies for our next push up unto the hills.

During my chat with the Gurkhas we had spoken of snakes and which was the most deadly. They warned me not to walk near banks, as the most deadly is the krait snake; it's only about eighteen inches long, but its poison will kill a person, if bitten, in minutes. I vowed to warn all our party on setting off, but I suspect the porters knew of these dangers; when I told Doug, he said, 'Oh Gawd!'

We would have to rest for another two days at least. I couldn't see Doug well enough to attempt the journey, and anyway, it would give us time to make sure we had all our needs. I was told the monsoons were nearing, so it would mean capes and boots on my list. It's the season when the blasted krait shoots out of the bank to bite.

The day passed quickly; by the time I had checked and rechecked our provisions for the journey, it was dusk, with our bobijee singing away in the kitchen, quite happy in his work.

Doug was much better; the pain and stiffness in both his knees had disappeared. He said, 'I'm all right!' But I said we'd give them another day at least, to make sure.

Captain Scott paid us a visit to enquire about Doug's condition, and of course stayed the rest of the day lounging in a chair on the verandah, drinking our rum. He did say there wasn't much to do at the depot, and asked if there was anything else we wanted.

I do believe he enjoyed our company; we made silly remarks, designed to raise a laugh – so different from the company he was among at the depot.

Our bobijee prepared a very nice chicken curry with chapattis, followed by huge slices of ripe melon. Scott said, 'Hurry back again after your mission!'

To sit out on the verandah after such an enjoyable meal and listen to all the weird cries from the jungle far below was out of this world, and will remain in my memory. It was fairly late when our guest shifted his bulk out of the chair to thank us for a restful evening – quite a change from the babble of the natives in the depot.

He was under the impression that we were off in the morning, till I told him it was the following day. At this he said, 'Oh well, I might see you again in the morning. Anything else you need?'

After he had left, I went into the kitchen to thank the bobijee for preparing such a excellent meal, only to find he had gone home, having cleaned up after the meal. We'd have to seek him out the next day; he would appreciate our thanks.

I returned to the verandah to enjoy another hour or so, and found Doug in much better fettle. All the pain had gone, enabling him to move about quite easily, and he said it would be all right for the day after next.

We sat out quite late. I had lit up one of my local cigars – a tobacco leaf rolled and tied round with bamboo string –

which gave me about an hour's puff! We retired about midnight.

I omitted to mention our meeting with a platoon of the Lushai Brigade (incorporating the JAT Regiment), who patrolled the Lushai and Chin Hills and wrought havoc among the Japs who infiltrated the borders.

In the spring of 1943, the battalion denied the approaches to the Silchar plain through the Lushai Hills to the Jap invaders.

It was quite interesting to chat with the Havildar (Sergeant). He gave me some very useful tips, when approaching a village, about speaking with the headman. You use your hands to communicate, and never turn your back on him!

While we were talking, his men were busy cleaning their equipment, a selection of Sten guns and bows with poison arrows. These men were tall ferocious warriors, very intent on their job, who gave no quarter; and as they wore practically no clothing, they were able to move speedily and silently.

On saying farewell to the Sergeant I wished him the best of health, and said I hoped we'd meet again on victory day! He was all smiles and thoroughly endorsed this dream.

I was awakened the next morning by the chattering and laughter from the porters in their scramble to prepare breakfast, as they lit fires to boil the rice and coffee.

Doug came into my room, fully dressed and washed, and ready to set off! He was quite a different chap from what he had been a few days' before, so it was my turn to get a move on. While I was washing, the bobijee prepared fried eggs and coffee, and during the meal, sitting out on the verandah, we both realised we'd look back to this rest as the best we had experienced. Very soon it would be time to move; the porters were all ready, with their loads slung on to backs and held there by lengths of webbing or thongs.

I didn't like the cloud I saw forming, and I thought, Here we go, the rains aren't far off, but we'll have to start. I had the porter in charge with me leading, and Doug bringing up the rear. As we moved forward, the column started to chant away in unison with every step. We made good progress. As I noted before, the sky had turned grey, and now we had drizzle. It hung heavily on the deep undergrowth, and as we brushed against it, leeches would drop on to us; there was nothing we could do but wait till we stopped for a rest.

Doug and I had pulled our capes over our shoulders, and we found the trail began to get very slippery with the rain. Subsequently, we were finding the going a bit rough, and I was glad when we arrived at a suitable clearing to rest and have coffee.

As we pushed on, the undergrowth seemed endless. We must have been on the move for at least two hours, when suddenly I could see ahead it was becoming much lighter and soon we came to a large clearing.

On either side of the trail grew tall bamboo grass, but at least we were free of overhanging branches and leeches. We'd just started to move out into the open when we sighted a clump of trees to our right full of fruit, and on investigating further, found they were loaded with oranges! Further on, we found grapefruit.

A small village round the corner welcomed us, and soon a fire was built and coffee and rice being heated. In the meantime, Doug and I were busily filling spaces in our kit-bags with the fruit. What a find! At least, it would provide plenty of roughage!

Sitting round the fire having rice and coffee, I thought about our situation. Here we were, miles from anywhere, surrounded by these near-naked natives, who were squatting around gaping at us, with some of the children who were more daring coming closer.

After a while, the villagers became quite friendly and wanted us to stop longer; but as the amenities weren't exactly up to scratch, we decided to move on towards a village called Uipui.

It was raining quite fast now – not heavily, but enough to make keeping our balance on the trail quite difficult for us. Consequently we were slipping all over the place, and cursing.

It became most uneven now, with dips and sloping gradients making the porters' job most difficult. I was sure they'd be glad to reach our destination.

My porter guide indicated it would take about another hour to reach Uipui, with about two hours before dusk; so we should have plenty of time to spare, as long as no mishaps occurred on this blasted trail. Coming to another clearing, I called a halt for a brief rest, in which the porters sat on their loads and jabbered way at each other, or smoked their cheroots and enjoyed a moment of peace.

On the trail again, I hoped it wouldn't be long. As we kept on saying, just round the corner! But at last we sighted the village from our hillside path, looking across the valley. It lay clinging to the highest point on the next range. I wondered if they had seen us; I wouldn't be surprised if they had.

I was right. We hadn't gone much farther when we were confronted by two tall natives running towards us. They immediately broke into huge grins and called out to our porters in their language, which they all understood.

I asked the porter with me, how did they know we were on the trail? At this, he moved his hands up and down, and at the same time cupped his hand to his ear as if listening, and of course I understood: the drums were beating out all the time!

During the day, as we were moving along the trail, we could hear the monotonous beating of drums – little did we realise that our whereabouts was being broadcast from village to village. Besides the drums, there was the incessant screech of the baboons flitting from tree to tree, making a hell of a din. What did we want wireless communication for?

On arrival at Uipui, we had to meet the chief and all his wives, together with some dignitaries, and drink local beer from earthenware mugs. It tasted b— awful!

After much jabbering, we were shown to the basha, which was to be ours for the night. Our porters camped close by, so at least we were assured of protection.

The inside of the basha had been cleaned out and a bamboo mat put down, but the stink! I had an aerosol container of mosquito spray which helped to minimise the smell, and in time we got used to it.

There wasn't much room, as two charpoys had been found from somewhere. At least, we wouldn't be roughing it on the floor. While we were sorting out what gear we wanted for the night, our temporary bobijee was busy cooking a meal over a fire outside the basha.

I went outside to see what he was preparing, to behold a pile of chapattis by the fire. So it seemed he was cooking for all of us. Wondering what to have with them, I thought – bully beef! I searched our provisions and found two tins.

Our porters started chanting, repeating the same tune over and over, which got a bit monotonous, but by then we should have got used to it.

We made up our beds, complete with mosquito nets, hoping for a restful night.

It was quite late when the meal was ready, but I must say it went down very well. We had huge chapattis, on which we spread thick layers of bully beef! It was past midnight when we finely crawled under our mosquito nets.

The sound of rain on the basha roof heralded the arrival of dawn; it was a sound that I wasn't looking forward to, but I hoped it would ease off later.

Doug began to stir, and called out, 'Good morning!' I said, 'Not so much a good morning at the moment,' and asked if he had slept well. He replied, 'Like a log!'

I must say these basha roofs must be woven quite closely, as not a drop of rain came through, for which we were very thankful. It would have been a nuisance packing our gear in a wet condition, as mould would set in with the humid heat.

By the time we had packed, the rain had eased off, with only a drizzle for the time being. We kept our fingers crossed!

Our bobijee came in to say our breakfast was ready – fried eggs and coffee. I asked him how he had escaped the rain. He explained there was a lean-to behind the basha. After the meal, we had our kit ready at the entrance of our basha for the porters to pick up. In the meantime, I enquired if the porters were all right. In reply, they just sat there with huge grins and waved their arms, so I took it they were all ready to move on.

It was still raining when we started, but the porters didn't seem to care; they were laughing and joking as they loaded their packs on to their backs. They pushed forward, bent almost double, using all their skill to keep to the slippery path.

Doug and I were finding the going most difficult. The groundsheets slung over our shoulders were very uncomfortable, as we had small packs on our backs, making both of us sweat till I was wet through. We were both slipping a lot, and trying hard to keep upright.

At about midday, at every bend on the trail, I was looking for a suitable dry area under the overhanging foliage. It was some time when I called a halt, much to

Doug's relief. The porters found dry firewood, and soon the cha and rice was being prepared, while Doug and I discussed further plans, and we both agreed we ought to make Mullianphui by dusk.

We all felt much better after a snack of rice and cha and a rest; the clearing up didn't take so long this time, and soon we were making the final slog to our destination. The light was beginning to fade when a fork in the trail appeared, and of course we had to decide, which do we take?

We decided to split the porters, each of us taking half, hoping to join up farther along the trail. Surely we would reach our destination at some time – hopefully together.

I watched as Doug disappeared into the jungle, with the porters chanting the same guttural song, leaving me thinking, Have we done the right thing? Anyway, it was too late now. I turned to my porters, who were standing at the fork, and beckoned them to follow me. I was taking the trail to the right, and hoping it would lead us to Mullianphui, our final destination for the time being.

The rain was still quite thick. I was sure I had a few leeches, as my shoulders felt a bit clammy – not the usual wet. Dusk was falling fast now and it was becoming difficult in keeping to the trail, when I realised there were no porters behind me. Where the devil had they gone?

I peered down the now darkened trail, but there was no sign; had they deserted me? I started to walk back, picking my way carefully, and found them cowering in the undergrowth and pointing, as if some terrible animal was about to pounce on them!

I cursed and shouted, all to no avail, and to prove there was no danger, I walked ahead, shouting all was *tekai* (all right). But I must say there was something, for I heard a commotion deep in the undergrowth – whether beast or man I shall never know.

I admit my heart was pounding away. Though I tried to scoff at their being afraid, I knew they were right.

Slowly they emerged out of the undergrowth, looking a bit sheepish, and formed in line. Off we started again, with the porters trying to pierce the half-light looking for any impending danger.

As we moved forward, my thoughts were of Doug, hoping he was coping all right. I believe the journey was wearing him down a bit; he was not exactly cut out for this slog.

I noticed too, that the gradient went gently uphill. Glancing down at the hills below, I saw that they were receding, with mist forming a barrier in between.

By this time my legs were beginning to ache, and I wondered how much farther Mullianphui could be. Daylight was fast failing, but we had to rest for a while, so at the next clearing I called a halt. At this the porters gave grunts of approval, but as the ground was still soaking wet, they had to sit on their haunches or find a low bough.

Two of them foraged under the dense undergrowth and found dry wood. Soon a fire crackled away, with a primitive tripod holding an earthenware pot of water over it. I asked, by making signs, how much farther we had to go? At this, one of them stood up, arching his arm to point over to the other side of the valley. I presumed he meant about a mile.

After cha and a short rest, we set off again for the last lap, feeling worn out and stiff with fatigue.

At last, peering ahead, I saw a faint light on the crest of the hill to our right, at which the porters shouted and danced about in their joy.

Mullianphui

January, 1944

Arriving at the post, I was hugely relieved to find Doug there. Apparently the trail he took at the fork was the correct one; it would be, wouldn't it!

The two chaps we were to relieve were overjoyed on meeting us, and had the bobijee prepare a meal straightaway.

After the initial introductions, we began swapping our experiences. It appeared they had been expecting us a week ago. Chittagong had signalled them to say we were on the way. Well, here we were at last, all together in this bamboo basha. It would be a bit cramped for sleeping, as there were only two charpoys; but in any case I didn't mind sleeping on the floor. I'd got quite used to it.

The bobijee cooked a very nice meal of fried eggs and rice on chapattis, followed by mugs of the local beer. During the meal we were being genned up on the local people and traditions, especially the chief of this village – a warrior over six foot tall, who was suspicious of all strangers. It would take a bit of tact and diplomacy when we were in conversation with him.

I asked the two men if they had the gist of the language, but they had only been up here for just over two months, and they hadn't bothered, as the bobijee translated for them. They told me we could trust him at all times. It appeared he was educated in Chittagong and spoke most of the local languages as well as English; he was a sort of civil servant and paid by the government. We would meet him in the morning during the changeover.

It was well past midnight when we all settled down. Doug and I were on rough mattresses on the floor; anyway, at least they were dry! Soon we all were in dreamland.

During our conversation the night before, I had the odious task of removing leeches off my neck, arms and shoulders by means of salt. They just dropped off! Their thin-skinned bodies were full of my blood, and they left a sore patch of flesh, which I was told would soon grow over. Doug was the same, but on awakening the next morning, all he had left was a slight itching. The two chaps we were relieving were already up and packing their kit in readiness to get away to make the trek down to Chittagong, a distance of about three hundred miles.

By mid-morning they were ready to move off with our porter corps of nine, and after handshakes, and wishing each other the best of luck, they moved off down the winding trail, through the village and into the dense jungle, and faded out of our sight.

Doug and I returned to the basha which would be our HQ for many months, and found our permanent bobijee there to welcome us, asking us if we would we like coffee.

Our observation post was about two hundred and fifty yards farther along the crest of this range which would itself be three thousand feet in height. From here we commanded a magnificent view of the Chin and Naga range of hills, stretching for hundreds of miles far below.

Doug and I decided to spend our first day in putting the rooms in the basha to our liking, which meant clearing out all the rubbish which had been left behind. I don't suppose the previous chaps had much regard for this when they knew they were being replaced.

The basha consisted of two bedrooms, each with a charpoy, table and chair. There were three-foot square openings acting as windows, with no glass, but a bamboo roller shutter above.

There was a verandah which ran round the basha on all sides, giving plenty of room to exercise or just lounge about and admire the panorama far below.

During our task of reorganising the interior, a sepoy arrived from the observation post to enquire if we needed help; if so, he would gladly give it.

Our sepoy's name was Cyril Sirren, and, as future events unfolded, I always looked upon him as being a most faithful and true friend.

He was an intelligent and well-behaved soldier, and one could see he would carry one's trust. So it was that we eventually built up a friendship in which he thought the sun shone out of my —!

By mid-afternoon we had the basha cleaned out and what furniture there was placed in the rooms to our satisfaction. This was done with the help of Cyril, who explained that he only came to enquire when we would visit the observation post, as the Sergeant in charge would need time to have the post ready for our inspection. Doug and I made it clear to Cyril our mission up here was only to make sure the equipment was in order; there'd be no bullshit on our part, as long as the communication with Chittagong was kept; that was the main object.

Cyril left about five, carrying our message that we would be at the post in the morning about nine, and to get the coffee ready!

The bobijee arrived from the village, bringing eggs, a chicken, and jungle vegetables: yams, *kolebeha*, a rough potato which is found quite near the surface of the topsoil, and, of course, bananas.

He also told the chief of our arrival, and asked if we would we pay a visit as soon as possible. We told the bobijee, on his return to the village, to say we would certainly pay a visit – tomorrow afternoon. We left it at that, hoping it would be convenient.

We'd had quite a busy day, and after a marvellous meal we sat out on the verandah for quite a long time before crawling under our mosquito nets.

I spent a most restful night – perhaps sleeping on a comfortable charpoy made all the difference, after roughing it on the ground. As I lay there, the morning chorus of all the birds and animals from below filled the dawn air.

I was thankful to the bobijee for putting up the mosquito net, as the room was full of the blasted things, while on the walls clung green lizards. They were about six inches long, having a high comb on their heads, and a long tail; they would have clung there motionless, till a mosquito settled near. Then, like lightning, they shot out a snake-like tongue to devour it.

They did a good job by killing off the insects, but I'm afraid the mosquitoes were too numerous. Nevertheless, it was fascinating to see how quickly they moved.

While I lay there watching the antics of the lizard-like creatures, the bobijee came in with coffee, and told me Doug was already up and having a wash outside under the lean-to. This was a good hint, and as I didn't know the time, I made the effort and crawled out from under my mosquito net to start another day.

During breakfast, we decided to inspect the observation post that morning, and in the afternoon have a chat with the chief. We would take the bobijee as interpreter, though I believe the chief knew a smattering of English.

The location of our basha and the observation post was well screened by tall trees and thick foliage, so to travellers down in the valley it was impossible to observe anything that would arouse any suspicion.

As we made our way along the beaten trail linking the units, we were struck by all the lush greenery about us: banana trees, and tobacco plants with huge leaves ready to be picked; while in the bamboo grass were numerous pineapples – not yet ripe, but ready in a few days.

On arrival at the post we were greeted by the five personnel with a very warm welcome – they'd had our approach under observation *nearly all the way*.

The IOC Sergeant introduced the four sepoys, Cyril Sirren among them, and asked us if would we like to check the transmission gear first, or have a meal. Then Doug said we should see the equipment first.

The bamboo observation hut itself was situated about thirty feet off the ground. It was built in between three trees on a platform lashed securely to the forks of strong branches. A rickety bamboo ladder led up to the hut. It was only strong enough for one person at a time, and as the Sergeant went up ahead of me, I could see why.

The hut itself was about eight feet square, and on entering, I saw how the equipment was well assembled, together with a bamboo chair and the usual cha making utensils. Narrow slits were put in each wall, so one could check on all approaches from different directions, having broad views of the Chin and Lushai Hills for hundreds of miles.

While Doug checked the transmitter, I enquired about supplies. Were they on time? Enough? Any stolen? To which the Sergeant said, given the conditions the porter corps had enough to go through in reaching here, the loads were ample, and if they were short at any time, the chief of the village would supply any needs.

The jenny (charging unit) and batteries were lasting well, giving no trouble at all, while the petrol supplies were ample; so all seemed well for the time being.

Doug came down from the post while I was checking the stores and suggested we should see what the staff had cooked. On entering their basha, we were met with a smiling welcome and a huge meal of curried chicken and rice, not forgetting the bottles of rice beer!

For reference we arrived up here on 4th January, 1944.

After the meal, and a few mugs of the local beer, we had to have a few minutes' rest before meeting the chief, and of course, it was an hour later when we slid out of our charpoys and made ourselves presentable, so as to give a good impression.

The bobijee accompanied us to act as interpreter and guide, and it was about three when we went down the winding trail to the village of bamboo huts.

As we made our way between the dwellings, I was struck by the utter filth, by the mangy dogs everywhere and the swine squealing, leaving their mess in and out of huts. There were fowls everywhere, while the women sat amongst it all, some with horrible ulcerated legs, and suppurating sores; heedless of all this, they sat there with huge toothless grins.

I would imagine the lifespan of a woman could be no more than thirty, as they were married off at the early age of eight or ten. The bride was then kept in purdah in the family till the age of puberty, to await the return of her husband.

I would say she would be fifteen or sixteen when the marriage was consummated. Then the husband would stay at home more often.

The style in which they had to live aroused disgust and nausea in Doug and myself. Disease was rampant, especially syphilis and gonorrhoea, revealed by the large swollen legs of the women, with pus seeping out from the broken skin.

What was pathetic was the complete resignation of the women: what had to be, would be; no guidance or medical advice from the outside world could help. It had been with them for ages – a way of life.

On passing the outer circle of the village, our bobijee led us to the centre where a huge basha was erected on large stilts about four feet high, a protection against marauding beasts; this was a feature of many large bashas.

To enter it, a wide ladder of bamboo led up to an opening. Here as we climbed up, a small group of natives appeared, led by a tall man. He was dressed with all the bamboo ornaments through his nose, ears and black hair, while his arms and legs were adorned with bangles of different colours; he was a man of about sixty I would say.

As we approached he held out his hand and said, 'Welcome.' I was most surprised, but as the bobijee explained later, the village had received many government officials on inspections in the past. On either side were warriors of different ranks, while at the rear were women of the household, giggling and staring at us.

Making signs for us to enter, the chief went forward into the large one-roomed basha, and indicated two large bamboo chairs placed at the side of his own. As there were no lamps, the interior was a bit dim, and it took Doug and myself quite a time to perceive different objects.

While his council were squatting in a circle on the sagging bamboo floor, Doug and I were getting used to the dim light. We could see a stone based fireplace set in the centre, with the smoke escaping through a large circular hole in the middle of the roof.

Approximately four feet off the ground, there was a foot-wide shelf, displaying various spoils of wars from the past; these included, to our horror, the shrunken heads of victims of wars between different tribes – large ones and small ones. I asked the bobijee to enquire if this gruesome decapitation was still practised, and the reply was, not so often now!

Directly above the chief's chair hung a large portrait of our Queen Victoria, to which the chief showed much respect, and when referring us to it, he put his hands together and bowed. I guessed that in colonial days gone by officials would often have passed this way.

In the meantime, while Doug and I were trying to distinguish the assorted spoils of war, the women were bringing in trays of food, including chapattis, curried chicken, yams, and all the fruits of the jungle. One large pot contained the local *Zophan* beer which was very potent; we'd have to go carefully with it, for from previous experience I knew it would make me a bit light-headed.

Our bobijee, meanwhile, was in deep conversation with the chief, explaining why we were there. He said that our equipment gave warning of the hated Japs, and that he must keep in contact with other villages to tell them to inform him if they knew of any patrols in the vicinity. The only means of contact between them were native runners, or transmitting by the use of drums – a language nobody could understand but themselves.

Our food was served on a huge green leaf, and we used our fingers, tearing off pieces of chapattis to convey the food. The meal was most enjoyable, especially with some swigs of the local beer!

I must say the chief seemed to enjoy it; he was making awful noises, belching and grunting, while all the time the women were fussing over him as he ate. When we all had enough to eat, Doug and I had to have a few puffs at the hubble-bubble pipe. You hold the tobacco bowl between your feet and draw the smoke through a three-foot flexible tube. This creates a bubbling sound as the smoke passes through a bowl of water attached to the tobacco bowl.

Altogether, the afternoon passed off quite nicely, considering the company we were in. After all, they had been headhunters only a few years ago, and given the chance, they might not be so far off it now! Near us, in the centre of the village, a huge fire had been lit, and of course we had to sit down on our haunches to watch the young men display their dancing skills. Round and round they went, chanting and waving.

We left the dancing and chanting natives still going round and round the fire and went to say our farewells to the chief. We found him well away, sitting on the verandah consuming rice beer from a large earthenware bowl by his side, while his women stood around giggling at the conversation.

Our bobijee explained to him that we were tired, and thanked him for all the hospitality and reception shown, and that we would put in a good report on reaching Chittagong later. As it was midnight by now, the chief allocated two tall warriors to escort us back to our basha, as there might be a few drunken natives around forgetting their manners! We arrived safely, asking the bobijee to convey our thanks to our escorts, who waved their hands and disappeared into the darkness. We sat on the verandah having a nightcap of rum, then crawled under our mosquito nets to drop off to sleep.

The night passed without incident, but for the mosquitoes trying to get through the net to me. Their presence was made known by the deep humming sound as they buzzed and dive-bombed about the room. Dawn came with the chorus of all the inhabitants of the jungle below, together with the rising sun making its debut above the range of hills hundreds of miles away. The air was quite fresh first thing in the morning, owing to the altitude, whereas down there in the jungle it was very humid and must have been in the hundreds at least.

The bobijee came in with coffee, and told me that Doug sahib was already up and washing, out under the lean-to. I took the hint, and crawled out from under my net to make a dash for the cold shower to freshen myself up.

Doug said he hadn't slept much, as his tummy was very painful. I told him to keep off the rich food and let it settle down for a few days; dry biscuits and rice was the order. In the meantime, I hunted through the medical supplies for treatment.

I found a white packet of indigestion tablets, and thought they might do the trick. Doug took two, and felt much better by lunchtime, which was a great relief; we knew the complaint could have only been indigestion.

After a light lunch of ration biscuits and rice, we decided to rest for the afternoon; I thought it would give Doug a chance for his tummy to settle down.

Before we rested, it was decided we would have a night's duty up in the observation post, to give the sepoys a break; perhaps we might get a signal from Chittagong.

The afternoon's rest did us both good. It was about six when I was awakened by the bobijee offering me a large mug of cha, and reminding me of our duty that night.

Dusk had fallen by the time we were ready; following the trail was a bit hazardous, as it was quite narrow and winding, but eventually the post came in sight, and the sepoys could be seen waving to us.

As we approached, two of them came running to meet us. One was Cyril Sirren, grinning and shaking my hand, and the other was just as enthusiastic, but not quite as likeable as Cyril, a chap I took to straight away for his bearing and appearance.

At the post, we were asked inside their basha to have tea and see for ourselves how they managed to live together in such a small space; and I must say they made use of every corner, considering that three charpoys had to be fitted in.

We stayed with them for about an hour, going over the routine of duties they had built up between the nights of duty. As we were taking over that night, all helpful tips were most welcome. Cyril volunteered to stay the night with us; he said he would make cha and look after us.

About eleven we climbed up the rickety ladder; there wasn't much wind. At this time of night the air was filled with weird cries of all the creatures around, especially the howl of wild dogs, beasts similar to the dingo. The blasted animals prowled underneath our basha making horrible cries, and I often had to shout and chase them off.

On entering the small observation hut, we could see that the transmitter and other gear took up most of the room. Three bamboo stools were the only means of rest, while a small oil lamp gave a low glow, just enough for us to distinguish different objects.

We each had a set of headphones. As I sat there listening to different call signs from all over the world, there wasn't one I could make sense of, but then it wasn't my job to decipher. Doug knew the code, and when we received it from Chittagong, he would wave to me to attract my attention, while he decoded the signal. The only signal we received was that they had acknowledged our position, and would give further instructions on this wavelength.

During one of Doug's tuning round the dial, we did get London, as the time here was early morning. I'm sure I could hear Jack Payne's band playing, even though the sound was oscillating. As we had confirmation from Chittagong of our position, we could rest to await further instructions; so for the next hour we were trying to get London, but with no luck.

We both felt much better in the knowledge that base was aware of the district in which we were operating. If we got short of supplies, we could signal for a porter corps to make their way up here, though I believe they were also using Dakotas to make the drops, which would be much quicker; in that case we would have to prepare a dropping zone.

In the meantime, Cyril was busy brewing up cha on a slow burning Primus stove, having found ration biscuits and a tin of fruit – what a meal! As the traffic in signals seemed to have quietened down at that time of the morning, we managed to have a break for five minutes.

As we continued our watch, I sensed the wind had risen quite noticeably, as the small bamboo room we were in began to creak and shift with its force. Cyril told us not to worry, as it had been much worse at times before, and it would take strong hurricane winds to dislodge it. The time now would be about four, and all the jungle below was awakening to the dawn chorus of the baboons, monkeys, wildfowl and wild dogs, and the shrieking cries of all the different birds. We looked as far as the eye could see over the range of hills, and the first tip of the morning sun began to make its appearance, emerging a little later as a huge fireball.

We had planned to come down at about five, after making sure all the equipment was as we found it. With Cyril sweeping and cleaning, the interior was as clean as a new pin when we eventually locked up and climbed down the ladder to report to the Sergeant in charge.

On arrival at their basha we were welcomed most heartily, and they thanked us for relieving them for a night.

The IOC insisted that we must stop to have breakfast, and chat about our travels and about England – of green fields, and the different shires and regions – and of course, London and Parliament, with its different parties debating opposing policies.

A hearty breakfast was prepared of bacon, eggs, and sausages; we hadn't tasted a meal like this for ages. We told them so and thanked them very much, at which they said we should thank Cyril, as it was his idea. A sort of rapport sprang up between Cyril and myself. I would spend hours explaining to him my way of life at home with my wife and son, Audrey and Nicky. I told him about the time I'd spent up here wondering how they were managing.

During our conversations, Cyril made it clear that he would work hard so that he could visit us after the war, and that he would write to memsahib to explain his wartime experiences with the *pugla* (mad) Sahib: I wonder!

Doug and I spent most of the day with the IOC, helping with any queries that were at hand, replying to different signals and maintaining the plant, including the jenny and storage batteries. Above all, we had to keep in touch with the chief at all times, in case there were any Jap patrols nearby.

If the post was in any danger of attack by the Japs, it had to be destroyed – by fire or complete destruction, by burial, or any means of disguising its existence. This would be a most dangerous job to put into operation; if detected it would mean the complete annihilation of the village.

We stayed with the IOC till about four, then decided to return to our basha, hoping the bobijee had cooked an evening meal, though we hadn't promised a definite return. We found, on arrival back at the basha, that the bobijee had, as usual, anticipated the time of our return, and as we approached the smell of cooking was very appetising. Soon we were tucking into chapattis and curried rice, followed by a mug of the local beer.

Dusk was falling fast, with swarms of mosquitoes swirling in the air, so it was time to cover our arms and legs with cream. This did help prevent the horrible swellings and itching. During our evening meal, not far from our basha, the loud sound of drums being beaten started up, together with natives chanting, making a hell of a din. I asked the bobijee the cause of it all, and he explained it was to celebrate a good rice harvest and that the drums and chanting would go on for days.

A huge fire was lit, and kept going while the festival was on. The young men continued leaping and chanting round and round, showing off their prowess to impress the young native girls, who were sitting around, wide-eyed and giggling.

A large cauldron, slung from a tripod over the fire supplied cha, while earthenware jars held gallons of the local beer. This was made from rice; it was very potent and as clear as gin and after a few mugs one had difficulty staying upright!

One of the dancers beckoned to me to join in, so with much laughter I accepted, falling in behind and holding on to the chap in front, and at the same time chanting and doing the soft shoe shuffle! I'm afraid I only managed one complete round; the beer was taking effect and I had to sit down – much to the amusement of the other dancers.

We stayed with the duty IOC for about an hour, hoping to get a signal from Chittagong, but had no luck. We heard hundreds of messages being transmitted in different codes and languages; I expect the Japs were also transmitting to their various units on patrol.

It was about two when we wished the chaps on duty all the best for the rest of the night, climbed down the ladder and made our way to our own quarters.

On reaching our basha, we found one oil lamp left on in the kitchen, together with a meal of curried rice and biscuits, thanks to our thoughtful bobijee. We did him justice by eating a small portion, then retired to our rooms to crawl under our mosquito nets and get a little sleep, if possible; though I doubted it, because the incessant monotonous beating of drums could be heard not far from our basha.

I lay there for ages, wondering how Audrey was managing. I'd have to write in the morning, and ask the chief to find a runner to take the letter down to Demagri, a distance of about thirty miles; from there by various means of transport it would take a week or more to reach Chittagong.

I spent a fairly good night; prancing around the festival fire took all the strength out of me, but in the process I'm sure better relations were made between us and the villagers. The bobijee came in with coffee to say a small detachment of the Lushai Brigade had arrived, and if possible they would like to rest for a while before pushing on to Demagri.

Doug came in to suggest we put on clean shirts and shorts, after which we found the small corps making camp not far from our basha. There were nine fighters led by a havildar (sergeant), all dressed in only loincloths with bangles and the usual bits of bamboo sticking through their nose and ears. These tall warriors, each carrying a Sten gun, had the usual weapons of the jungle slung from their shoulders – huge bows, quivers full of arrows with poisoned tips, and blow-pipes, while slung from a thin hide belt they carried the deadly Gurkha *kukri*.

The Sergeant said they had been operating around Ijal and fought many skirmishes with the Japs. They had been successful in seeking out Japanese positions to report to HQ. After eight months they had been relieved, and were looking forward to returning to their families and resting awhile before taking further orders.

During our conversation it was established that there were three WOU posts situated at villages towards Ijal, the distance between each being about twenty miles. I wondered if HQ had any ideas to signal us to slog for sixty miles on inspection!

During cleaning out of the lean-to where we washed, the bobijee found a portable gramophone, complete with three records, all in a terrible state. I suppose the previous chaps had left it behind. I resolved to wash and clean it thoroughly and see if it worked.

A native had just arrived from the village carrying vegetables which grow in abundance in the jungle – yams, wild potatoes (*kolebeha*) and roots that make up the natives' daily diet. The chief had sent them, hoping it would be a change from our tinned food, and I asked the bobijee to convey our deepest thanks, and said we hoped to pay a visit soon.

The bobijee said he had sighted a herd of deer not far from here, so we decided to go down to tell the chief, and very likely a hunting party would be formed to locate the herd. On returning, the bobijee said if the hunt was successful, we would be eating venison tomorrow! Just before dusk, a huge portion of the meat was sent up, so it appeared the hunt was successful; there was enough meat to last quite a few days.

Before retiring last night, Doug and I took a stroll along the ridge to check the IOC at the observation post, mainly to see if there were any signals for us regarding further movements. Wonders of wonders, a coded message had come through instructing us to proceed up the ridge to check the post at a place called Choullong, a village about the same size as this, manned by five Pathan IOC with a sergeant in command.

Returning to our basha, we spent about an hour discussing plans for the next day: how many bearers to have, and what provisions to take, and the need for a native who was conversant with the trail. I reckoned the village was about fifteen miles distant. I doubted if we'd make the journey in one day, so we'd have to take groundsheets and blankets.

We would have to get up as early as possible, to arrange with the chief to pick out trustworthy porters with knowledge of the trail.

We sat out on the verandah that night till quite late, discussing what we should take on the visit, and finally decided on as little as possible; with the benefit of previous experiences we could now plan our loads. We'd take the bobijee to translate, with only two bearers. In this way, the party would be able to keep together – much better than a straggling line. It was so quiet and peaceful; the chanting and dancing had temporarily ceased, though it wouldn't be long before it would start up again. I guessed they had stopped for rice and rice beer. Before they resumed their din, we decided to turn in for the night.

During the night the sweat rolled off me, saturating the bed, the oppressive air being broken only by the drone of mosquitoes as they circled round and round. It was therefore a great relief when dawn was marked by the rising sun piercing through the gaps in the bamboo wall. I could hear someone moving about, and presently the bobijee came in with coffee, saying Doug Sahib was up and washing, and breakfast would be ready soon.

After breakfast we made our way through the village to the chief's basha to ask if he would detail two trustworthy natives to act as our porters and guides to the village of Choullong, which would mean being away for three to four weeks. On reaching his basha, we were made most welcome, and he answered our request by immediately sending for his choice of people for our needs. During the time these chaps were being found, we were made most welcome. Mugs of cha and bowls of fruit were presented by his women, who at all times stood just behind his chair, giggling and chattering away.

I was fascinated by the large photo portrait of Queen Victoria framed above his chair, and asked the bobijee to enquire how he had obtained it. The chief stated that it was presented to his father by the then DC (District Commissioner), who organised local hunting parties and frequently passed through the village. This explained his smattering of English. After shaking hands with the chief and thanking him for his hospitality, we finally left and made our way back to our basha. Prior to our leaving, he gave his assurance and the two porters would be reporting to us in the morning at dawn.

Arriving back at the basha, we were met by our grinning bobijee who said he had made chapattis and rice for lunch. Afterwards we would have to make arrangements and organise what we needed to take for our trip to Choullong. We hoped to start at dawn.

The weather was fairly favourable – quite close, but we were getting used to the humidity. There was a light wind, but I reckoned it would be misty in the morning.

The dawn broke with the usual crescendo of noise from the inhabitants of the jungle far below, which we would soon be among, threading our way towards the distant villages of primitive people. We had a light breakfast of hard issue biscuits and coffee; we had learned our lesson from previous trips when we'd marched on full stomachs!

By about nine we were ready: two porters and our faithful bobijee, loaded with packs high on their shoulders; Doug and I wore only shorts and a loose shirt, Doug carrying a Sten gun, while I had just a bamboo walking stick. Sandals were our footwear, and often we didn't wear them, as our feet had become hardened to walking barefoot.

By ten we were ready to move off. We checked round the dāk bungalow and locked up, making sure all the kitchen utensils were hidden away in the lean-to.

Heading our small party was the stocky warrior who had assured us he was conversant with this trail, as he often used it to visit a relation. Threading our way past isolated bashas leading down to farther open plots of land, we could see far below the dense jungle which we'd be entering soon, and it certainly didn't give us much cheer.

We were all very lively. Doug and I didn't say much, but the two porters were talking and chattering away, and in between would chant away at some native song. I asked the bobijee how far it was to Choullong. After rolling his eyes around and shaking his head, he said he thought about fifteen miles. At this, Doug and I both agreed we certainly wouldn't be able to reach it that day.

We had been on the trail for about three hours, stumbling and trying to keep a good foothold, with the sweat pouring off us, so it was a great relief to the others when I called a halt at the next clearing. The porters soon had a fire going with the water boiling in a crude earthenware bowl, held over the fire by a tripod of stones.

While we were resting I enquired if there was a village nearby where we could stop over for the night, and was told by our guide that there was, but it would mean a slight deviation to our left off the trail. Anyway, I thought over the alternative of staggering on, and decided to make for this village, called Chamoon.

Branching off the main trail, we entered a much smaller one leading into dense undergrowth, through which we had to plod along in a single file. What with the sweat and heat, I wondered if I had taken the right decision. Then suddenly the overhanging undergrowth cleared, and gave way to a stretch of open country stretching for miles. What made it more amazing was the sight of orange and grapefruit trees, bearing loads of fruit; it was surely a Utopia to us.

Amongst the trees were built the usual bashas, constructed on log supports about four feet off the ground, away from any animals that might venture in to attack. Our guide went ahead to locate the chief and explain who we were, and as he went forward I was struck by the absolute emptiness of the whole village. We waited for about ten minutes, when suddenly the whole place burst alive – natives and children came running out to meet us, shyly at first; then, as they got more confident, they came up to us to stare and giggle.

While the children were running around, a deputation of elders approached, led by an imposing figure, dressed in the full regalia of coloured feathers and ornaments.

As he drew near, I could see he was suspicious, and he looked aggressive; this was not the formal greeting we had experienced with previous village chiefs.

Our bobijee had the presence of mind to go forward to have a few words with the chief, with the result that by the time they had reached us he seemed less suspicious. He clasped his hands together and gave the customary bow – what a relief!

I must say, Doug and I both felt our hearts pumping overtime! Our porters played their part in easing the tension by chatting away in their lingo, and after a short while smiles appeared all round, with the chief beckoning us to follow his party into the village.

There were about a dozen bashas forming a circle, in which smaller bamboo huts made up the village, with mangy dogs and swine running about in between the dwellings, dropping their dung and whatever in and out of the huts. What with the squeaking and grunting of the animals together with the children screaming and shouting, and of course the smell, I said to Doug it would be better for us to make our stay there as short as possible. In the meantime we would have to stop the night – augh!

We were given to understand that a basha had been allocated for our use, just outside the main circle, and three warriors had been detailed to look after us, and to keep guard through the night. Judging from that precaution, it would seem we had found quite a friendly village! Better than we had thought at first. The bobijee and porters camped just outside our basha, giving Doug and me assurance of our safety, though I must say we both didn't get much sleep.

I couldn't sleep much; the stink and movement of rats kept me awake most of the night, so it was a relief to see the early sunrise penetrating the thin walls of the basha. It was then about four; the dawn was heralded by all the cockerels and early birds venting their early morning chorus to mark the start to another day. Looking across to where Doug lay, I could see he was fidgety, so after a few moments I called out, 'Good morning!'

He replied, 'How do? What a bloody night!' From that I presumed he'd had about as good a night as I did.

The bobijee looked in to see how we were, and to promise coffee as soon as possible, but I must say we both spent a miserable night. By now the whole village was beginning to stir, with dogs barking, and children shrieking in their morning games. The bobijee came in with the coffee, and to say the porters were loading up again, ready to move out of this rat hole! Even they couldn't stand the conditions!

We didn't stop to have a meal, as I believed we all wanted to get moving. I took the bobijee along with me to thank the chief for letting us stay there for the night, but when we arrived at his basha, it appeared he had gone out hunting for the day; so that let me off that duty. I only hoped we wouldn't meet the gent during his headhunting trip!

We were soon on our way, thankful to leave such a hole. If I'd known beforehand what a dump we were walking into, I'm sure we would have struggled on towards Choul-long and made camp at a suitable clearing.

It seemed the recent experience and keenness to get away again put new heart in the porters, for as they swung into their familiar gait, they were soon chattering and singing the occasional tribal chant; my only hope was that it would last till we arrived at our destination.

After about two hours of progress on the narrow trail, pushing forward, sometimes against thick overhanging undergrowth, Doug and I decided to have a rest, and soon a suitable clearing came in view, just the job.

I do believe our bobijee and the porters welcomed the rest. Our previous night's stop at Chamoon wasn't a restful experience; we were all on edge and glad now to be away, and leave it all behind.

Very soon we had a fire going, and could look forward to coffee and chapattis, and perhaps five minutes' snooze, which we would all welcome. Our final destination was Choullong, a much larger village. Within its boundaries was the IOC post we were to inspect; I believed it to be manned by a small core of Pathans – men from the northern states of India, of which Pathan State is one.

After a welcome rest, we all felt much better, and after clearing all signs of our stay, set out on our last few miles. By this time, the wind had risen quite forcibly, and I began to wonder if we were in for a storm. We had left the cover of the undergrowth, and the full force made it most difficult to keep upright. We had to hold on to any branches that were near for support.

We were now following a trail winding round the edge of a steep hill. It was a sheer drop of hundreds of feet, if we were to slip. Glancing across the valleys far below, I wondered what life existed down there, if there were any Japs. Our bobijee and the guide were leading the party, when suddenly they turned and shouted, 'Choullong!' They pointed across the valley, and we could just see a village situated on the crest of the hill, about a mile away.

We had to follow the winding trail down the steep hill to reach a plateau before entering the thick undergrowth. Then we began climbing again, and by this time I could see

Doug was feeling the strain; he didn't look at all well. I offered to call a stop to rest for a while, but he said he'd make it to our destination and have a good rest then.

Up and up we climbed, grabbing hold of any branches to steady ourselves, until after about an hour, our leading guide stopped. He held his hand up to signal us to listen, and in the distance we could hear someone approaching. Very soon we were met by a Pathan IOC sepoy who was all smiles and very glad to welcome us. He said we had been in their sights for quite a long time; they'd seen us making our way across the opposite ridge, and followed us when we broke cover now and again.

His post had received a signal from Demagri that we were somewhere up here, and they should help us in any way we wanted. He explained also that a basha was at our disposal and had been made ready. After hearing all this, we found the remainder of the journey much lighter; even Doug seemed brighter at the thought of having a long rest.

Choullong

It wasn't long before we came in sight of the observation post. It was built on the highest point of the ridge, partly hidden by a clump of tall trees, but with a commanding view of the Lushai and Chin Hills. The village lay below in a hollow, out of sight to travellers from the plateau below. I gave full marks to the IOC who must have had some harrowing experiences in finding and setting up these posts.

On arriving at our destination we were met by a sergeant, who seemed very pleased to meet us at last, having heard so much about us over the wireless from Chittagong.

Having made sure our porters and bobijee were billeted in a suitable basha, we were shown our quarters – a large basha situated not far from the camp. It benefited from a marvellous view from the verandah which circled the whole building. Doug and I would certainly rest here for a few days.

The Pathan cook had prepared a meal of chicken curry and rice, together with a bottle of the local rice beer. After this we both felt much better, and looked forward to a good night's rest. Before retiring, I walked over to the bobbie's basha to see if they were all right, and was met by laughter and singing, with the assurance that all was well!

The Pathans had even had mosquito nets erected over our beds, which they themselves didn't use. This was a thought for which we were very grateful – I still had swellings over my arms and shoulders from previous visits of the blasted insects.

I did sleep well. I felt so exhausted after the previous few days' travelling, and this charpoy felt so comfortable that it wasn't till about nine that I was shaken up by the bobijee enquiring if I was all right! Doug was already washed and moving about, and came in to say breakfast was laid out on the verandah.

During the meal we decided to visit the observation post to check all the equipment and to ask if there were any messages for us. The three Pathans on duty had spent a quiet night, continuously hearing coded signals being given from various outposts throughout Asia, but none were for us. While Doug checked the transmitter, I checked the jenny (charging unit) and storage batteries. I also went through all the stores and equipment, so that I could report to Demagri if there was any deficiency in stock.

By the time we had checked all the equipment it was past noon and we were looking forward to a meal. Then the Sergeant appeared, to say he also was up half the night with the sepoys and had only just woken up; if he had been aware we were here, he would have come out earlier. We told him we had checked everything and asked about getting some food.

Returning to his basha, we found one of the sepoys had prepared chapattis and fried eggs, and of course rice, with mugs of the local beer.

After the meal, I wandered along a trail leading through undergrowth and came to a wide open space, from which I got a marvellous sighting of miles of hill ranges stretching far below. I felt so isolated up there and I was thinking we'd have to trek down below later on.

I rejoined Doug and the Sergeant at the basha to discuss when we should move on, and it was decided that as Doug still had a touch of stomach trouble, we would have another day resting, and start the day after tomorrow, hoping his discomfort would have eased.

On several previous occasions he had complained of pains. Luckily we had in our medicine cabinets a mixture for the relief of tummy trouble. The hour was quite late when we eventually made our way back to our basha. It was just a short walk, but the air was filled with all the cries of the night prowlers, some sounding very strange.

Arriving at the basha, we were surprised to find the bobijee waiting up, full of smiles. Gathering together his *poen* (skirt), he quickly disappeared into the darkness for home.

After a nightcap of the local beer, we sat out on the verandah for quite a while; it all was so peaceful, and the fact that Doug was feeling much better made us both feel at ease with the world. We'd have a day off tomorrow in readiness for our trip to Mullianphui.

I was awakened by the jabbering of many personnel, and peering out of my open shutters I could see the camp was full of men of the IPC (Indian Pioneer Corps). They were all helping to build a fire in order to cook a meal. There were about twenty of them, moving about freely, having dumped their 40 lb loads in a huge pile, leaving two men to guard the loads against theft.

I had just finished washing when Doug came in to say the Corps was under armed escort, led by a jemadar (lieutenant) who would like to discuss accommodation for one night. Talking it over, we decided they could take over my room, while I put my charpoy in with Doug. The IPC armed guard could make use of the verandah. The jemadar was deeply grateful when he learnt of our plans. He apologised for putting us to such trouble, and promised us any stores we might be short of – he couldn't offer much, but would make up a little of any shortage we might have.

Doug and I appreciated the co-operation, and invited him and his Sergeant to a meal in the evening at about seven. I contacted the bobijee to suggest a meal, and he said a chicken curry would be the most popular; there were plenty of ingredients for it available. The bobijee also promised that he would collect bottles of the local beer; I didn't know if our guests would bring any whisky, but I hoped they would.

Doug and I changed into long trousers and clean shirts, I said to Doug that if we made a good impression, he'd spread the news farther up the line!

Dusk had fallen by the time our guests arrived, full of bullshit and clean *dhobi* (clothes). I told them not to dress up and suggested we let our hair down!

I could see they were a bit inquisitive about our rank, but we didn't help in any way. We told them we were on a special mission and left it at that; the observation post was out of sight; which was a good thing. If the porters saw it, one of them would let it slip out in conversation with any native he met.

The evening passed off quite well. The Jemadar spoke quite good English, and talked of his home in northern India, of his brothers and sisters, and the way of life in his village. Of course, he spoke enthusiastically of London, asking a lot of questions about the Houses of Parliament, Buckingham Palace, and many other places of interest.

He was a tall figure, with a military bearing, and by the time we'd had a few glasses of his whisky, we were well away, all enjoying the company.

It was nearly midnight, and with all our cares and worries about our future far away, we could relax and chat about our experiences up here among the different tribes. We were sitting out on the verandah, and glancing towards the dying embers of the campfire, round which the porters were all sprawling – some asleep, others talking in low tones; in a while I decided to call it a day and bid our guests goodnight.

Our friend said he would be off at first light, but before leaving he would remember to leave us some provisions, whatever he could spare. They would be left in the lean-to out of sight. The time came for us to part. Doug and I shook his hand and wished him and his supply porters a safe journey to their destination.

It must have been about two in the morning by the time we got our heads down. We dropped off straight away – the first time for many a night.

I must have slept soundly. When I heard the voice of the bobijee saying, 'Cha, Sahib!', the sun was well up and shining through the bamboo wall.

Apparently, the Jemadar with his IPC had left quite early before sunrise. It must had been a very quiet departure, as I didn't hear a thing. I immediately asked the bobijee to look behind our basha under the lean-to, hoping our friend had kept his word.

Sure enough, a small heap of provisions had been left in the corner, covered over by bamboo matting. He was a true gentleman; I reckoned he would keep his word.

All the provisions were in small lots: coffee, cigarettes, rice, sugar, flour, and, wonders of wonders – a bottle of Rosa rum! He certainly knew how to move quietly; I'd heard nothing. I walked over to where the porters had made camp, but it was most difficult to locate the exact place. It had all been restored to its original state.

Returning to our basha, I found Doug sitting out on the verandah tucking into a breakfast of rice and fried eggs. It looked a very appetising feast, and I was soon enjoying it too. I asked Doug if he'd had any tummy pains lately. In reply he said sometimes the pain was unbearable, then it disappeared completely. This was a symptom, I thought, of gastric trouble; he would have to keep off fatty foods.

The village below seemed to me to be very quiet. I said to Doug, 'Let's go down and enquire, the place looks deserted.' On leaving our basha, we were met by our bobijee who explained why the village seemed so desolate.

A child had died and would be cremated that afternoon. The whole village was in mourning. The procession was due to start later in the day; the child's body would be borne on a little bier above the heads of those leading the cortège to the place of cremation.

By contrast, if an elderly person died the whole village celebrated with an orgy of dancing and feasting! There is some sense in that philosophy, I suppose.

We decided that after a midday snack we would join in the procession to watch the proceedings.

By mid-afternoon I could hear the procession had started. The low notes of the drums mingled with the wailing of the bereaved following. Doug and I scrambled down the trail to join it at the rear, meeting strange looks from the natives. Some of them glared at us, but the majority accepted us in their midst. The procession wound its way along the narrow trail for about half a mile, till finally a clearing was reached which had obviously been previously prepared; there were garlands of flowers everywhere.

In the centre, a high pyre built of bamboo had been erected, and soon the ceremony started. The covered body of the child was placed on a bed of bamboo grass, which was lit by the chief mourner. No real emotion was shown; they all had their eyes fixed on the pyre as flames engulfed it completely.

The cremation was soon over and there was just a pile of ashes left; I don't believe they were collected by relatives. The whole gathering just dispersed, leaving the dying embers disappearing into the ground.

Doug and I were asked to have a meal with them, but we declined, making signs that we had duties to attend to. However, our presence at the funeral did, I believe, foster a closer faith between us and them. By this time, the sun was sinking towards the horizon, so we decided to give the IOC a visit in the hope that there might be a signal for us.

On arrival at the post we found two sepoys on duty. Both of them seemed very pleased to see us, and immediately made coffee. They said all was quiet, with no signals received all day – perhaps the night would yield something.

We decided not to spend the night there in the hope of receiving a signal, but left the post at about midnight and made our way back to our basha. The sepoys on duty promised to contact us at once if an urgent message was received.

On our way back, we were accompanied by our friends, the baboons. They swung from bough to bough among the highest branches of the trees that formed a camouflage line, deflecting the inquisitive gaze of travellers who might stray into this area.

The continuous shrieking and crying of the packs stayed with us as we made our way along the trail. I often thought it was a certain indication of our presence, but our friends in the villages pointed out that it was customary for the baboons to make this row whenever they were on the move. We soon arrived back at our basha, put up the bamboo shutters and prepared to crawl under our mosquito nets; but before that, we had to have a stiff drink of rum during our last recap of the day's happenings.

During breakfast of fried eggs and rice the next day, we decided to make plans to move down to Mullianphui on the following morning, and at least make a start on the slog. Our first duty would be to contact the chief to ask him for the services of two trustworthy porters; that would mean taking the bobijee as interpreter. Having located the bobijee, we set off down to the village hoping the chief would be available, and in good humour! Upon our reaching his basha he emerged on to the verandah in a most jovial mood; he was all smiles, and glad to meet us.

While his women were preparing coffee, we explained to him we would be leaving in the morning, and asked him to recommend two staunch porters conversant with the trail in the direction of Mullianphui. This was a distance of about twenty-five miles, which would take at least two days. Luck was with us, for it appeared that there were two natives from that village here on a visit. They would be returning at any time, so the chief immediately sent a runner to ask them to report to him.

The coffee arrived, served in large earthenware bowls, together with a large container of the local rice beer! During our talk with the chief, conducted through our bobijee, we only sipped the beer. From previous experiences, we knew it was most potent, and a clear head was required!

A native reported he had found the two Mullianphui men, and that they were waiting to know when we'd start in the morning. I told the bobijee to bring them in and let us have a look at them. We were confronted by two tall warriors, dressed in very little, with all the usual bamboo ornaments through their ears and nose, while bangles adorned their arms and legs.

To think that a few years ago they were headhunters! Looking at them, I could well believe it. Recently with the opening up of these territories of hitherto unknown ranges of hills and valleys, these tribes had come to accept that a much larger conflict was raging around them.

I asked the bobijee to tell them to be outside our basha at dawn the next day, so that we could get away as soon as possible. At this they made signs of acceptance and hurried away.

The bobijee assured us they would keep their word, so we had to leave it at that and trust them; though I did think the presence of the chief carried some weight. I didn't think they'd let us down.

By the time we had reached our basha, the sun had started to sink over the valleys, creating a wonderful aurora of all the colours of the rainbow: what a wonderful sight! We stayed up till the early hours, packing up small incidentals that we would want on the trek, till at last we had it all organised for an early start.

No sooner had I got my head down than the cheerful voice of the bobijee was saying, 'Cha, Sahib,' and I could see the early morning sun streaming through the gaps of the bamboo wall. I could hear Doug splashing about in the lean-to and decided it was time I made a move towards getting my kit together, so we'd be ready to move out as early as possible.

Our two porters hadn't turned up and I hoped they wouldn't let us down; they seemed quite a reliable pair. During our light breakfast snack they arrived, grinning and bowing, and arranging the loads between themselves with the bobijee's help.

By ten thirty we were ready to take to the trail again. We said our farewells to our friends in the village and the Pathan sepoys at the observation post, wishing them all the best for the future.

Our trail led us along the crest of the range for about half a mile, then descended steeply down into the deep undergrowth of the jungle, during which we all had a devil of a job to keep upright as the trail was so slippery and steep.

Soon we were in the deep jungle again, with all the heat and insects closing down; and of course, our friends the baboons had found us. There was a large troupe of them, shrieking in their high-pitched cries and swinging from bough to bough, following us all the time. In places the trail was quite narrow, so we had to maintain a close lookout on the banks in case our friend the dreaded krait snake decided to shoot out.

At all times there were numerous exotic birds in flight, together with highly coloured fowl, so there was no need to go hungry! We kept close together. As our porter guides knew the way, I had them leading – just in case there were natives ahead with poisoned arrows keen to practice on strangers!

By now it was about noon, and we had made good progress, so I sent the bobijee up front to tell our guides to look out for a suitable open clearing in which we could rest for a while to have a meal and coffee. Ten minutes later a suitable opening in the undergrowth appeared, and quickly a quantity of wood was collected, enough to boil water and make cha.

As we sat around the fire our presence was noted by many types of inquisitive creatures of the jungle, especially the monkeys. They just sat up in the branches staring down at us with their large round eyes, wondering what sort of species we were!

The two guides picked quite a lot of fruit – bananas and oranges, together with some berries that I'd never seen before; I was told they were nutritious, containing lots of iron and calcium.

It was a good idea to have built a fire, for as we were eating, large animals were heard prowling around in the undergrowth not far from us. Our guides were continually casting anxious looks at the deep undergrowth, wondering what beast would show itself.

I do believe the incessant chattering and laughter of our porters made the prowlers think twice before coming closer!

We made a point of not stopping there too long. After coffee and biscuits, the small fire was put out and all signs of our short rest were disguised. We swept the marks away by dragging branches over the ground.

We were soon on the trail again; I believe the porter guides were grateful for it. As we got into our stride, while they were jabbering away, they looked at Doug and me in appreciation and, I hope, a better understanding.

Before reaching Mullianphui, the bobijee said we'd have to go round or through another village, and in his recollection, at his last visit the natives were most friendly. The chief especially had made them very much at ease, so it was decided that when the village was located we'd contact the chief first.

The trail we were on was becoming dense with the overhanging foliage. The bobijee had warned us of this earlier, and said that we would eventually emerge out of the undergrowth on to open land. Here, the trail wound its way down a rock face and a treacherous hillside with a gradient of one in ten.

I would say we were about five hundred feet up, and looking down into the valley below, we could just see the bamboo roofs of a village deep in the forest well camouflaged by the different colours of the vegetation. I said to Doug, 'I wonder if we have been spotted yet?' We still had about two to three hours to go.

I could hear the drums beating, but as we approached, looking ahead over to another range of hills, we could see a party of natives making their way towards us. They all looked very ferocious, with their spears and arrows, and chanting away with some tribal challenge! As we came near, the chanting stopped, with all of them blocking the trail and looking for us to make the first contact.

I sent the bobijee ahead to explain who we were, and assure them that we were friends, out on patrol and seeking out the dreaded Japs, who were intent on destroying their villages. After quite a long session of waving arms and glaring in our direction, the tension eased and soon we were rewarded by huge grins; they were telling each other that we were there to safeguard their villages.

Beckoning us to follow, we were led down through deep undergrowth till we caught sight of our friends' village – a cluster of about a dozen bashas forming a circle built on open ground, away from the jungle and dark foliage.

Following our guide, we were led to the largest basha, where we could see a gathering of a few elders had assembled to meet us. Our bobijee went ahead to go through the same procedure of introduction as before, and soon large earthenware jugs were placed on the verandah, each full of the local rice beer, together with bowls of fruit. Our porters were being treated similarly, so Doug and I presumed we weren't destined for the cooking pot!

Meanwhile, we were the main attraction for the villagers. They stood around in small groups; some seemed friendly, while others stared suspiciously. I wouldn't have liked to cross their paths! The children seemed to have no fear; they were laughing and running around all the time. After a few mugs of beer, we were all making signs, trying to overcome the language problem; and by the time we began making preparations to leave, a good liaison had been established between us.

After thanking the chief for his hospitality, we decided to push on the trail for Mullianphui. When all our farewells had been made, the sun had started to sink, so we would have to make the most of what was left of daylight.

As we picked our way along the rough trail, I said to Doug it was obvious we wouldn't make Mullianphui by nightfall, and we'd have to look out for a suitable clearing to camp for the night.

As we slogged along, our friends the baboons had formed a school and were shrieking and making a hell of a din, leaping from tree to tree; while in the distance one could hear the drums of villages warning each other of our whereabouts.

At last we found the going much better. There was green grass growing between shrubs, while the overhanging branches grew less dense, giving much better light on the trail.

We came at last to a plateau of small shrubs and grass, with banana trees loaded with fruit – what a sight! After sweating and cursing the tangled tree roots we had to stumble over on the way, it was very welcome.

We decided to make camp, and set to clearing a space in which we could make a small fire to cook a meal. We would keep it going throughout the night to warn off any inquisitive prowlers that might venture near. Soon we had a nice pot of rice boiling away, while the bobijee was busy making chapattis on a crude slab of metal.

By this time daylight had gone, making the glow from the fire all the more welcome, and soon we were all sitting round it on our haunches, picking at the rice and chapattis served up on a large green leaf.

Doug and I had previously cleared spaces in which to bed down, not far from the bobijee, while the porters had made a watch roster to maintain guard and keep the fire going. I didn't sleep all that well. The ground was most uneven, while the air was full of the cries of different night prowlers, the most prominent being the wild dog.

The dawn came, with the porters jabbering away and chanting and singing as they got the breakfast ready. The early sun cast arrows of light through the canopy of the treetops above us. After a light splash of water over our faces, Doug and I felt a bit fresher, and made ourselves ready to have a light meal and get on the trail again.

The bobijee had fried eggs ready in no time, together with a mug of cha. We were ready to move within the hour. Having removed all traces of our camp, the porters loaded up, and we set off for our last few miles to Mullianphui – and a nice rest, we hoped!

The trail led us through many different aspects of the jungle. Sometimes we were on high ground, looking down on the dense foliage below, at one time the porters stopped to point down below where we could see a small herd of elephants grazing. I hoped they wouldn't come our way, but the bobijee put my fears at rest, saying the wind was carrying our scent in the wrong direction.

Meanwhile, the trail began to descend gradually down into the dense undergrowth again, and soon we were sweating and trying to swat the clouds of mosquitoes looking for a good meal! There were numerous snakes of all sizes partly hidden under the carpet of leaves, so at all times we were on the lookout.

Still we pushed on – the two Lushai porters leading, with the bobijee and me and Doug following. We must have been quite two hours on the trail when I decided to call a halt for coffee and a rest before reaching Mullianphui.

Mullianphui

January, 1944

Nearing Mullianphui, we could see the village on the crest of the hill, half hidden by trees. There was no sight of our observation post, which was a good point in its favour. It seemed to be just a few huts, and if a Jap patrol saw it, I didn't think they would bother to investigate.

We had to follow the trail down into the valley, then to climb up to where we saw the few huts. By now we had been observed, and several children came running towards us, laughing and dancing.

It was good to be back there. The bobijee had gone ahead to get the kitchen fire started and soon we were stretched out on our charpoys to look forward to a long rest.

Our basha had been well looked after while we were away. I think the bobijee had made arrangements for it to be checked periodically by a relation.

We both felt much better for having a rest, and enjoying a nice chicken curry the bobijee had prepared. We decided to go along to the observation post later on, to try and contact Chittagong and obtain news, if there was any.

I would have to check our stores, and make a list of what we were short of, hoping we'd contact Chittagong. Then it would be up to them to contact Demagri, to make up the load and enlist enough porters for the delivery. Each porter could carry 50 lbs, secured by a sling from the forehead, the weight being evenly distributed by the porter bending forward as he went along.

I once had young *chikos* (boys) aged about twelve carrying loads. They all had a cheerful outlook and laughed at the least quip; I don't believe they ever went to school. They lived on their wits, leaving home at an early age to mingle with others doing whatever came along to earn a rupee. They would sleep in any shelter available, and always had a cheery outlook and a ready grin.

We decided to man the observation post that night, perhaps we might have the luck to contact Chittagong; if so, we could indent direct for more supplies, hoping they'd pull their fingers out and act as soon as possible. In the meantime I sent a runner to the post to inform the duty IOC sepoys that we would take over duty for the night. I said it would be appreciated if one sepoy could be on duty to assist, preferably Cyril Sirren.

After a light meal of rice and chapattis, we decided to make our way along the ridge to where the post was situated – a distance of about five hundred yards. The trail passed through deep vegetation where yams and wild potatoes or *kolebehas* were plentiful, together with pineapples, growing amongst the bamboo grass.

Looking down over the *khud*-side or hillside as we made our way, we could see quite a lot of banana trees loaded with fruit, and I said to Doug we could collect a branch on our way back later. As we looked ahead, the site of the post came in view – just a clump of tall trees, giving the passing traveller no hint that hidden away was a wireless transmitter post, capable of giving urgent immediate calls to the outside world.

We were met at the base of the post by our sepoy friend, Cyril Sirren. He seemed delighted that we had decided to do a night's watch with him as a cha wallah and general help.

Climbing the rickety bamboo ladder, we entered the small hut built between the branches, and were again struck by the ingenious way the equipment was assembled, with every appliance to hand.

The first job for Cyril was to brew a mug of cha while Doug and I inspected all the gear, noting that all was in perfect condition – clean, and in working order.

The hut had no windows. Small slits in the bamboo gave us the only view we had of the hills and jungle down below.

Having made ourselves as comfortable as possible, we put on the headphones. Doug moved the dials in an effort to home in on our frequency, which was becoming increasingly difficult, as more operators were arranging different wavelengths. This made it very frustrating for us trying to pick out our calling sign.

It would be about two in the morning when Doug waved his hand to me to signify he had at last contacted Chittagong. The signal wouldn't last long, so it was up to us to make our requests for supplies and give our position as quickly as possible, hoping our signal and code would be understood. An affirmative was received, followed by 'out'.

Putting our headphones down, Doug and I heaved a sigh of relief that we had at last contacted base, and could be sure that our request for supplies would be acted on *ek dum* – straight away! In the meantime, Cyril had prepared a meal of rice and chapattis. Soon we were tucking in and feeling much better in the knowledge that we had at last contacted HQ.

We stayed on duty, listening to dance bands and the jabberings of different operators from all over Asia. The danger was that the Japs might decipher some of them. The crescendo of all the calls of the jungle dwellers came with the dawn; for miles around the air was filled with the cries of the awakening beasts and birds.

Looking through the bamboo wall of the hut, I could see the sun making its arrival over the crest of a range of hills hundreds of miles away. It sent a golden glow of warmth penetrating deep into the valleys and announcing another day to all.

By now Doug and Cyril were awake. Doug was complaining of feeling stiff, while Cyril was busy making coffee and asking if we had made contact during the night. If so were there any orders? I explained that I'd only had time to put our request for supplies before being cut off, but at least they knew where we were.

After consuming two mugs of coffee, we decided to return to our basha to have a good rest. On our arrival, our faithful bobijee soon had breakfast ready – eggs and fried rice. I'd be glad when more supplies reached us; perhaps we'd get sausages and bacon!

The village below was beginning to stir now and I could hear the laughter and cries of the children as they ran out to play, while the women started to rekindle the fires to prepare the morning meal. We both felt a bit tired, so I suggested to Doug we should have a few hours on our charpoys before making any other plans for the day. We needed to rest our stiff and aching limbs after sitting up all night.

It was about eleven, with the sun nearly at its height, that the bobijee came in with coffee to say Doug had gone to stretch his legs for five minutes and wouldn't be long. After a quick wash down in the lean-to, I felt much better, and decided to raid the bobijee's supplies, to find flour and fat, and so on to see if it was possible to make a suet pudding! I found the local flour (maize ground down by stone) a bit rough, but it would do. I also needed a lump of fat, and bicarb, which I knew we had. I chopped off a hard lump of fat to make the suet, bunged it all together, wrapped it in a piece of rag and dropped it in a earthenware bowl of boiling water... and hoped for the best!

Having made sure my pudding was simmering in plenty of water, and having told the bobijee to keep an eye on it, I decided to go down into the village and try to locate Doug; but after wandering through the maze of bamboo bashas to no avail, I reckoned he must be back at our base, wondering where the hell I'd got to.

During my walkabout, I was struck by the friendliness the natives were showing. I guessed the chief had broadcast to all that we were there in their interests; the bowing and clasping of hands told it all. Many offered gifts of fruit, but by hand signs I had to refuse, for on close inspection I saw the fruit wasn't exactly fresh.

Most of the time I was surrounded by many *chikos*, laughing and dancing round and round, hoping to win my favour; but I treated them all equally as they guided me along around the many twisting trails around the village.

There was no sign of Doug, so I made my way up the incline to where our observation post stood, partially hidden amongst a clump of trees on the crest of the hill. Two IOC sepoys were on duty, but up to now they'd received no signals from Chittagong. Perhaps some would come during the night watch. I had been waiting anxiously for news of any reply regarding my request for supplies.

Reaching our basha, I found Doug sitting out on the verandah. 'Have you seen your pudding?' he asked me. I hurried round to the lean-to to inspect my culinary project, to find the pudding had risen to an enormous size – overlapping and hanging over the rim of the crude earthenware pot!

With the help of the bobijee, it was lifted out and placed on the table and the wrapping cloth removed: it was perfect. In the store we had a few tins of jam left. What a treat it was! I gave the bobijee some; he had never seen one before, and promised he would tell his village pals how to make it. Then he made his way down to show them a portion!

Doug tucked into some and thoroughly enjoyed it – anyway, it soon disappeared.

After eating all that pudding, we hadn't much room left for lunch – just a little rice, and a few ration biscuits which were very hard and difficult to swallow!

While we were resting on the verandah, a native appeared from the direction of the village carrying a cockerel and some eggs – a gift from the chief; so we'd be well fed for the next few days. I thought then that I should have sent him a portion of my pudding.

Later on, our bobijee came on to the verandah carrying a huge bunch of tobacco leaves, still green. We'd have to spread them out on the roof of the basha to dry out, and in doing so they would turn brown. I could then roll a leaf tightly and bind it with bamboo string, and hey presto! I had a nice fat six-inch cigar!

By the time I lit up and clouds of smoke were rising, all the mosquitoes disappeared, leaving us free from bites. We could then enjoy the cool fresh air, while gazing down at the panoramic sight of hills and jungle stretching for hundreds of miles far below.

We stayed out on the verandah till midnight, discussing our plans for the future; we weren't sure how long we would to be up there. As we hadn't heard a word from Chittagong, it would appear to us that we might be entirely forgotten!

Our rations were very low. We only had a few tins of issue biscuits and bully beef, condensed milk, carrots, and a few tins of fruit. We decided to do the following night's duty and try to contact HQ. We had been lucky in that the villagers had supplied all our needs, and we certainly felt none the worse for eating produce from the jungle.

Before creeping under our mosquito nets, I wrote two letters, one to Audrey and another to Whiteleaf hoping the rations would arrive soon. If they did, they could take my letters down to HQ on their return journey, which would take a matter of four to five days, as they'd be travelling light.

During the night I perspired incessantly – the humidity was so bad that the sweat ran off me, making the charpoy soaking wet. That, together with the continuous hum of the mosquitoes trying to get through the net, made the coming of dawn a great blessing. At first light I slid off the charpoy to get some fresh air on the verandah – what a relief! I had acquired quite a few sores, which began to itch like the devil. I'd have to find some powder or grease to ease the irritation.

While I was cooling off, Doug came out of his room complaining of the close heat and flopped down to enjoy the fresh air. As it was quite early, the bobijee hadn't arrived yet, and I decided to make some cha; perhaps it might make Doug feel better. I thought then he looked a bit peaky and a little thinner, but he seemed quite cheerful.

The wind had risen quite strongly, and I hoped we weren't in for a storm. I wanted to enlist some natives to repair the roof of our basha – there were quite large gaps showing. It would mean threading and weaving bamboo grass to knit between larger branches, which made quite an effective seal.

The bobijee arrived to get breakfast, while Doug and I freshened ourselves up in the lean-to, after which I must say we both felt much better. I think we both had a sleepless night. After a meal of fried eggs and hard biscuit, we decided to wander down into the village to ask the chief for the services of two natives to repair our roof.

It was mid-morning by the time we reached his large basha. Women were sweeping and cleaning around, and I made signs to ask if the chief was about. He appeared at the opening to welcome us. His wicked old face was covered by a huge grin and his hand was outstretched for us to shake; I suppose he was taught this by hunting parties in the past.

I explained to him that our roof let the rain through. Could he recommend a couple of men to repair it who were conversant with the work? While they were being sent for, two of his woman presented us with coffee; we declined the huge maize biscuits – they looked as hard as bricks! Within minutes, two young natives were taking orders from the chief, who explained what we wanted doing and told us they would start the work that afternoon.

Thanking the chief for giving us his immediate attention, we made our way up the trail to our basha. By this time – midday – the heat was most oppressive making the sweat run freely, which irritated the sores. This made life a bit unbearable; the only comfort was when we stretched out on our charpoys and tried to cool down.

Back at the basha, the bobijee had laid out a light lunch of bully beef and ration biscuits, with bananas and grapefruit and coffee to follow. After this, we had a rest in preparation for a spell up in the observation post that night, hoping to hear from HQ that supplies were on the way up to us – what a sight that would be!

The sepoys at the post at all times kept a sharp lookout down into the valley to detect any small column making its way towards them.

After lunch the two roof repairers arrived, complete with all their materials; so it looked as if we wouldn't get much rest!

In fact, we both had quite a restful afternoon. The two natives repairing the roof were very quiet, weaving the bamboo to make a waterproof layer. I don't believe they were up there long. We only had about an hour's rest before enquiring how the job was progressing – but they had already finished and gone home! We'd have to pay them later.

To help supplement our rations, we followed the trail down the hill to where a small plantation of bananas grew. Using our kukris, we selected and cut two boughs heavily laden with fruit, slung them over our shoulders and staggered up the hill to our basha. Here we stored them underneath our charpoys, to ripen off in darkness.

As we were on duty that night, we wouldn't be eating here, so we gave the bobijee the rest of the day off. He would come in later to look after the place during the night – I guessed he would have a *bibi* to keep him company!

Doug was still suffering from a painful tummy; he had to be careful when eating. He kept mostly to bully and biscuits, which didn't exactly help his stamina.

In my request for rations, I had asked for some medicine to help Doug. I fully expected them to send bicarbonate of soda!

It was about six when we made our way along the narrow trail up the incline towards the post. I must say, whoever planned the site for the post had found the ideal spot. It was in a clump of trees situated on the crest of the highest hill of the range, giving a wonderful view of chains of hills rising from the jungle far below. Arriving at the post, we were met by Cyril Sirren who was most pleased to see us; as usual, he was very interested in our chats about London – Buckingham Palace, and all the sights of interest.

We climbed up the rickety ladder and settled down in the confined space to make ourselves as comfortable as possible, while Cyril was making coffee on the small Primus stove. It would be a waste of time for us to try to contact Chittagong before midnight as the air would be full of codes being transmitted, filling up all spaces available. We would have to wait till it quietened down. In any case, I believe HQ was fully conversant with this practice in the past.

Outside our small bamboo hut, the din of all the night prowlers could be heard, with their weird guttural cries. It's a good thing a huge fire was kept going all night outside the IOC basha. The air was heavy, oppressively hot, and the air was still. Sweat poured off our bodies, setting up an uncontrollable urge to scratch and scratch.

We had been sitting there with headphones on, waiting to hear our call sign amongst all the others, when, at about two in the morning, Doug stamped the floor and waved his arms to attract my attention. He was indicating that he was receiving a coded signal, and proceeded to take it down.

Apparently they had been transmitting on this frequency for the last two days, with the definite assurance that a porter corps of nine carrying supplies, with two Lushai Brigade volunteers in charge, were on there way up to us – a journey of about six days.

Doug affirmed we had received the signal, and indicated that we would now shut down for the night. Looking through the slits of the bamboo wall, I could see the dawn breaking over the range of hills stretching for miles below us, and once again I wondered what people were out there.

Doug was about to disconnect the transmitter and remove his headphones when another signal came through, to warn us that a Jap patrol was nosing about in our area. We would have to shut down immediately and take all measures to keep our presence undetected, keeping very very quiet.

I had the idea of sending a hunting party down to get more information of their whereabouts. Doug and I hurried down to ask the chief if he agreed to our request. Luckily he was at his basha consulting with a few elders, and on hearing of our plan he immediately summoned five ferocious looking natives, complete with all the gear for hunting, to go down and seek the Japs out.

After seeing the hunting party off, Doug and I sped back to the observation post to make sure that no fires were lit. We asked everybody to stay inside their bashas and keep quiet. Just as the sun began to sink towards the range of hills below, the hunting party returned to report no sign of the Japs. In fact, I could still hear the drums from villages within a radius of about ten miles sending the all clear message.

Phew! That was a sticky moment. I dread to think what would have happened to us if we'd been caught. The bastards were capable of indescribable torture, one of these being to slash through the ligament just above the heel, leaving the victim unable to walk; if no help arrived, the maimed person would certainly die.

We spent the next hour or so with Cyril Sirren and two sepoys making sure the coast was clear. During this time we had further confirmation from the surrounding villages that no signs of the Japs could be found. Then we decided to return to our basha to rest and clean up after a rather nerve-racking day. On our way back to our basha we met quite a few natives, who seemed pleased to see us. They showed this by putting their palms of their hands together and muttering the greeting, '*Collome*,' or a word to that effect. No doubt all the villages around would be on full alert, keeping scouts posted to report if any Japs were located in the area.

The bobijee had managed to barter a few pounds of rice for a nice chicken down in the village, so tonight it would be curried chicken and chapattis. I would have to see if he could find two natives to show me where wild vegetables were to be found down in the jungle. Yams and *kolebeha* were amongst many wild vegetables growing in abundance, together with pineapples and bananas.

Among many dangers in the jungle were the traps the natives set to catch wild boar. The principle was that highly sprung bamboo branches, hidden by plenty of dead leaves, were laid in the boar's tracks. When the trigger was set off, a spear would find its victim in a flash and kill it instantly. This very fate happened to a dog that had started to follow me. It happened so quickly; I heard a loud yelping behind me, but by the time I ran back to investigate, the dog lay dead.

On returning to the village I told the bobijee to send someone to go down and bury the unfortunate animal.

Sometimes these bamboo spears were set high up in the trees, so when we had to contact a village not in our territory, I took the bobijee and local natives.

We would give the transmitting a couple of nights' rest, allowing plenty of time for the Japs to move away from our territory, and for Cyril and the other sepoys to have a clean-up around the site.

We arrived back at our basha at about ten to find the bobijee had prepared a nice meal of curried chicken and rice and chapattis. This was very acceptable, as we'd had quite a tense day. We'd be glad to crawl under our mosquito nets and try to sleep.

I must have dropped off straight away, for on awakening I found the room full of sunshine. The air was echoing to the chorus of all the birds and animals, while geckos (lizards) moved like lightning devouring mosquitoes on the wall of the basha.

The head of the bobijee appeared, wreathed in smiles, asking if I would like coffee. I was told Doug Sahib was up long ago and had gone down to the village to enquire if there was any news of Jap movement. It was when I had washed and was halfway through my fried eggs that Doug returned, to report that all was quiet. The distant drums of the villages for miles around had become silent, so it was apparent the Japs had moved away.

The bobijee said he would do some *dhobi* (washing), but would have to wait for a woman to fetch more water. This involved a journey down the khud-side of about one and a half miles! I would have to go down myself one day to see what the conditions were like.

Another must was to have my hair cut – I must have looked a sight. Perhaps the bobijee would have a go. But on asking, he just laughed and waved his arms, and suggested I got one of the sepoys, which I thought was a good idea. Later I would ask Cyril Sirren.

Still no sign of our rations; the sepoys were keeping a constant watch down into the dense jungle below for any sign of movement. From up there we were able to scan the likely trails for miles around.

I sent the bobijee down to the sepoys' basha to ask Cyril to come up to see me; I thought he would say no if told of my request. When he arrived, he seemed a bit bashful at the thought of attempting the task, but after I had convinced him no blame would be put on his efforts if he made a hash of it, he agreed to cut my hair.

Actually, he made quite fair job of it. At least it wasn't hanging over my shoulders!

He doubled up with laughter at some of my remarks – especially when he seemed to be pulling the hair out by the roots! Doug said it looked passable, and even asked Cyril to have a go at his hair, perhaps the next day.

The rest of the day passed uneventfully. That night we hoped to hear by bush telegraph of the progress our ration supply was making. Doug and I would have a stint at the receivers; we'd try to contact Chittagong to confirm the sighting of our supply train on its way to us.

The thought did enter my mind that there might still be a Jap patrol about. I hoped they hadn't intercepted our supply team.

By now the sun had disappeared behind the range of hills far below, leaving the rest of the daylight fading quickly, so after we'd had a wash and tucked into a meal of eggs and rice, it was time to make our way to the observation post.

During the night, Doug and I spent the time listening for our coded signal from Chittagong; it was about three o'clock when Doug waved his arm and pointed to his headphones to signify that he had made contact.

Would we confirm receiving our supplies? And would I check the post at Choullong, a village about four miles down the ridge, within the next day or so. Doug replied that we hadn't received our supplies yet, and that I would make preparations to inspect Choullong as requested. We climbed down from the post at about five just as dawn was breaking – what a glorious sight! The mist had nearly cleared to give way to a glorious sunrise. A golden glow was spreading over the range of hills for hundreds of miles, while the inhabitants of the jungle were giving vent to their chorus of dawn cries.

Walking along the narrow trail leading to our basha will always be imprinted in my memory. We were flanked by thick undergrowth, with tall trees giving us perfect camouflage. Anyway, the Jap patrol had no inkling we were there. I was very thankful there weren't any baboons in the trees – they would certainly arouse suspicion with their noise. Perhaps it was too high up there.

On reaching the basha we were greeted by our faithful bobijee to say he had our breakfast of fried eggs and rice cooked and ready to serve on the table out on the verandah. Afterwards we'd have a short rest before I planned my needs for the trip down to Choullong. We both slumped, stretched out on our bamboo chairs, and dozed off. We awoke to the hum of a swarm of mosquitoes – the blasted things were all over us.

We were both covered in bites; the bobijee was most concerned, and blamed himself for not checking us out there. He immediately went down to the village to see if a potion could be obtained.

During his search, the chief's son heard of our trouble and straightaway knew what would cure our bites. A little later the bobijee arrived back, carrying a small earthenware bowl containing a thick gooey liquid. It was green in colour and looked awful! The bobijee rubbed the stuff all over our bodies, and within half an hour the itching had gone! We were both very stiff, but the swelling had gone down and all we had to do was rest and wait for the potion to do its job.

Meanwhile, the air became quite heavy, with clouds gathering down below forming a sheet between the hilltops and the jungle – a sure sign of bad weather to come. Soon, a few spots of water began to make a rhythmical pattern on the corrugated roof of the lean-to. Within a few minutes all hell was let loose: torrential rain burst down, and Doug joined me to stare through the slits in the wall of our basha, praying that our recently repaired roof would withstand the pressure.

The storm lasted for about fifteen minutes, with torrents of water gushing down the khud-side taking in its path any lightly constructed building. On our travels we had struggled through monsoons, battling against steady rain, but it would be difficult to keep upright during this storm. Soon the worst had passed over, and a frightened bobijee came in to see if we were all right. He jabbered away in Urdu, waving his arms to express his concern for our safety. We spent the rest of the day inspecting for damage, but luckily there was none. We'd have to check our observation tower.

On reaching the post, we were greeted by Cyril Sirren and another sepoy. Both had been on duty during the storm and had experienced a frightening time. The fragile hut had swayed to a dangerous angle, but miraculously had not shifted an inch; apart from one or two bamboo sections being out of place, the unit seemed quite safe.

No damage could be seen to the transmitter or any of the fixtures, and after listening to a babel of call signs Doug and I concluded no harm had been done. As we didn't start relaying our call sign till about ten at night, we were lucky that the storm had passed earlier. Cyril made cha, and during conversation I informed him of my intention to go down to Choullong and check the small post for provisions, etc. He said he wanted to come along, but I assured him I'd be all right. We passed through the village on the way up, and apart from negotiating a rickety bamboo bridge slung over a deep ravine, we found the trail was quite open and well used.

Having been assured that the post hadn't been damaged, we prepared to return to our basha, telling Cyril we'd spend a few hours with him later that evening in the hope of further news from Chittagong. As we were about to leave, a native runner informed us that our ration party was only about two miles away, and would arrive in the evening.

Doug and I straightaway returned to our basha to make space in the rooms to store the loads where they would be safe. As we made our way back, we stopped at a clearing to look down into the jungle below, trying if possible to notice any movement; but as it was very far down and dusk was falling, viewing became very difficult.

For the next hour or so we both were busy making room for the provisions. Not till we had done that, and found a secure lock for the door, did we sit out on the verandah to have cha and await the arrival of the porter corps.

It wasn't long before we could hear the chanting and laughter as the porters came up from the village to our basha. As they came into view, the Lushai Brigade Corporal in charge came forward wearing a huge grin, clearly wondering whether to salute or shake hands!

After shaking hands and the usual greetings, I showed the Corporal where to stack the loads. While he supervised this, I told the bobijee to prepare a meal and a charpoy, though I wasn't certain whether the Corporal would stop the night or return after a short rest.

It took only a short time to put the load into the space provided, and as there appeared to be plenty of light before sunset, he decided to start the return journey after a meal and a short rest. He had put it to the porters, and that is what they wanted to do. So there it was: after a huge meal of chicken curry and chapattis and about half an hour's rest, they were all ready to return to their villages, or get part of the way. It appeared that was why it took so long for them to reach us – they enjoyed many rests.

The sun was beginning to sink when at last they waved goodbye and made their way down into the village, passing through it to descend on the trail leading into the dense jungle. We stood outside our basha peering down, catching sight of them now and again as they emerged from cover, to be lost again from view as they trekked into the deep undergrowth.

Doug and I spent the rest of the evening sorting all the provisions and rechecking the items as we stacked it all away. I noticed they had sent cigarettes and two bottles of Rosa rum!

We sampled the rum before retiring, deciding to leave the main unpacking until the morning, for Doug and the bobijee. I would be starting early on my trek to Choullong, and had spent most of the evening preparing what I had to wear and carry.

I was woken up by the bobijee at about five with a nice mug of coffee and the familiar words, '*Tekai*, Sahib,' spoken with the usual wide grin. I looked through the narrow space that served as a window and could see the sky was overcast, giving off a light drizzle – not bad. I had a light breakfast of rice and biscuits, said 'Cheerio!' to Doug and slung my holdall over my shoulder. After putting on my cape and selecting a stout walking stick, I set off.

For the first two or three miles, the trail zig-zagged through deep foliage and trees. Sometimes it was covered in deep bracken, while at other times it was quite wide and clear, winding its way down to the forest of jungle and bamboo grasses below.

It took me two hours to reach the entry into the jungle, but as the descent was gradual, I felt no tiredness, and strode on in order to get as much of the journey behind me as possible, and reach Choullong before dusk. My friends the baboons had found me; a pack of them were shrieking and jumping from tree to tree, high above my head. As I looked up at them, they stopped to glare down at me, keeping their distance at all times.

At least the villages around were aware of my location, for I heard the drums beating faintly in the distance, a reassuring sound that told me they were keeping their tabs on me, even though I couldn't see them. Now and again I heard noises – grunting, and the snapping of branches – but I pushed on. I had yet to see any large animal; it was probably a wild boar. Pressing on, I would soon be in sight of the footbridge that would signify that I had another two miles of the trail to negotiate. I hoped that someone had been sent out to meet me, to show me the way to the post.

Rounding a bend, the trail began to widen; far ahead I could see tall bamboo posts and realised that it must be the structure of the bridge. This I would have to negotiate to cross over the deep ravine below. On reaching the bridge, I had to sit a while on the bank to gaze at it. At each end, thick twenty-foot tall bamboo posts were sunk into the ground. These were held in position by bamboo ropes running from the top of the posts and anchored at the base of trees nearby.

The bridge itself was made entirely of bamboo mesh, interwoven to make strong panels and lashed together to be tough enough to withstand heavy loads. I would say the span was about one hundred feet. While I was taking it all in, a fresh wind started a slight swaying, causing the whole sagging structure to ripple. As I looked down into the ravine, tall trees seemed like matchsticks; at the same time, it was very difficult to see the base.

After making sure my equipment was safe, I started to cross. As the width of the bridge was only about four feet, I was able to hold on to the bamboo rope on either side. Keeping upright by this method compensated for the sagging of the bamboo mesh flooring.

I had to stop twice; the swaying and bouncing movement began to make me feel quite dizzy. I didn't dare look down; it must have taken about ten minutes, and by the time I'd reached the other side, the sweat was pouring off me.

After scrambling up the bank at the other side, I discarded my packs in order to have a rest and cool down, and to gaze at the crazy bamboo bridge I had just crossed.

It was only when standing up after resting that I realised my legs were beginning to stiffen and ache like the devil – a good pointer that I must keep going: no more long rests.

As I pushed on, the trail became more even. There were no more bamboo branches to avoid, laid to conceal sprung spears set up in the overhanging branches. These would kill or maim the intended recipients – members of invading tribes.

Choullong

I rounded a bend on the trail, and the next range of hills came into view, with the sight of a village on the crest partly hidden by trees. This must be Choullong – at least I hoped it was! – about ten minutes' slog away. I said ten minutes! It must have been two hours later when I finally reached the village. On the high ridge above were clusters of tall trees, in which I guessed the post was situated. I could see children running towards the bamboo huts. I presumed they had seen me, and were telling their parents.

Nearing the huts, I was met by a Pathan sergeant with a welcoming smile and greetings; he explained he'd had me monitored most of the way, either by native scouts or by the bush telegraph.

As we neared the observation post, children came running towards us, laughing and trying to hold on to my arms, while at the same time the Sergeant was also finding it very difficult to keep them away. Arriving at the post, I was surprised at its size. I was expecting a much smaller unit. The basha they shared as rest and sleeping quarters was quite large – much larger than I thought.

I explained that I would have a clean-up and wash, and then take a short rest before inspecting and getting the layout of the unit. In the meantime, I met the three sepoys who made up the complement of this isolated post. They all seemed very glad to meet me. They were Pathans – tall men, taking pride in their appearance and bearing – a strong point in their favour. They were very faithful chaps. The

Sergeant explained that a dāk bungalow was situated just outside the village and had been got ready for my arrival. He told a sepoy to show me the way; it was a short distance along the trail.

I was pleasantly surprised at the size and setting of the bungalow. It was built in an open compound of rich greenery, surrounded by a fence of bamboo. A native bobijee had been assigned to me; it appeared I would be looked after. Like most others, the bungalow was built high off the ground, away from any prowlers that might be tempted to enter.

The accommodation was the same as others: two beds and a sitting room, with a spare open space at the rear for any surplus gear. The bobijee had prepared a nice chicken curry, so after a welcome wash and with clean clothes on, I felt much better and decided I'd done enough for the day.

As we were relaxing on the verandah, one of the sepoys arrived with mail. It appeared the runner called in there on his way up to Mullianphui; it was just chance that I was there on inspection. There were three letters: from Audrey, Whiteleaf and John East. So for the rest of the evening, I was hanging on to every word. It was lucky the runner called in there, as it would be quite a time before I got back to Mullianphui. I settled down to write replies. Audrey seemed to be coping – though of course she would say that, even if the going was rough.

I had a fairly good night. My charpoy had had many sleeping on it; the centre was sagging deeply. I'd have to see if there was room for shortening the bamboo twine so as to straighten the whole bed.

Looking through the narrow bamboo window, I could see that it wasn't very nice outside – heavy mist together with a slight drizzle. It wasn't all that warm, either; but then we must have been about three thousand feet up.

The local bobijee came into the room carrying a large mug of coffee and offering the usual cheerful morning's greeting. He said breakfast would be ready soon, and would I have it on the verandah? It was rather bracing outside, having a wash in cold water under an open lean-to, with the mist and rain swirling round!

After a breakfast of fried rice and eggs, I felt much better, and proceeded to get ready to visit my friends at the observation post, to check and to see what help I could give. On arrival at the post, I was met by cheery greetings. Everyone wanted to shake my hand, asking all sorts of questions and in the meantime brewing up coffee. It appeared that they each did three months' duty on transmitting and deciphering. They looked after themselves and had to keep the camp clean and tidy.

The chief of Choullong had been well briefed by the military as to why we were there, and erecting these posts. In fact, he felt safe in the belief that the Japs couldn't harm him! I hoped he was right. In the meantime, I spent most of the day in checking the equipment and stores, noting some parts that were showing wear. I made a list which would be coded and sent to HQ for action. One of the sepoys informed me that dinner was nearly ready; would I like to freshen up?

They did me proud: chicken curry with vegetables from the jungle – roots of wild potatoes, *kolebeha* and many other roots, together with large chapattis and a mug of the *Zophan* beer. One of the sepoys began playing a zither-like instrument, making what to me seemed a continuous wail; but then they all began to clap hands and chant and were well away. Talking to the Sergeant, I told him I would need to make plans to return to Mullianphui in the morning. That gave me an excuse to get away from the awful music and chanting. As it was late, he instructed a sepoy to see me back to the dāk bungalow, for which I was very grateful, as there were natives about all night, stealing and quarrelling.

On arriving back at the bungalow, my first act was to pour out a stiff Rosa rum and commence gathering my kit for an early start in the morning. It must have been about three when I finally crawled under my mosquito net to try and get some sleep, sweating and listening to the insects dive-bombing just over my head. I was relieved that the bobijee had put the net up.

It must have been just before dawn when the native bobijee brought the coffee in and told me that *pani* (water) was falling. Looking though the slits in the bamboo walls, I could see it was indeed drizzling. Oh well, I'd have to put up with it. It would mean the trail would be slippery, but I'd have to chance it. By nine I was ready to push off, and after thanking the Pathans for their hospitality and waving goodbye, I set off down the hillside into the jungle, keeping to the well-worn trail.

After about half an hour, my give-away friends were swinging from treetop to treetop, screeching at the top of their voices, gazing down as if to say, You are trespassing! I dreaded the thought of a Jap patrol hearing and interpreting the cries, but then villages for miles around had their scouts out.

Finding a nice open clearing, I decided to have a short stop, resting on a fallen tree. I didn't dare sit down for small snakes lived under the bamboo leaves and branches, and it would be fatal if I were bitten far away from base.

Pushing on, I came to the bamboo bridge. It wasn't swaying so much this time, the wind being quite light, so off I went again! Making my packs secure, holding on to the bamboo rope on either side and taking short steps, I gingerly made the crossing. I suppose the natives took it in their stride and ran across; anyway, I was glad to have made it.

By now I was beginning to feel groggy and a bit weak on my pins, as I made my way along the uneven trail. I believe it was a touch of malaria, as I felt a bit shivery and weak. Until then I hadn't seen or met a single soul; it all seemed so unreal, the baboons' shrieks mingling with all the weird sounds of the other jungle creatures and multi-coloured birds. Together they made a continuous chorus echoing for miles around. I was now following the trail leading towards open ground on a steep hillside. Soon the trail was in the open, with no vegetation on either side, giving a clear view of the jungle far below. My main job now was to keep a firm foothold, as the trail became more uneven and narrower all the time.

On rounding a bend, the next range of hills came into view, and at last I was sure I could see Mullianphui perched amongst a clump of trees high up on the crest. When I got off this treacherous length of the trail, I would look for a clearing and rest for a while. Leaving the uneven trail on the hillside, I was glad to enter the cover of the overhanging trees and bamboo grass. I was still looking for a clearing in which to rest, when suddenly I was confronted by four tall natives, all decorated with bamboo ornaments and carrying nasty looking spears.

Momentarily, we were all surprised; they stopped in their tracks to stare, while I managed a weak smile and tried not to look alarmed. At the same time I uttered the Lushai greeting, which sounded like '*Collome!*' At this they seemed to relax, and conferred amongst themselves. After a few seconds, smiles began to replace the scowls and they started to jabber away, standing aside at the same time to let me pass. Phew! As I passed, I looked up at the faces of these six-foot headhunters, and thanked God they had apparently met military personnel from the observation posts before.

As I slogged along the trail, a feeling of weakness and that I was perspiring more than usual overcame me. I was beginning to feel quite shaky and hoped I wasn't in for a bad dose of malaria. On reflection, I had quite a lot of mosquito bites, evidenced by the lumps on my arms and legs, which itched like the devil. I hadn't much farther to go before reaching Mullianphui, where the first job would be to have a dose of pamaquin, hoping it would quieten any signs of fever. As I neared the village, a number of *chikos* came running to meet me, laughing and making shrill welcomes; most of them I could recognise, and it took me quite a time to pass through and take the path leading up to our basha.

As I got nearer, Doug and the bobijee came down to greet me. I think Doug was pleased to see me again; we'd both had our differences, but managed to get over them by making a joke, or interesting ourselves in other subjects.

After a wash in the outside lean-to, and putting on clean clothes, I began to feel much better. I relaxed in a comfortable chair on the verandah, waiting to sample the bobijee's chicken curry; but first I sipped a mug of Rosa rum, and related my travels to Doug.

2nd February, 1944

After a good night's rest, I awoke to find the bobijee with the usual morning greetings and a mug of coffee, asking if I'd had a good night. I said I felt fine, and asked after Doug sahib. I was told he was in very good health and would be in to see me soon.

Getting off my charpoy and standing up, I realised how weak I was; I had to stagger round to our bog, and afterwards I lay down and had a rest. Doug came in to see how I was coping and to say he had signalled HQ to report my return, and to tell me to take it easy. Noting how weak I looked, he said he thought it must be a touch of malaria, and I should rest for a while.

We were both in a poor state; his right knee had swollen and was looking very nasty. He couldn't recollect twisting or knocking it, and would have to relax for a while.

The bobijee had been given a large tortoise by a native of a hunting party, and proceeded to prepare it for a long boiling session! He said the meat was very good.

I made the bobijee strengthen my charpoy by criss-crossing the bamboo base to correct the deep sagging. Perhaps I would be more comfortable in the future!

The weather had turned very misty. It was humid, with plenty of mosquitoes buzzing about – not a very good day. Perhaps the wind would freshen up to clear it all away later. In the meantime, I staggered about checking what supplies we had.

I did think that by the time of my return the rations would have arrived. We would have to make do with jungle produce, and help from the villagers; anyway, we'd be scoffing tortoise tonight!

After a meal of chapattis and rice, we both decided to rest for the afternoon. That night we would be up in the transmission hut with the duty sepoy, trying to contact the base at Chittagong for any news – especially news of our rations!

I tried to rest on my charpoy, but the blasted mosquitoes kept up their dive-bombing over my head. Even though I had the net all around, they crawled through the smallest hole. What with perspiring and itching from sores, I gave up the idea of resting and got up to move around.

It was a good thing I did, for a native arrived at the basha to speak to the bobijee. He told him one of the villagers, while cutting bamboo, had cut his leg deeply with a *dah* – a long curved knife, about two feet in length – a very lethal weapon.

On arriving at the native's hut, I was met by his wailing family, all showing signs of great distress, and taken to where the poor chap lay. He had indeed inflicted a very nasty wound. I had my first aid box, but the contents were sadly not up to full strength, as from time to time they had been used in various emergencies. I had plenty of rolls of bandages and lint, together with bottles of iodine, so I proceeded to wash the cut and prepare it for dressing.

While all this was going on, the native showed no sign of pain, not even when I applied plenty of iodine. He winced a little, but still had a cheerful outlook and took great interest in what I was doing. When I had at last tightly bandaged the wound, he broke into a babble of his lingo, and grasped my hand in appreciation, thankful that it was all over.

A meal of curried chicken and rice had been prepared by his wife, together with earthenware bowls of the local *Zophan* beer made from rice. I had to have some, but all the time I was thinking of my tortoise meal awaiting me at the basha!

Making my farewells to the villagers, I realised time must be getting on, as dusk began to close in. I had to hurry back to honour the bobijee's repast that he was attempting to prepare for us.

Doug met me at the steps of our verandah to enquire if my efforts at dressing the native's leg were successful, and was most relieved when I said all went well. I told him the chap seemed most grateful; anyway we'd have to wait for a few days.

After a wash and change of clothes, we sat out on the verandah, tipping back a mug of the local beer and enjoying the panoramic view spreading far below us. We could see over deep forests and ranges of the Lushai and Chin Hills, and wondered if the blasted Japs were out on patrol in the dense jungle.

The bobijee came out to say our tortoise feast was ready. It certainly smelt nice; he had fried the meat, putting in a few herbs and spices, and set the meal on a large plate for us to help ourselves. There was also a dish of jungle vegetables – yams, *kolebeha*, and roots, all making a very tasty meal. We sat there gorging the very tasty tortoise and saying, 'What a feast!' There was plenty left over, so it would be cold tortoise on the menu for a few days.

It must have been nearly midnight by the time we decided to turn in. We had no news from the post; we'd have to wait till morning for reports, if there were any.

I had quite a fair night's rest. I woke up a few times to listen to the mosquitoes buzzing round and round; it was a good thing I'd put my net up. The bobijee came in with coffee and said Doug sahib was in much pain with a swollen knee. He must have twisted it at some time; after coffee I would see how he was.

Also the *pani* wallah's wife gave birth during the night to a stillborn child. I would have to go down to the village to ask if there was anything I could do to help. I checked that Doug was comfortable and I was surprised to find him up and hobbling round his room. He explained that the swelling had gone down, leaving the knee a bit painful, but, like me, he would rather keep going.

I went down into the village. My first call was to see how the birth had been handled, and I was startled to find the woman up and doing her housework! When I was on these visits, I always had the bobijee with me to interpret the language. I was surprised to learn that her husband had already buried the body, and she was clearing up all the mess!

Leaving her, I made my way to the hut of the native whose leg I had just dressed. I found him sitting outside and he was very pleased to see me, telling his wife to make coffee as he offered us seats. I enquired how the leg was, and he was all smiles, jabbering away at the bobijee, saying that he was very thankful for the job I had done! He also said he would always be at my service, if required!

On returning to the basha, I found Doug still limping about, but he said the pain was much easier and he was able to bend the knee quite often. I could see the swelling had gone down, so all he had to do was to keep the weight off and take things lightly.

After a meal of curry and rice, plus a mug of the local rice beer, I decided to write to Audrey and Whiteleaf. This took me the best part of two hours, trying to express my feeling at our being so far apart, and wondering what the conditions were at home – thoughts that were prominent in my mind at all times. I would have to ask the chief to despatch a runner to deliver the letters to Demagri, a journey of about three days.

That night Doug and I spent a couple of hours with the duty sepoys up in the observation hut. We took turns with the headphones, listening to all different call signals; eventually, it was Cyril Sirren who waved his arms to attract our attention, indicating that he had found our call sign, and we immediately began to decode.

We were warned of Jap patrols, and told our rations were on the way up, but as the Japs were in the area, time would be the main factor. The party had to make frequent reconnaissance sorties as they went along. But as the porters were fully conversant with all the different tracks through the jungle, I reckoned the little yellow men would be outwitted.

We returned to the basha at about midnight, to have a *chota* of rice beer, then crawl under our nets and try to drop off to sleep. The continuous droning of the mosquitoes shortened our sleeping time. The air was quite heavy, and at times I was bathed in sweat, making my sores itch like the devil, as I waited for the dawn to break.

I must have dropped off, for suddenly I heard the voice of the bobijee saying, 'Cha, Sahib.' He wore a grin from ear to ear, and said Doug was hobbling around on the verandah, trying to relieve the stiffness in his knee. He was in fact feeling a bit better; also, my patient with the wounded leg had sent up a large chicken and eggs, and said the deep cut was mending quite well.

So it would be curry that night, and chicken. Meanwhile the wind had risen, and we hoped rain was on the way, as everything was very dry; besides, it would test our newly repaired roof.

The bobijee said that the chief had sent off a runner with our mail. It would take at least sixteen days as we were two hundred and sixty to three hundred miles from Chittagong; in an emergency, we would of course signal.

Doug and I were both feeling a bit off colour, he with a bad tummy, while I felt very weak and shivery. The bobijee said I should be in bed, in the warm, and should rest. The chief was trying to help; he sent up a huge side of swine bacon – ugh! To look at it was enough to turn one's stomach over! I told the bobijee to lose it discreetly amongst his friends.

One of the Sepoys had contracted a nasty bug. He was feeling very weak and was off his food, and had been like that for a week. If it continued, I would arrange to have him taken down to Demagri by stretcher.

We decided to do a stint up in the look out that night, as the wind and rain seemed persistent, we might as well occupy the night listening to all the coded signals and different music. I didn't think there would be a message for us, as we were fully up to date. We were just waiting for supplies, hoping of course that the little yellow men were kept at bay.

After a meal of curried chicken and rice, followed by a *chota* of the local rice beer, we made our way along the ridge on the well beaten track that twisted between dense undergrowth – not forgetting our friends high up in trees, shrieking as they swung from branch to branch.

Arriving at the observation post, and climbing up the bamboo ladder, we entered the small hut to find two sepoys sitting before the sets, each with headphones, intent on trying to decipher our call sign from the maze of codes that filled the atmosphere during darkness. They were both pleased to see us; one was Cyril Sirren, who at all times made me most welcome. He maintained I was a *pugla* (mad) sahib. I attributed that to some of the ventures I had attempted in the past.

10th February, 1944

Cyril made us some nice curried rice and cha. Being a cheerful chap, he chattered away all the time, asking questions about life in England, and saying how much he would like to have the chance to visit London. I tried to explain to him about all the harrowing times the population were being put through. I told him about the day and night bombing, and about our of homes being reduced to rubble – not to mention people losing families and friends. I said it would take many years to rebuild, so his ambitions would have to be put on ice for a while.

The rest of the night's stint was spent listening to all the different signals, and at the same time trying to decode; but one had to be very skilled to be able to achieve this. We did have dance bands continuously playing in the background, but our efforts to hear English being spoken were unsuccessful due to all the oscillation filling the air. No signal came from Chittagong. I guessed they thought we had already received our rations, so they couldn't be far away; perhaps tomorrow they'd arrive.

I climbed down from the post at about four. Dawn was just about to break, and looking down on the forest far below, we saw the mist beginning to lift and we could hear the cries of all the different jungle creatures awaking to another day. I wondered if any Jap patrols were out there. If so, our friends would start up the jungle drum telegraph, giving warning to villages within a radius of about twenty miles.

As we made our way along the ridge, our friends were following us, swinging from tree to tree, gibbering away and staring down at us; they must have got used to our movements by now. We both were beginning to feel a bit off colour. Doug was suffering from a bad tummy and knee, while I felt weak and shaky. I hoped it wasn't a dose of malaria. I would take mepacrine tablets on reaching the basha.

On our return, my first job was to find the malaria tablets. Then I took a swig of the local rice wine, and we both retired to our charpoys to rest for a couple of hours.

It must have been quite a short rest, for I was soon woken up by loud jabbering just outside my room. Easing myself up off my charpoy to look through the shutters, I could see clearly that the rations had arrived. Doug was already out there, showing the porters where to put their loads, while the bobijee began to organise lighting fires on which to boil rice for the porters.

I was soon up, checking the contents of each bundle, assisted by the Lushai Corporal in charge. He spoke quite good English and was cheerful with it. There were five porters, each carrying 90 lbs on his back; they leaned forward all the time as they struggled along the sometimes difficult trail. The Corporal told us of warnings by local tribesmen of the Jap patrols in the area, but it was obvious the natives were much more experienced in jungle tracking, besides being familiar with all the trails.

There were sacks of flour, sugar, rice, and dried fruit, together with tins of dried potatoes, mixed fruit, and fish. They'd also sent us a complete first aid kit containing small packs of bandages. In one load, there were tins of dried milk, together with packs of issue cigarettes and matches. As the loads were stacked away, each item was crossed off the list, and when everything was stored, it was time for the porters to organise a fire to prepare a meal. The chief had sent up a large chicken, which was soon in the pot, secured by a tripod over the fire.

It was past midnight when Doug and I eventually crawled under our mosquito nets to rest, but the natives were making a hell of a din, singing and dancing round and round the fire.

I couldn't sleep: my tummy was painful and churning round and round, and added to this I felt very weak and shaky. I must have dozed off, for I was awakened by awful pains. The mattress felt wet and sticky, and upon looking down, I could see it was covered in blood. It was then I realised it must be a touch of dysentery. All I could do was to put up with the terrible pain in my tummy and keep my legs tightly closed!

Doug and the bobijee were most concerned at my condition, and after changing the sheets to make the bed more comfortable, they took it in turns to be at my side most of the day. The pain became unbearable; it seemed as if a devil was scouring the lining of my stomach with a knife. I couldn't eat any food. I just lay there, hoping the pain would ease off, constantly trying to stem the flow of blood and matter from my rear.

The bobijee was most upset and decided to seek advice from the chief, who immediately came to the basha to see my condition for himself. He confirmed straightaway it was dysentery. He then told the bobijee to inform me that the potion he prescribed wouldn't be ready till the morning, and that I would have to lie still and try to sleep.

Off he went, leaving me feeling weaker as the day wore on; I must have lost pounds. All the time I was keeping my legs tightly together. Doug or the bobijee were always with me, for which I felt very grateful; sometimes I dozed off, thinking of Audrey and home.

It must have been about five when Doug woke me to say the chief had arrived with my medicine. In walked the tall warrior, grinning from ear to ear, holding a small earthenware bowl containing my dope – a deep brown liquid. He said I mustn't drink it till morning. I asked the bobijee what the medicine consisted of, and he replied that it was juice made from soaking tree bark. He didn't know the name, but the different tribes often used the vegetation around them as medicine. Some were very crude, but the results seemed good.

I hadn't eaten much for a couple of days. Mainly I ate the dry biscuits that were issued in our rations, hoping they'd help make my insides more solid. All the time, I looked forward to the day when I'd be able to tuck into a square meal. Doug was with me most of the time, chattering about what was happening with the signals to Chittagong. He had informed them of my condition and they in return hoped for my recovery; as we were three hundred or so miles apart, there wasn't much they could do to help.

I spent a restless night and was glad to see the dawn, with the arrival of the bobijee and the usual, '*Tekai*, Sahib?' He offered me a huge mug of coffee, but before drinking it I remembered the potion I had to take first, and asked the bobijee to fetch it from where I had placed it. There was about half a cupful of the foul liquid, and as I was still passing blood, I had no further option but to close my eyes and swallow the lot. It wasn't so bad – it tasted like black coffee, yet much stronger – but the smell! I nibbled a dry biscuit and settled down to try to doze off, but it took a long time before I did. It was daylight when I woke up. Doug was moving about in the other room, and on my calling out, he came in to enquire how I felt now, to which I was pleased to reply that the pains in my stomach had completely disappeared, and I felt much, much better!

By the evening I felt much healthier. The pains in my stomach had completely gone, also the loss of blood, and as the evening wore on, my strength was rapidly returning – and it all happened during just a few hours!

Shortly before dusk, the chief arrived to enquire about my health, and showed no surprise at my quick recovery. He told the bobijee the medicine never failed, and was widely used, as dysentery was rife in most villages. I told the bobijee to convey him my warmest thanks, and that I would never forget him or the potion that so quickly cured my dose of pain and weakness.

I even had a meal of rice and biscuits before trying to drop off to sleep, and it wasn't till the morning that I realised I'd had my first restful night for many days.

I lay there feeling on top of the world. All my pain had gone, and I was feeling stronger all the time; I wonder what tree supplied the medicine?

I asked what was the chief's name. It was something I couldn't pronounce – Veihban Thango; the bobijee wrote it down for me. I addressed him as 'Chief', while the bobijee acted as interpreter; in that way we seemed to converse quite well.

Just before midday an army officer arrived, heading a small platoon of Gurkhas, nine in all. After the usual introductions – his name was Lieutenant Hunt – he said his job was to locate a fifth columnist who was believed to be infiltrating in this part of Lushai. He gave as close a description as possible of the bloke, and said if we did have any suspicions, not to apprehend him, but to signal HQ at once.

Lieutenant Hunt stayed to have lunch of curried rice and a few drams of the local beer, while his Gurkhas built a fire to prepare their rice and chapattis. We assured him that we would notify the chief that there was an enemy agent working in this area, and for him to tell all the elders to keep a sharp lookout, and God help the spy if he was caught!

At about three, Lieutenant Hunt decided to push on up the trail towards Ijal, a distance of about a hundred and twenty miles, which would take six to seven days if all went to plan. Doug and I stood on the ridge looking down to the jungle, keeping the small party in sight as it weaved its way down among the overhanging foliage, until at last it was out of sight.

On the way back to our basha, as I was feeling much better, I decided that in the morning I would enquire in the village as to where the water was drawn; perhaps it would explain my touch of dysentery. I still felt a bit unsteady; I must have lost pounds. I could tell by the way my clothes hung on me.

The rest of the day was spent in checking all the rations; in the humid air we had to move perishables to cooler and shadier corners of our storeroom, and while keeping them covered, we had to allow fresh air to circulate. Most of the tinned meat and stews were kept below ground. I had deep storage holes dug in the corner of the room, covered over by sheets of meshed bamboo matting, allowing the air to circulate.

Doug and I decided to spend a duty with the sepoys up in the observation tower. Perhaps we might get a signal from HQ. Before moving off, we tucked into a nice meal of chapattis and rice prepared by the bobijee. He promised to look after the place all night. The post was about five hundred yards up on the high ridge, obscured by densely set tall trees. It was impossible to locate from ground level – the chaps who found this spot certainly knew their job. We were greeted at the post by Cyril Sirren together with another sepoy, and were made most welcome.

18th February, 1944

The night was very still and humid, broken only by all the weird cries of all the animals from down below deep in the jungle. As we settled down for the night my main hope was that we contacted HQ and received further instructions. Also, we could tell them of my quick recovery from my dose of dysentery.

In between taking turns with the headphones, Cyril was busy preparing a curry and chapattis, which would be ready in about an hour's time. It was Doug who first heard our call sign, and beckoned Cyril to join him; they were both decoding. After acknowledging HQ, Doug gave the news of my recovery, and said all was well. The contact lasted only about a minute, and then the signal was lost, fading away in the crowd of different codings that filled the atmosphere.

Reading from Doug's scribble, it was apparent that we were to move from here to farther up the ridge – to make for the District Commissioner's office at Lunglei, and from there to proceed farther up the Lushai and Chin Hills toward Ijal – a large village where different HQ were based.

An Indian jemadar (lieutenant) of the IOC was on his way up to relieve us, due to arrive in a few days' time, so it would give us time to pack ready to move off.

After a good night's sleep, I felt much stronger, but I'm afraid Doug was still suffering from a painful stomach. At the best of times he didn't give the impression of being a pillar of strength, but he had courage. I suggested that if he could manage it, we ought to follow the *pani* women down the khud-side to where they drew the water.

I asked about the distance from the bobijee, who grinned and said it was a good mile! Doug said he could manage that, so when the women came in sight making their way to go down, we followed at the rear, much to the amusement of all.

They were tall women, and carried large earthenware containers balanced on their heads. They were graceful and sure-footed as they picked their way down the trail on imprints made by *pani* wallahs in years gone by.

As we descended, the foliage gave way to tall trees, and of course, hordes of baboons and other species of monkey were all shrieking at our presence. The women just laughed at us staring up at them.

We came at last to the waterhole. About a dozen women sat on boulders, dipping the garments in the water and pounding them repeatedly to release the dirt. Some were actually squatting in the water! My mind boggled at what was going on. I would give the size of the hole as about ten feet by six feet, and about two feet in depth.

I thought it must be spring water, but on further examination I saw a small trickle was coming through the stony ground from higher up; there must be a stream farther along.

But the water lay stagnant – and the colour! It was a murky deep brown – and this was our drinking water. No wonder I had dysentery.

I immediately made signs to the *pani* woman not to use this water, and to show me the main stream farther along the valley. It was only five minutes' scrambling through the undergrowth, and on reaching it, I was relieved to find it much cleaner. I told the women to collect it here before it entered the stagnant hole.

I'm sure they understood. Anyway, I could check it as it was carried up.

I staggered back to the village. My first job was to find the chief to tell him of the awful state in which we found the waterhole, and of our instructions to use another outlet. He seemed quite pleased, and then calmly said he wouldn't know about the stagnant water, as his water was carried from quite a different source in the opposite direction!

I had to check the supplies and make an inventory of all stores to be handed over when the Jemadar arrived. During the check, I found the tinned vegetables very low. I'd have to tell the bobijee to send his friends down into the jungle to dig up a few Yams, *kolebeha*, and other root vegetables that grew in abundance down there. Doug's health was now much better; his tummy had recovered from those awful pains, and his appetite had returned. I hoped that by the time we had to move on, he'd be his old self again.

During one of our contacts with HQ, they signalled that they had a Dakota making regular reconnaissance flights over our area, and if we could be located, it could make a drop of essential supplies. I wondered what they would be.

After a lunch of curried rice, we were both sitting out on the verandah enjoying the cool breeze, when I began to feel a bit weak, and developed a thumping headache. Doug suggested I ought to lie down for a while; so off I went, and by the time I'd reached my charpoy, I was shivering like the devil, and realised a touch of fever had arrived.

I spent the next two days on my charpoy, shivering. I couldn't keep still, and the sweat simply rolled off me. Doug and the bobijee kept a constant watch over me, trying at times to make me eat; but as fast as I had a mouthful it all came up.

I took regular doses of mepacrine, which did help in keeping the temperature down, but I felt so weak.

The air was very still and humid. It must have been over a hundred degrees outside, and the sweat was still running off me. I must have lost pounds – if only the shivering would stop! It had to stop soon.

It must have been on the third day that I felt a bit stronger. The shivering had gone, leaving me worn out, so it was up to me to try to regain my strength and move about.

The bobijee made a nice hot chicken curry, and after a bowlful, I felt much better. I decided to get off my blasted charpoy and move about.

I was dressed and in the process of clearing the room, when Doug came to ask how much I had improved, and to say he was very pleased to see me on my feet again.

He had received by bush telegraph news that the Sikh Jemadar would arrive up here some time tomorrow, so we would have to make room in the basha for him. He'd expect some quarters of his own.

I spent the rest of the day writing letters to Audrey and Whiteleaf, hoping all was well at home. They were in my thoughts at all times. It was very difficult to put into words the emotions that one kept bottled up.

At about five, the bobijee came in to say our IOC Jemadar had been located on the trail about a mile away, deep in the jungle. He could push on to reach here today or camp overnight; anyway, we were all ready to welcome him.

During the night we spent most of the time listening for our call sign to come over but had no luck; perhaps the Jemadar had instructions to pass on to us when he arrived up here.

We were awakened in the early hours by the babbling of native voices just outside our basha, and going into Doug's room, I found he was already up and dressed, ready to greet our IOC relief. We were wondering what sort a bloke he was.

Out on the verandah we were greeted by a tall Sikh Jemadar, immaculately dressed, wearing khaki shirt and shorts, together with campaign ribbons and medals, and sporting a neat moustache on his weather-beaten face. He gave us a proud smile as we shook hands.

After the introductions, I took him round the side of the basha to show him his temporary quarters, and explained our working routine.

In the meantime his three IOC sepoys had erected a large tent which would be their billet during the changeover.

It was mid-morning when I suggested that we should go down to the village to introduce our friend to the chief, and to see the conditions the local people lived in.

I think the sight of the tall military figure impressed the reception party, so much so that they couldn't take their eyes away.

Our bobijee served as translator, while the women of the household served up dishes of different delicacies, together with bowls of the local rice beer. During the meal we were all squatting cross-legged on the sagging bamboo floor, scooping up the food with our fingers.

As our eyes got accustomed to the dimness of the interior of the basha, I could see the Jemadar was staring at all the shrunken heads displayed on narrow ledges surrounding the walls. He raised his eyebrows to give me the wink.

It was past midday when we finally thanked our host for a courteous meeting. I was glad it turned out well; now our friend could go down into the village in the knowledge that he had been accepted.

While walking back to our basha, the Jemadar suggested that as we had had a meal he would like to have a ramble further along the ridge, to see what the conditions were in respect of density of jungle and ease of travel. Off we started, taking two sepoys just in case we wanted help, keeping to the narrow trail while at the same time taking in the panoramic view of the of jungles ranged below.

We came at last to a clearing of tall elephant grass and were steadily following the narrow trail, when suddenly my companion gripped my shoulder, saying, '*Asti! Asti!*' [Careful!] We could hear a loud swishing noise coming in our direction, and as we stood transfixed to the ground, a huge snake – its girth must have been at least eight inches and its length seemed to be endless – passed swiftly ahead, disappearing from our sight and made its way into the tall grass. Phew!

We waited, listening for any further approaches, and it seemed ages when at last we started to talk. The sepoys were obviously very shaken, while the Jemadar remarked, 'That was close!' We decided to make our way back to the village – we'd had enough for one day!

On arrival back at the village, we enquired at the chief's basha if anyone could tell us what type of snake it was that shook the life out of us. We were told it was probably a python or something similar.

While at the chief's basha, we were informed that a welcoming party had been arranged in honour of the Jemadar taking over the observation post. It was due to start that evening, and a messenger had already left an invitation at the post. I must say the chief was well up to modern ways!

During the afternoon, a sepoy came to our basha with a coded message stating we would have to dismantle the observation post before leaving on our next assignment, and leave no trace of it ever having been there. The Jemadar was to report back at Demagri, while we make our way up the ridge towards Lunglei, a distance of about fifty miles.

For the next few days we'd be very busy. I would be seeing the chief to organise porters to transport our gear, while in the meantime all hands were needed to dismantle the high lookout. Doug and I had plenty to talk over during our evening meal; in the morning I'd go down to see the chief, while Doug put a few things together and started pulling down the post.

Due to this sudden change of events, we had to postpone our dance round the evening fire. I wasn't sure whether the party would take place or not; all our time now was taken organising our move away; I reckoned it would take two days to clear the camp and restore as near as possible the original layout.

As we prepared for bed, we remarked that just as we'd made the place habitable, we had to pull it all down – all but our basha. I told the chief he could make it his meeting house for different functions. It was up to him. He thought it was a good idea, and a pity to break up a well-built dwelling.

Before finally climbing on to our charpoys, I wrote to Audrey stating the change of plans. It would probably be quite a few days before I'd have the time to write; and if I had the time, I'd be worn out!

Over breakfast of rice and fried eggs, Doug and I planned our day of action. First we would move all the transmitter gear from the hut – a precarious job, as the bamboo ladder wasn't all that secure. I'd take the weight, while Doug would have a rope running from the transmitter round his waist, taking the rest of the weight.

In the meantime, in case we all overbalanced there were four sepoys ready to catch us! The exercise went quite well; we had all the gear down in about an hour, with the sepoys transferring it along the ridge to our basha.

By dusk all the equipment was neatly stored away, leaving the empty hut perched high up in the fork of the tree. I told the sepoys we'd set it alight in the morning, and burn the whole lot down; we'd spend the rest of the day clearing away all the evidence of it ever being there.

We were about to leave the site when the chief's son arrived and was amazed at the desolate scene, and asked the bobijee where it had all gone. He couldn't believe we could have done all that work in such a short time. The bobijee told him there would be a huge fire up here in the morning.

22nd February, 1944

Over breakfast, we discussed the best way to dispose of all the bamboo building material, which by now had built up to a huge pile in the centre of the empty compound.

Rather than make one huge fire, which would attract attention from people below, we decided to break the huge pile up into small lots. These would be carried farther up the ridge to be burnt, thus making the fires less obvious.

The chief's son came up to see how we were managing; he was getting quite friendly, I thought. He even gave the bobijee his name, scrawled on a bamboo stump. He also offered to have all the firing to be scattered about by some of the young men from the village, an offer we gratefully accepted.

By dusk, small fires could be seen along the ridge for miles. They could be taken for campfires, which were usually lit at sunset after a day's work; so I don't think any suspicion would have been aroused.

Well, that was that: where the post had been was open scrub. Looking across I recalled many nights of waiting for our call sign and wondering if perhaps we had been forgotten.

We had been invited to the chief's basha that night for a farewell supper and drink. I said to Doug we should thank the family for all the help they had given us; after all, the village had been well accustomed to British hunting parties on their way up the trail after game.

I asked the bobijee to accompany us to the party – he was always indispensable for translating, and this kept the conversation flowing. It was better than sitting there staring at each other. My mind turned funny when the chief's eyes were fixed on us for any length of time – what was he thinking?

On arrival at the chief's basha, we were welcomed by four tall warriors dressed in nothing but a few bangles and ornaments, holding at the ready wicked looking spears. They clasped their hands together in welcome and escorted us along the long verandah to the main entrance.

On entering the dimly lit main room, we had to concentrate on where to step. All we could discern was a group of natives squatting in different parts, taking up most of the space. They were all jabbering away in high-pitched voices. At the far end sat the chief, a heavily decorated figure wearing different shapes of bamboo. He had bangles of ivory round his legs and arms, while on his head he carried a tall plume of coloured feathers taken from various birds of the jungle.

On either side were women of his household – about six or so – preparing earthenware bowls containing rice and fruits that grew in the jungle in abundance, together with tall jugs containing the local *Zophan* rice beer.

Placing the bobijee within earshot, they gave us two bamboo armchairs, set by the chief's side.

During the meal, and amid guttural sounds of eating, I got the promise that there would be eight porters outside my basha for the day after tomorrow, early in the morning. They would help sort out all the equipment into loads of 90 lbs for each porter, and be ready to push off as soon as possible.

The rest of the evening was spent in watching the young women dancing round the fire in the centre of the basha – a fire which was always kept going, supplying the only means of light. The smoke and fumes spiralled up to a hole at the highest point in the bamboo roof. I wondered why it didn't catch fire, but apparently no fire had been caused yet. By now, most of the guests were getting tanked up. The air was full of laughter and chatter; I'd had my fill of curried rice and beer, and as I glanced across at Doug, he gave me the nod, as if to say, that's enough.

It was past midnight by the time we took our leave. The chief insisted that two warriors should see us safely home; our bobijee said he would look after us, but at this time of night we could meet a drunken reveller, who might just revert to his past practices!

Relaxing on the verandah before retiring, we both talked of our experiences, good and bad: of my malaria and dysentery, and Doug having leg and stomach troubles. He still felt a bit fragile in that region. As long as he was careful what he ate, he said it would pass. It was really out of this world sitting out there. It was not too close that night – or perhaps we were both getting acclimatised to the oppressive heat.

The bobijee had left a chapatti and rice on the table, together with a large earthenware jar of the local beer, so by past midnight we were both feeling pretty free!

Tomorrow would be our last day here – a day which would be spent in checking the loads assembled for the porters, making sure all were equal.

By the time we crawled under our mosquito nets, the air was full of the blasted insects, and I had to be careful when getting on the charpoy not to let them under the net.

I slept for about five hours, to be woken up by the bobijee with a mug of cha. Doug Sahib was already up and had gone for a stroll, I was told. By the time I had washed,

Doug came in saying the air was a bit heavy and he was wondering if a storm was on the way.

As we had already said farewells to the chief and his family, the day would be spent on checking for our final departure. The bobijee had done most of the work clearing out all the rooms. I expect as soon as we'd left, the chief would take over – or his women! I wandered outside the basha to have a last look round and gaze down into the jungle far below. To think that we'd be down there soon, plodding along the trail!

Before dusk, Doug and I strolled along the ridge to have a last look at the space where our observation post once stood. The natives had certainly done a good job – branches and bamboo bracken left no trace that anyone had been there.

As we looked across, we both recalled our nights of patience, waiting for signals.

24th February, 1944

Dawn was about to break as I peered through the slits of the bamboo. I could see a huge pile of wood being prepared in the compound for a fire to cook the different meals for breakfast.

Later on the bobijee brought in mugs of coffee, and said that our eight porters were outside ready to load up, and would we pass them as suitable?

On meeting them, I gave credit to the chief. These natives were magnificent chaps, all at least six feet tall, clasping their hands together and giving Doug and me the welcome word, '*Collome.*' It's a word I always used when meeting the Lushai.

By approximately nine o'clock, after a hasty breakfast of rice and issue biscuits, we were all ready to move off. Cyril

Sirren and I were leading with Doug bringing up the rear, and as we passed through the village on the way down, many natives waved. The *chikos* ran ahead, laughing and dancing around us, till the distance from the village became too great, and they all disappeared to make their way back.

Down and down we plodded, the open hillside giving way to more and more foliage, which got steadily closer as we neared the fringe of the jungle. As we entered, the porters started to chant a tribal song; I believe it was to ward off any inquisitive marauders that might have a go. In any case, they were well prepared; besides the packs on their backs, they carried spears, while round their waists belts carried wicked looking knives, such as the *kukri* and *dah* which they used most effectively.

We were deep into the jungle now; high above us our friends were venting their disapproval at our intrusion, swinging from bough to bough, always keeping us in sight. The air was much closer in here; the sweat was running and we were beginning to itch all over our bodies. At the next stop I would have to rub cream on.

After we had covered about four miles, a suitable clearing appeared in which we could rest for a while. In no time the porters had a fire with the rice pot over, and were sitting around till it was cooked. Doug and I found a suitable log to rest on and chat about our aches and pains. His right leg was giving him trouble; it was very painful when he put his full weight on it, but he said it would be all right till we stopped at the next village.

I asked the bobijee how far it was to the village, and its name. It was called Salui, and we had about four miles to go; so the sooner we pressed on, the better.

The porters spent about half an hour sweeping and trying to restore the campsite to as near as possible to how we found it. They covered the ground with fallen foliage, to try to disguise the beaten ground; though the weeds and young shoots soon grew up again.

The trail by now was beginning to lead us to more open spaces. We were leaving our friends chattering away high above us, as the jungle began to recede. The added daylight made us feel better, and the porters' rendering of their chants became stronger.

By now we were in single file. The bobijee was leading, with me next and Cyril Sirren heading the porters, leaving Doug to bring up the rear. We were well out in the open now, and the trail wound round the hillside, enabling us to look down into the dense jungle far below. Suddenly, the bobijee halted and pointed down at a herd of elephants grazing in a small clearing not far from us. The wind must have been in our favour, or else they would have noticed us.

We had another mile before reaching Salui, a village that was tucked away from the main trail. The bobijee said that little was known about its people, they kept well to themselves, being totally independent. I wondered what reception we would get.

Rounding a bend, we could see the village ahead, with children playing, and most of the women sitting in front of their open bamboo bashas, gossiping or weaving cloth.

The children saw us first, and in no time the whole village was deserted. They all hurried into their huts and hid from view. We stood back, waiting for someone to reappear, but no one did. One of the porters volunteered to enter and call out a welcome. As he was doing so, a tall bearded native appeared to speak to our porter, and after a few exchanges they were both all smiles, beckoning us to enter.

As we urged our porters to come forward, dozens of children came running towards us, stopping a few yards away to gaze at us with wide open mouths. I don't suppose many white men ever came this way. Like all principal dwellings, the chief's basha was the largest. It was built in the centre, raised on thick three-foot logs, with a short ladder leading to the open main entrance.

A verandah wound round the whole perimeter of the basha, having a three-foot bamboo meshed fence on the outside, to prevent people falling over – especially after a night on the local beer! On entering, we were met by a tall native, a chap of about forty, decked out in the usual bangles and feathers. He seemed quite pleased to meet us and greeted us with his hand outstretched. I thought, Not so native after all!

After the greeting, we were shown bamboo chairs, and the women came forward with bowls of fruit. Meanwhile, bobijee was explaining to the chief who we were, saying it was to his advantage we were in these hills, locating the Japs and reporting back to HQ.

He did say a hunting party had encountered a Jap patrol. It would be about two weeks ago, but nothing came of it; the Japs stood aside to let them pass, as they couldn't speak the language. They thought fighting would be a waste of time; besides, it would be to their advantage to keep in with the locals. No sightings of them had been reported since.

During the evening, in which we were offered various prepared dishes, the bobijee kept the translation going, while the smoke from the central fire swirled more densely as it made its way towards the hole in the highest point of the basha.

To add to the smoke, each of us was offered hubble-bubble pipes to smoke. Each pipe was about three feet in length, and from the mouthpiece to the actual bowl there was about three feet of flexible hose. The bowl had two compartments – the top filled with tobacco, and the lower with water. As one draws to extract the smoke, it has to pass through the water – hence a horrible gurgling sound is emitted while it is in operation.

The locally grown tobacco was very strong, and after a few puffs we both were feeling a bit dizzy. It was Doug who had the sense to stop, after which I gratefully followed. We nodded our approval to the chief, who seemed highly amused at our discomfort.

By this time the party was well away; natives were bent double prancing round and round the fire, chanting and getting more excited as they danced. Some, I thought, were getting out of hand, so I suggested to the chief that we should rest.

We were escorted to a sizeable basha, but on entering we found an awful smell of rats and dung. There were two charpoys and nothing else. We just lay on top of them to await the dawn.

I hardly slept. What with the awful smell and the squeaking of rats as they scampered over the ground, I was thankful for the charpoys. Doug was restless most of the night, so it was a great relief when at last day began to break with the start of the dawn chorus.

There was loud groaning from Doug, and he asked if I was all right. I said I would have been had it not been for his snoring! I could hear natives moving about, and presently the bobijee came to enquire if we were ready for coffee. By now, most of the camp were up and preparing breakfast. Makeshift fires were heating up water for coffee and rice, while others were collecting their belongings ready for the next trip.

By about nine, we were all ready to start again. The porters had their loads on their back, held by wide bands of bamboo twine. When on the move, they all leant forward to spread the load more evenly. I believe the village we were making for was Uipui; we had come through it on our way up here.

We had to get into single file now, as the trail was getting more uneven and the undergrowth much denser. Cyril and I were leading, and we had to use our kukris to clear the way.

At times the trail would lead us to the open hillside, where our footholds were very precarious; a slip would mean a drop of hundreds of feet down the khud-side. Following the twisting trail, we came upon an open clearing and were face to face with a herd of buffalo. They were all lying down and stared at us as we approached.

Cyril said, 'Keep going, Sahib! Take no notice!' We were about eight yards away, and the porters had by now stopped chanting. I said, '*Asti! Asti!*' meaning 'steady', at the same time feeling very shaky myself. As I made my way forward, the beasts just lay there, chewing away, making no effort to follow!

I asked Cyril why the buffalo took no notice, and he said they were seldom hunted, and in any case, they were safe if left well alone. After we had followed the trail for about four miles, I called a halt, having found a large open clearing away from the undergrowth. It was a place in which there was plenty of dead wood, so we could easily get a fire going.

Very soon the pots were hanging from the tripods with water boiling for the rice, while two of the porters were slapping and shaping chapattis to be cooked on the hot stone.

As I sat by the fire scooping up the rice with my fingers, my thoughts were always of home, wondering how they were getting on – if they could only see me now! The natives were jabbering and laughing as they ate. Doug said his leg was giving trouble; a pain went shooting up it directly he put pressure on it. Added to this, his tummy was out of sorts.

We were now making back to Mullianphui, a distance of about ten miles, but the village of Uipui would be our next stop. We'd have to rest there for the night; though as far as my recollection went, it was a bit of a stink hole. However, we had to give Doug a rest.

We followed the same procedure as before, and cleaned up the campsite, leaving no trace of our being there. Having accomplished that, the porters loaded up, amidst grunts and laughter, and off we marched, aiming to make Uipui before dusk.

After about an hour's march, I decided to send two of the porters ahead to warn the village of our arrival, hoping by then a suitable basha would be ready.

Near the village, we were met by all the children running circles round and round us and laughing. They seemed to be glad to see us again.

Leaving our porters near the chief's hut, Doug and I climbed up on to the main entrance to be met by the chief and the elders, while the women offered us mugs of the local beer. We had to squat on the floor; poor Doug found it most painful, as his legs were so stiff, but he managed it. During the meal we explained through our bobijee that we were now on the way down to Mullianphui and probably wouldn't be up this way again.

We were assured that our basha was much better than we had been allocated before, and our porters would be camped not far away. If there was anything we wanted, we should let him know. I believe Demagri must have heard of the way we were treated on the way up.

Out came the hubble-bubble pipe; an hour sucking that blasted thing made us both feel sick, but it had to be done. It was quite late by the time we left. The reception given to us was very good, and we both tried to show our appreciation. I do think HQ must have shaken him up.

The basha in which were to spend the night was quite the opposite of the one we spent in on our way up. This one was nearly new, and clean inside and out – what a relief! There were two nice charpoys, while the floor was covered with bamboo mats. I said to Doug, 'What a difference!'

The bobijee had prepared us a nice pot of coffee; I didn't expect him to wait up but was glad he had. We chatted for quite a while, before getting on to our charpoys. There were no mosquito nets; we'd have to cover our faces and hope to snatch a few hours.

The bobijee and the porters were just outside, so I didn't think we'd get any inquisitive natives visiting during the night.

I forgot to mention that my feet were getting very painful. The soles were covered in blisters. I would have to rub fat on to them, hoping that by the morning they'd be less painful. It was well past midnight when everything went quiet. The chattering of the porters outside stopped, so now we could get an hour or two of sleep.

The noise of the porters just outside woke us up; I swung my legs on to the floor, and gently put pressure on my feet. I found they weren't so bad, and hoped that use would ease the pain. Some of the blisters had flattened with the soaking in oil.

Doug was up, complaining of his tummy and knees – we were a couple of poor souls! We'd have to rest there for the day; I didn't like the place, but we had no option. We'd have to massage and exercise, hoping to get relief from our stiffness. I must say that using the local vegetable oil did help to relieve the pain.

I had a chat with the bobijee to explain our plans about having a rest for the day, and to have a fresh start the next morning. He said the porters would welcome the rest; it would give them time to check their loads and make them more secure, if necessary.

We both welcomed the day off. Most of it was spent stretched out on the charpoy, trying to swat the mosquitoes as they came near. Outside I could hear the porters beginning to chant a tribal song; they seemed quite a good crew.

At about five, the bobijee came in with earthenware pots in which he had cooked rice and chapattis. We both had to sit cross-legged on the floor and scoop it up with our fingers.

9th March, 1944

Before we retired last night, our main job had been to assemble and get ready the light packs we were to carry ourselves. Thus at the last minute everything would be accounted for, and we should get off before break of dawn.

After a light meal of rice and biscuits, we were all ready to move off. The porters were sitting on their packs, ready for us to lead the way; but first I had to say goodbye to the chief and thank him for the evening meal and the help he had given. Though I didn't like the chap, I had to pay my respects. That done, we finally moved off, the bobijee and I leading, with Doug and Cyril bringing up the rear.

Before we started, I remarked to Doug that I felt a bit groggy, and hoped it wasn't another touch of malaria. I felt very shaky on the pins, and a bit unsteady; but perhaps it would go off as I pushed forward. Mullianphui was about eight miles off along a rough trail that wound in and out of the undergrowth.

Sometimes it was narrow, and we moved in single file, then it widened out to allow more room to spread out as we pushed forward. We had done about three miles when I had to call a halt. A good clearing appeared in which we had room to brew coffee and rest – besides, I felt knackered. The porters soon had a fire going and the coffee made, but I could feel myself getting weaker as we sat there.

We started off again, with my assurance that I'd be all right once we got going again, but after about a mile I had to give in. I just couldn't stay on my feet. I was shivering all over, and sweat was pouring off me. I had indeed another touch of malaria.

Doug and the bobijee conferred about what to do, and it was decided they should make a bamboo stretcher. While some porters cut bamboo poles, others were busy stripping the bark to form a pleated bed to be bound to the poles. In no time, I was dumped on the stretcher, while two sturdy natives trotted along the trail carrying yours truly, chanting a weird song as they moved forward.

I don't know how they managed it; they still had a load on their backs, yet they were cheerful and watching me all the time. I do believe we were now covering the ground more quickly, as before I had been dragging behind. As we jogged along, I had to grip the stretcher tightly, as the trail dipped every way. At least we were making better progress. I could see Doug was limping badly, but he uttered no word of complaint. During a stop for a short rest, I asked how much farther it was, and they said they reckoned about a mile.

We decided to send the bobijee ahead to inform the chief of our arrival. Perhaps he would prepare a basha so that I could lay down straight away. I still felt weak. When we got settled in I would check through what stores we were carrying. I might have some mepacrine; that would at least bring my temperature down.

We arrived at Mullianphui before dusk, with the children running to meet us. As we entered the village, the chief and some elders approached to welcome us. He was concerned to see me on a stretcher. As our former basha had been taken over by his council, he made the IOC basha available. It had been all cleaned out and charpoys were fitted.

The bobijee soon had the place ship-shape. Before cooking he had found the mepacrine, and after taking two I was soon stretched out on the charpoy, waiting for the shivering to stop.

Mullianphui

10th March, 1944

I spent quite a fair night. The shivering had gone, but I felt very weak. Looking through the gaps in the bamboo walls, I could see the sun rising over the jungle far below, a very colourful sight as the rays penetrated different layers of cloud. The mosquitoes had their bombing practice; they were diving about in droves. I had to swat a few to try to keep them off.

My faithful friend, the bobijee, arrived with the morning coffee. I believe he was pleased to see that I was much better. I asked him if Doug was up yet, and was told he had gone for a short walk to ease his knee, which seemed much better. He would probably come and see me on his return. As I put my feet to the floor to stand up I could feel I was much stronger. I was definitely better; the shivering had gone, so it was up to me to build myself up again.

Doug was surprised to see me up and walking. We decided to rest there for a few days before the push down to Demagri. I wondered if they knew we were here; later I would send a runner down.

I suggested to Doug that we should take a stroll along the ridge to survey the site where we had our observation post – if we took it slowly, it would at least help to build our strength up: what a couple of old crocks!

Later we came to where the observation post was situated; it was all covered in small trees and bamboo shoots –

all traces of our hours of duty were overgrown. I still recognised the distant views if the valley below. We stood there taking it all in for the last time before returning back to the village. I couldn't help looking back as we neared our small temporary basha.

By the time we had returned, the chief had paid a visit with presents of chicken and fruit, and left a message with the bobijee asking us to spend the evening at his basha. Arriving at his basha, we were met by three elders at the entrance, tall warriors who could easily have been head-hunters only a short while ago; they still carried bamboo spears.

As we entered, the chief came forward, clasping his hands together in a welcoming gesture and asking the bobijee if I had any repeats of my bouts of dysentery. He was pleased to learn that all symptoms had gone.

As we sat down on the sagging bamboo floor, the women came forward with earthenware bowls filled with rice, chapattis and all fruits of the jungle. While we sat there, cross-legged, scooping up the food with our fingers, I gazed round the room, and noticed that there were no extra heads placed on the ledges! Perhaps they had grown out of the habit.

During our conversation, carried on through the bobijee, I asked for five porters to be outside our basha at dawn the day after next. The chief nodded and grinned, as if as to say, 'It will be done.' The evening passed with the natives dancing round and round the fire in the centre, while the local *Zophan* beer flowed freely, supplied by the women from large earthenware jars.

By midnight, Doug and I were feeling a bit light-headed. What with the smoke and drink, we felt it was about time we made a move. The chief insisted on providing an escort to our basha – the locals by now would be up to all tricks. So, after shaking hands and saying we'd never forget the hospitality that was shown us, we eventually made tracks back to our basha with our guides leading, while the bobijee said he could take care of us just as well!

11th March, 1944

We sat up late last night, enjoying the cool air and listening to all the cries of the different jungle dwellers far below. We wondered what people were out there, and were thankful that we were so high up on the ridge of the range. It was too far for the hunters to climb in their quest for game.

I was woken up by the bobijee with the usual greeting and a mug of coffee. He told me Doug was still in bed, unable to get up because of the pain in his knee. It was very frustrating; I would try to find out if there was any embrocation left in our small store. I was lucky to find a small drop left, and applied this to his knee, massaging the stuff in for about a quarter of an hour, after which Doug said it was much better.

During the morning, the chief paid a visit, bringing with him a large deerskin and a pair of sandals made for me by one of the village women. On inspection, I noticed how well they were made; the hide for the soles was quite thick, while the uppers were of chamois-type leather. Remarkably, they fitted quite well.

He stayed with us for quite a while, with the bobijee acting as translator. I believe he had got quite used to us being there; perhaps he thought we kept the Japs away!

He also promised five natives to act as porters when we were ready. I said it would be the day after tomorrow. By then, I hope Doug's knee would be functioning.

I still felt a bit shaky. I took a couple of mepacrine tablets; they generally did the trick, stopping the shivering and keeping high blood pressure down.

After a light lunch, I decided to wander down the trail, through the village, and to take a last look at how well we were positioned away from the deep jungle below. Making my way, I met quite a few villagers. Some recognised me with a formal wave, while others clasped their hands together and stood aside.

I must have strolled quite a way, noticing the different trees and shrubs, when I realised the light was closing in fast and I had to hurry back before sunset. I only just made it. As I was nearing the village, I was met by the bobijee; Doug had sent him to see where I had got to.

On returning to the basha, I was surprised to be met by Doug, limping a little but looking quite cheerful and saying his knee felt much better. He hoped that after another day's rest it should be strong enough to get moving again. After a nice chicken curry, we sat out on the verandah discussing our plans for packing up. We aimed to move off at first light the following morning, that is, the day after tomorrow.

I had a restless night. I had several sores breaking out, caused by the oppressive heat and sweat. I felt like scratching the skin off, and got off the charpoy in the early hours to search for powder which might take the itching away, but to no avail. I spent the next few hours before dawn sitting out on the verandah, looking down on the range of hills and the jungle, before seeing the tip of the sun slowly appear, heralding the new day.

As the light improved, I searched our small store of medical supplies and eventually found a small bottle of calamine lotion. When applied, this certainly relieved the awful irritation, allowing me to lie down for another hour or two.

The bobijee woke me with the usual cheerful greeting, telling me Doug Sahib was much better and would like to see me as soon as possible.

The calamine lotion had certainly done the trick, as the sores were beginning to dry up, and the itching had nearly disappeared. I felt a bit shaky as I stood up, but gradually felt better as I moved about; and by the time I went to see Doug, my strength began to return.

I must say, I thought Doug looked a bit thin and weak, but he was quite cheerful, saying his knee was much better, and that he'd be fit to move off in the morning.

The rest of the day was spent checking and preparing our loads, and looking around to see if there was anything we might have forgotten.

At about four, we were surprised by a small squad of Gurkhas making their way to Ijal. There were about twelve of them, and they asked if they could camp with us for the night. They wouldn't interfere, as they carried all their provisions, and would camp away from our basha.

I explained to the Sergeant in command about our plan to move off at first light for Demagri. He said they'd be off about the same time. They were all IOC on relief to report at HQ Ijal – a journey that would take about two to three weeks.

I suggested they had a meal with us. Our bobijee said he could get a nice chicken from the village, together with vegetables, and make a good curry. The Sergeant was most pleased; they would have time to clean and check all their equipment.

After washing and putting on clean shirts, Doug and I strolled over to their camp, to find most of them busy. They were sharpening their long curved kukris, weapons famed for their effectiveness in the hands of Gurkhas.

To sharpen them, they used large smooth stones, bringing the knife backward and forward in a circular motion till the edge was as sharp as a razor.

They were very friendly to us, laughing and cheerful, and offering us what food they were having at the time. We declined, but we did have a few mugs of their beer. They showed us considerable respect – I think they were puzzled as to what rank we held.

We stayed at their camp for about an hour, and then shook hands with them and said goodbye. I didn't expect to see them in the morning, as they would be off before dawn. The Sergeant thanked us for our companionship and help, and said he'd certainly mention us to HQ.

On returning to our basha, we made sure all our kit was ready for the porters first thing in the morning. It was our last night there; we couldn't let it go without going outside to sit and listen to all the strange sounds from down below in the jungle.

My heat rash sores had stopped itching, so I hoped to have a good sleep. We had stacked all our gear, ready to move off. Now for our last night at Mullianphui.

We woke up quite early, ready to move off by about six. The porters had loaded up, so off we started. The next village we were making for was about five miles off. It was called Salui, and we'd been through it on the way up. I reckoned we'd have to rough it, but it would be only for the night.

As we pushed down towards Salui, I recognised sections of the twisting trail. Some was in the open, while other parts were very narrow, leaving no room to alter one's stride. In the open, the trail was dry, while deep in the undergrowth, due to the overhanging branches, it became very slippery, besides being uneven.

As we came within two to three miles of Salui the sound of drums could be heard. Our porters listened, and could read the message that we had been located and runners had been sent to guide us in.

Near the village, our baboon friends disappeared from the treetops as quickly as they came. I remarked to Doug how quiet it was now! Soon we were met by the children, laughing and dancing round and round; I suppose it was quite an event for them to see white men again.

Entering the village, I noted that the natives sat outside their huts to welcome us, whereas before on our way up they all disappeared: a sign that we were trusted. Sometimes, from the looks of the young men, I wondered!

The chief seemed to be more friendly. He explained to the bobijee that he'd had our basha thoroughly cleaned, and had two charpoys put in. He hoped we would have a better stay than before. I suspect Demagri must have heard a word or two of our stinking night, and told him to clean up for when we returned.

The basha was certainly better. We noted that the floor was covered by a bamboo mat, while in one corner was a table on which stood an earthenware bowl full of clean water! Meanwhile the porters were busy preparing a fire to cook their meal, chanting a song at the same time. I saw that they had obtained two chickens from the village.

Doug and I were invited to the chief's basha for a meal and a natter. We would take the bobijee as interpreter. I guessed it would be another evening swilling rice beer; at the same time we would both have to be careful what we talked about.

In the evening, as we made our way to the main basha in the centre of the village, I thought – what a situation! Doug and I were on our way to have a meal squatting on the floor amongst a tribe of headhunters, all glaring at us, and wondering what do these white men do, and why are they here? During the meal of chicken and rice, our bobijee was busy translating, and as the time passed, the chief and elders seemed to relax. Amid all the belching and grunts, the time went quickly.

It must have been past midnight when we eventually staggered out to make our way back to our basha, the chief having insisted on a native to accompany us safely back.

I spent quite a fair night. As we had no mosquito nets, our friends were having a ball. All night they kept up a continuous humming, together with a few dive-bombing attacks. Most of the time I covered my head under my blanket.

Dawn came at last. The porters were busy outside preparing a meal of rice, which didn't take long. Then it was all hands to loading up for the last eight miles to Demagri. The morning was quite clear once the mist had cleared. It was nice to feel cool; later we'd be sweating, making our sores itch, and we'd have to loosen our shirts.

The sun began to rise as we finally made our farewells to the chief and all the natives. To see the elderly headhunters and the children waving was quite a sight. I often wished I'd been allowed a camera – what an interesting film it would have made!

As we wound our way down into the jungle, the trail became more uneven and the undergrowth more dense; sometimes we were bent double avoiding the branches, but thankfully not for long. The blisters on my feet had by now dried up, and with the help of the soft hide sandals the women had made, I was able to jog along quite comfortably.

After two hours a suitable clearing came in view, and we took a welcome rest, with time to cook a meal and make coffee. Very soon a fire was blazing away, with tripods supporting the pots in which rice was being cooked.

Doug and I took out some hard issue biscuits, and having found a large fallen log to sit on, we were grateful for the rest.

While we were eating, I noticed a few nasty looking snakes of different species going in and out of the carpet of leaves. As long as they didn't come up my leg, I'd leave them alone! While most of the porters were resting, movement could be heard in the undergrowth not far from us. It was some animal or an inquisitive native. As it was so dense, they'd have to show themselves, if they were friendly.

The short rest was very welcome, and the porters, when reloading for the last slog, seemed much more cheerful. They even started to chant their favourite tribal song, at the same time laughing and cracking jokes; they were looking forward to seeing their families again.

The trail we were on led us halfway down a sloping hill-side, through the dense undergrowth and trees which grew on either side. At one small clearing I called a halt, to point out to Doug a cluster of huts far down into the valley, saying I hoped it would be Demagri. The porters were all nodding and waving their arms in agreement, so off we started on the last lap.

On entering the depot, we noticed some building changes. Some of the old huts had been replaced with ones much better built and spaced apart, giving the whole camp a better appearance. While the porters rested, Doug and I made for the supply Major's office, to report our arrival and to find where our dāk bungalow had been moved to.

Illustrated Weekly

MARCHING SAGA OF THE MEN THEY SUPPLIED

CARRYING 50 lb. on their backs, men of a battalion of the 9th Jat Regiment, while part of the famous Lushai Brigade operating in the Lushai and Chin Hills, covered—on the map—nearly 550 miles over mountainous jungle country. Actually, each of them marched more than 1,000 miles on foot—an average of five miles a man for every day of the campaign.

If the Afghan War of 1879 the battalion had honoured its title of "light infantry" by carrying out a phenomenal 700-miles march through Baluchistan to Kandahar and Kabul, and back to India *via* the Khyber Pass. In this war the battalion has again proved itself worthy of the title.

When the present battalion crossed the flooded Barak river near Tipaimukh, even mules had to be left behind and all supplies for the men were dropped by air. In the spring the battalion denied the approaches to the Silchar plain through the Lushai Hills to the Jap invader.

After the enemy tide had been turned, the battalion worked its way down the western flank of the Fifth Indian Division's advance along the Tiddim road and pursued the retreating Japs into Burma. This task had a special significance for the 9th Jat Regiment as this battalion had taken part in the first Burma campaign. Most of the men had met the Jap before when they marched and fought 1,100 miles from Martaban to Manipur. Now the tables were turned.

The battalion established a block on the Tiddim road in their first action and held it for four days against heavy enemy fire, till the Fifth Indian Division broke through to link up with them. The leading troops who relieved them were men belonging to the battalion.

Here Naik Fateh Khan, of Palandri village, Poonch State, won the M.M. After a brush with a Jap patrol, in which two of his three men were wounded, he fought his way back 1,000 yards, carrying a wounded man.

Fighting other road block actions in which 49 Japs were [redacted] the battalion pushed south. To the Punjabi Mussalman company went the honour of being the first troops of the South-East Asia Command to re-enter Burma when they occupied Khuaivum, a village across the border.

But chief marching honours went to the battalion's Rajput Mussalman company, which moved from Champai, astride a track leading from the Tiddim Road, and came north to link up with it. The company passed within 500 yards of Kennedy Peak before the Fifth Indian Division had taken Tiddim and rejoined the battalion at Heili, to move with it and re-occupy Falam early in November. The same company caught up with the Japs at the end of November and shot up a boatload of them crossing the Myittha river.

The whole battalion then made their way 50 miles down the Myittha valley, and during the greater part of December were operating against Jap positions north of Gangaw, where their historic march eventually ended.

Demagri

14th March, 1944

The IOC Major was surprised to see us. He and the other liaison officers had repeatedly made enquiries as to our whereabouts but all had drawn a blank. Where the b— hell had we been? Anyway, it was nice to meet up again.

He explained that Captains Robinson and Scott were out on a short inspection of supply dumps and would be back tomorrow. In the meantime he would detail a couple of sepoys to help carry our kit up to the dāk bungalow.

On entering, we noticed all the rooms were tidy and clean, and the floor was covered with fresh matting – what a change from the stink of some of our previous nights! While Doug and I sorted and packed away different items, the bobijee was busy in the kitchen preparing our evening meal. We both felt whacked. I felt an aching in all my joints, while I knew Doug still suffered from pain in his right leg.

After a wash down and a change of clothes, we felt more relaxed, and later during our meal of chicken curry taken out on the verandah, we were truly able to unwind. Our faithful bobijee made sure we were all right before going to his quarters next to the kitchen – a corrugated lean-to. It was past midnight when we at last flopped on to our charpoys, thankful that the bobijee had put the mosquito nets in place, though the oppressive heat made us perspire and itch.

Apart from a few scratches during the night, I slept fairly well, thanks mainly to being in familiar surroundings and having a fairly comfortable charpoy. Looking down into the valley far below, I could see the sun rising above the jungle treetops, giving out dazzling rays of different colours. I could hear the bobijee moving about in his kitchen, so I hoped to see his cheery face soon bringing in the coffee.

When he did, it was to say that Doug Sahib was still asleep, and perhaps it would be wise to let him rest. As I drank my coffee, I could hear all the calls and cries of different animals way down in the jungle; up here we only got small monkeys darting about, with exotic coloured birds flying everywhere. If it weren't for the heat and mosquitoes, plus a few snakes, life would be tolerable.

After a cold wash and shave, and dressing in clean clothes, I found Doug awake and feeling much better. He'd had a good night, and the pain and swelling in his right knee had nearly gone; so today he shouldn't put much weight on it. After a snack of biscuits and rice, we decided to stroll slowly down to the supply depot and contact Captain Scott or Robinson. We'd see if there had been any mail or further news regarding our movements. It would also give us a chance to check the gear we had left in store.

There was no sign of our liaison friends, so we decided to contact the Supply Major and ask for two or three IOC sepoys to help to carry the gear up to the observation post. It was quite tricky lugging the heavy transformer and other gear up the rickety ladder, but once inside the small hut, we positioned the different units as we had them before, and in no time everything was in place for operation.

One of the sepoys had brewed tea, and while we were enjoying a mug, Captain Scott appeared at the top of the ladder. He was all smiles and seemed very glad to see us. He wanted to know where the devil we had got to, and insisted we told him during dinner at his place that night.

It would suit us quite well, as we hadn't planned for the evening. Also, while he was there, he could take a list of all the provisions we needed to carry on. He promised it would be seen to at once.

We had decided beforehand not to transmit till the transmitter had been well positioned and tested, so it would be the day after next. Having made sure the post was securely locked, we made our way back along the ridge to our bungalow. There we found, to our surprise, all our provisions stacked in the lean-to, with the bobijee sorting them out to put away in different places.

As we had been invited out, our first job was to strip down and have a thorough wash. We had clean clothes – we even put long trousers on! After weeks in shorts, we both felt a bit overdressed.

Arriving at the depot at about seven, we were met by a sergeant of the IOC who showed us to the officers' quarters – a bamboo hut, which on the outside looked derelict. The bamboo panels between the posts had seen many a storm; I wondered if they could keep the rain out!

On entering, we were surprised how well it was furnished. There was a thick bamboo mat, with deep armchairs and sofas carefully arranged with room to spare. Captain Scott came forward to say, 'No "bull", chaps. Come in; we have invited the Supply Major, but we doubt he'll turn up. We believe he has a *bibi* in his basha, so he'll be kept occupied!'

Out came the rum. It was very strong, and went by the name of Rosa; I'd never seen it back home, but our hosts maintained it was dropped to isolated posts in five-gallon jars by Dakota planes. If we were making our way up the northern ridge towards Imphal, we'd probably sight the drops.

During our conversation they spoke of a General Festing, who had taken command of 36 Division – men from Scotland, Wales, Lancashire, Sussex, and Gloucestershire – who had fought the Japs in north and central Burma for over a year. They'd fought through monsoon rain, across great rivers, over swampy country and through dense trackless jungle – and still kept moving. They were known as 'Festing's Killers'. The Japs hated him; sometimes he rode on a donkey; sometimes he tore around in a Jeep.

15th March, 1944

By midnight our conversation was in full swing, helped by a few rums and mugs of the local rice beer. I don't believe they wanted us to leave, but we had to check the duty IOCs. Perhaps they had picked up a signal referring to our movements.

It would give us a good chance to surprise them; I often wondered if they had a kip on the job.

We climbed up the bamboo ladder quietly, hoping to catch them out. As we reached the small entrance to the hut, there they were, waiting! They said they heard us coming. Never mind, we had a good laugh.

After having coffee, Doug and I took over and put on the headphones, trying to decipher our call sign from the hundreds of others that filled the air.

It was about four when Doug waved across, indicating he had picked up our call sign, and was writing it down. It was to say we were to stay put till further instructions, and to put out native hunting parties, as the Japs were on patrol in this area.

It was dawn when we eventually packed up. Looking down into the jungle, we could see the heat haze beginning to thin out, revealing the thickly packed trees and undergrowth. A sepoy made coffee, while we disconnected the transmitter – just in case the Japs had the means to detect our post. It was about four when we at last arrived back at the bungalow, and straight away we crawled on to our charpoys, making sure the mosquito nets were in place. We got what rest we could before the village awoke with the usual cacophony of humans and animals.

I forgot to mention that the bobijee had requested time off to visit his bride-to-be, a child about eight years old. The custom was to choose a bride at about that age; then they both had to wait till the bride reached thirteen or fourteen. In the meantime, on no account must she be seen out with another male!

He was given the job of looking after us because of his knowledge of local languages and English, together with his familiarity with different tracks through Lushai. He was paid by the government through the DC at Lunglei, collecting his money whenever he was in the area.

He was an intelligent looking chap, about five foot ten, slim, with black hair cut in the Western style, and always wore a *poen* (skirt) made by the local women. He was always cheerful, though by nature a quiet chap. We were lucky to have him.

I woke to the sounds of hordes of mosquitoes. They seemed to appoint a certain time in the morning and evening to hold a bombing session, at which they go all out, and then retreat to assemble for the next raid.

I had a lot of heat sores that constantly itched. Applying the local mustard oil did reduce the inflammation, but didn't heal the sores.

I eased myself off the charpoy to make coffee and enquire how Doug was faring. Before retiring, he'd been suffering pain in both knees.

On entering his room, I found it was empty, and guessed his knees must be a bit better. So after a quick wash in cold water, I wandered down into the village to find him.

Halfway down the hill, we met. He had obtained a stout bamboo stick to lean on, and was making good progress. He said he'd got fed up with lying down and had to try to loosen the joints. He said the pain was much better and was easing off as he exercised.

Later in the evening, Captain Scott arrived, to ask how we were, offering us a large bottle of rum in the hope it would help!

During furlough in Chittagong, he'd learnt about some troop movements. Units of the Lushai Brigade were on their way up towards the Lushai and Chin Hills, and a small corps of the 9th JAT Regiment would be passing through here – could we accommodate them?

We learnt also that the Lushai Brigade had marched over one thousand miles through dense jungle, averaging ten miles a day, to engage the Japs, pushing them back across the Tiddum road to a point where General Festing's 36 Brigade were waiting.

It was this brigade that pursued the Japs back across the border into Burma, and occupied a village called Khuaivum, awaiting further orders.

Just off our bungalow was a fair sized clearing, dotted about with small trees and decayed undergrowth, which seemed just the place.

Doug and I sought out the chief to request native labour to clear the field of all bracken straight away, as the unit of 9th Brigade would be arriving any day now.

He said men would be in there at dawn tomorrow, with implements, to make it all clear enough for the men to erect tents, and promised all the *pani* (water) they'd require.

Our bobijee was still away, making sure his young bride-to-be was behaving herself; we expected him back any day – we certainly missed his service!

It was a very interesting day, learning of the Japs' retreat: we should keep an all-night guard, up here, and warn the chief to do likewise round the stockade of the village. By the time we had paid a visit to the village and returned to our bungalow, the daylight had gone. After a snack of biscuits and rice, we made tracks to do a stint up in the observation post; perhaps Cyril had received a signal.

17th March, 1944

We were on duty till about four. Coming over the air were signals from all over the East. We had to concentrate to try and find ours, but to no avail. Perhaps, as the Japs were so close, it was too dangerous to transmit.

The two sepoys who were to relieve us had coffee and biscuits made, so it was about 5.30 by the time we returned to our bungalow, only to find it surrounded by khaki-clad troops, babbling away and busy erecting tents.

As we neared them, a sergeant came forward to salute; I wondered why, but then, I wore only shorts. He was very smartly dressed, and asked if it was all right to camp. We both welcomed him, and said if we could help in any way, to let us know. He stated that they carried plenty of provisions, and hoped to keep as quiet as possible. They would be off at first light in the morning.

I had quite a good night's rest; the mustard oil certainly eased the itching. Looking through the bamboo slits in the walls, I could see our friends of the JAT Regiment had made an early start – the small paddock was empty. I found Doug up and about, in the lean-to, about to fry eggs. He said that his legs felt much better – the pain in his knees had nearly gone.

After breakfast, we both decided to pay a visit to our friends at the supply depot. Captain Scott was there with the Major in charge, and asked if we needed more supplies. Of course, we were glad to accept what they had to offer.

As it turned out, the reason why they asked us was that a Dakota had made a drop a few days previously, so we were in luck.

Two carboys of Rosa rum, each containing five gallons, had been dropped, but they could only retrieve one. At a later date a search party would have to cover a large area of jungle and get the other one, unless of course some fat old chief had already found it!

We were lucky with the rations: plenty of cigarettes, flour, rice, lard, marge and tins of fruit, together with corned beef and biscuits. I signed for the lot and got a promise that it would be sent up to our bungalow in the morning.

I suggested that, if it was all right with Supply, I would see the chief and borrow some natives to form a search party in trying to find the firewater – a suggestion with which they all agreed.

After a light lunch, we set off down into the jungle together with three tall natives, who wore very little else but a leaf to cover their goolies. They had bamboo rings through nose and ears, and black hair plaited to reach half way down their backs. They'd been given strict orders to guard me while searching for the firewater.

We met a small hunting party, who on seeing me looked a bit suspicious, until my escort put them at their ease. It was then that they talked of a strange object floating down out of the sky, and waved their arms in the direction they thought correct. We bowed and put our hands together, and set off as directed, but after an hour's search we had to give up.

I guessed that villagers had found the carboy by now, and in our travels we'd be offered a drink of our rum!

Arriving back at the depot, after about three hours' searching, we were glad to have an invitation from the Major to have an evening meal at his basha, which we gladly accepted. During the meal we could discuss our afternoon search, and what direction we had taken.

By the time we returned to our bungalow, we both felt whacked, and had to stretch out on our charpoys to rest before washing and preparing for the evening.

We arrived at the depot at about seven, and a sepoy met us to show us where the Major's basha was. It stood halfway up a hill overlooking the depot. I supposed he could sit on his verandah and keep an eye his domain, especially on the natives, who darted about as quickly as the jungle beasts.

On entering his basha, we were met by the Major dressed quite informally in slacks and an open-necked shirt, showing no rank. 'Come in, chaps! Have a rum!' he said, open-handedly. There were about four others – our friends Captains Scott and Robinson, together with some IOC officers. They all seemed pleased to have our company and to be interested in our travels.

The evening was spent swapping yarns – mainly about home. Captains Scott and Robinson were both very interested, as they had their homes in Berkshire and knew Buckinghamshire pretty well.

By midnight we were well away. I didn't want to break up the party, but as we were expected by the sepoys up in the tower, to relieve them of some of the duty, we decided to get moving.

On arrival at the post, the two sepoys reported that no signals had been recorded. The air had been filled by messages, none of which they could decode; so we suggested they have a rest and make some coffee, while we took over till morning.

It was as dawn was breaking that Doug picked up our signal. When decoded, it told us that a column of British troops were on their way up the line making for Manipur to fight the Japs behind their lines.

It was later that we learnt of the Chindits, a small squad of men highly trained in jungle warfare under the command of Colonel Wingate, who were causing havoc to the Japs behind their lines.

We decided to keep the news to ourselves till further confirmation as the movements seemed to get nearer, we would have to keep awake!

I had quite a restful night. Outside my net, the mosquitoes were active in trying to get at me. There seemed to be quite a large horde – perhaps they had brought up reinforcements!

I forgot to mention of our bobijee's return from visiting his young bride-to-be. It was yesterday when he arrived back, all smiles, to say everything was *tekai* – very good.

When the bobijee came in with the morning coffee, he had news that a Jap patrol had been located about four miles away, heading this way. It was under close surveillance, maintained by native scouts from village to village. As the bobijee was speaking, I could hear in the distance the beating of drums sending warning messages to villages far ahead to warn them of the danger.

Doug and I straightaway made our way up to the post. We instructed the IOC to stop operations, disconnect all installations and make no movements.

In the meantime, we got natives to go down into the jungle and cut down a few small trees to help to camouflage the tower, so that it would be more difficult to locate from below.

There were plenty of natives carrying out the work, all laughing and chanting away. In no time, the observation hut was completely covered and the natives returned to their village.

As the post was out of commission, we made our way down to the supply depot to warn our friends of the Jap patrol. Although they had scouts posted at strategic lookouts on the highest points of the ridges within a radius of ten miles, they hadn't as yet received any warning, but could hear the distant drums.

We'd have to lie low now, and at the same time instruct the villagers to go about their usual chores. If the Japs looked up to the ridge and saw the villagers going about their lives as usual, they might decide to stay down in the valley, and not to make the long and steep climb up here.

Sitting out on the verandah, we could still hear the drums sending messages to villages far away up the Lushai and Chin ranges of hills.

Tonight, we'd have to rest between spells of lookout: no lights of any kind. In any case, the nights weren't pitch-black – there was always a luminous light which one could see to move about in.

After consuming a few rums and issue biscuits, we decided that I should take the first watch, and we'd change over every two hours; in this way we could at least make sure no prowlers could surprise us.

Doug went to his room, while I sat to listen to all the weird shrill cries coming from far below deep in the jungle. The air was most oppressive; the sweat was running off me all the time. My heat rashes had long since healed, so I was grateful that most of the irritation had eased.

I spent most of my watch wandering round the compound of the bungalow, looking down into the jungle far below and wondering if the Jap patrol was still down there. I hoped they had given up searching. A slight breeze sprang up, giving relief from the oppressive heat and providing a spell of fresh air.

On rounding the rear of the bungalow, I distinctly heard a movement a few feet away. Peering through the half-light, I was relieved to find Doug looking for me.

The time would be about three; in the distant hills the village drums could still be heard, keeping up their coded jungle messages of warnings about any Japs in the vicinity. They in return must have been frustrated by the continuous beating of drums, covering an area of many square miles.

Looking down over the range of hills, I saw the sky beginning to reflect the morning glory of the sunrise, with golden rays piercing the heavens in colours too wonderful to describe.

We decided to keep watch for another hour or so, during which more coffee was brewed to wash down our very dry issue biscuits. They were tasteless, but would have to do till breakfast.

Later, as the sun rose to herald another day, the jungle down below became alive with the awakening cries of all its inhabitants – a momentous chorus that will be forever imprinted in my memory.

Doug and I crept under our mosquito nets to catch a couple of hours' rest. The sun by now had cleared all the hills, its rays piercing through the mist to presage another hot and sticky day. I couldn't sleep. Mosquitoes were making a hell of a din trying to penetrate the mesh of the net; one or two managed to, dive-bombing down above my face, till at last it became hopeless. I slid off my charpoy to have a welcome cold wash down in the lean-to leading from our rooms.

Over a breakfast of rice and eggs, the bobijee said he had enquired down in the village of the whereabouts of the Jap patrol, and it seemed that our friends had given up the idea of penetrating further into the dense undergrowth and were moving back up towards the Chin Hills.

These reports were supplied by local headhunter scouts, who shadowed the Jap patrols at all times. Little did they know they were under such close scrutiny; perhaps it was the reason for their moving out.

We both decided to lie low for the next two days – no fires – and keep our movements outside the village as short as possible. Captain Scott sent word by a native runner that all was quiet at the depot. They had scouts posted within a radius of ten miles who confirmed the Japs had withdrawn, making for the direction of the Chin Hills.

Before lunch, the bobijee asked permission to have another couple of weeks off; he was still worried about how his child bride was keeping. It appeared there had been tribal warfare amongst the villages north of Mullianphui. Doug and I could see the poor chap was concerned, so we told him to get off first thing in the morning; he promised to be back as soon as possible.

The village he was heading for would be about fifty-odd miles away, so it would take at least two to three days. He would have to keep a steady jog along the trail. We told him to take what provisions he needed, and that we hoped he would find his betrothed safe and well. After shaking hands with us and expressing many thanks, he retired to his room to prepare for an early start.

Three sepoys delivered a small quantity of rice, dehydrated potatoes, flour and 7 lb tins of corned beef; now Cyril could cook some sort of a meal for us tonight. By seven o'clock we had all systems working, with the help of the two IOC sepoys sent up by the depot.

It was about midnight that contact with Chittagong was made. One of the sepoys started to wave his arms about to attract Doug's attention, at the same time handing over the headphones for him to decode.

The good news was that a convoy of nine porters, each carrying 50–90 lbs, with a Lushai Brigade sergeant in command, was on its way up here. They'd started three days before, so it all rested with the weather conditions prevailing.

At the moment, heavy rain was beating down, together with sheets of lightning, making the jungle far down below visible: what of the convoy with our food supplies? We hoped they had found shelter.

Added to the intense heat and mosquitoes, soon the walls of the hut would be covered with leeches. We would have to be careful they didn't drop off and attach themselves to us, as the only way to remove them off the skin was with burning cigarettes or salt.

I wrote letters to Audrey and Whiteleaf, and would send them down to Chittagong by the next runner from here.

We were both getting a bit fed up, stuck here with no news. We both wanted to move up to Lunglei and from there to the higher range towards Ijal, where I believe there was a District Commissioner over the whole region.

A native from a village farther down the trail had news of a porter corps making its way up here; he stated it to be about three days away. It certainly could be ours; I would give it another day and send a scout to check.

We were at the bungalow, having left two sepoys in charge at the post. The time was now midday, with Cyril preparing some sort of a meal; I guessed it would be mainly bully beef – the IOCs won't touch the meat as it's against their religion.

The meal Cyril had prepared was quite good – a bully beef stew with chapattis followed by coffee – not bad. He said he would do better next time!

He told us the *dhobi* wallah would be up to collect our washing later, and asked us to put all the clothes in a heap outside.

It was very humid after the storm; the air was full of insects – I'd have to rub some cream over my skin. It was too humid to put a shirt on, so all I wore was shorts.

For tonight's meal, to get away from bully beef, Cyril was preparing a native spread. We had *kolebehas* or jungle potatoes, yams (swedes), pineapple, grapefruit, rice, and huge melons.

With tobacco growing just outside, I suppose we could have lived self-sufficiently!

My first job after breakfast the next day was to try to contact the IOC Major at the depot and ask for a sepoy to replace the bobijee for a few weeks. My preference would be Cyril Sirren, a chap we both liked and trusted, and who had already stood in for the bobijee.

By mid-morning, Doug and I were at the supply depot seeking out the Major. We asked at different bamboo built stores until we found him squatting on a tea chest, checking through lists of stock, working out when to signal Chittagong for the next load. If no porter corps could be formed, a Dakota would drop supplies in a clearing previously used, depending on the urgency.

He knew we were short of provisions, and thought we were after supplies, and was relieved when he learnt of our request. He said of course we could have Cyril – he would be glad to get away from duty. After instructing the Sergeant to find Cyril, he found a bottle of rum in one of the filing cabinets, and soon we were swapping all the latest gen. Gone was rank, as apart from Captains Scott and Robinson, we were the only white chaps around.

Cyril arrived at the basha looking immaculate, in a uniform all neatly clean and pressed. It was a credit to him, and showed how proud he was to wear it.

Thanking us for detailing him, he suggested he should go straight up to our bungalow to sort things out while we were having a drink and chat.

During the testing of the transmitter and other gear, Doug found a faulty valve that wasn't giving full output. There was no hope of a replacement, so we hoped it would still function.

Captain Bartlett arrived up here, to have a drink and chat, or so he said. He was cheesed off, it appeared, with being attached to the supply depot. His position was liaison officer, but as there were no companies to liaise with, what the hell was he doing up here? Anyway, he did promise to scrounge what there was to spare and send it up as soon as possible.

By four o'clock, Doug had all the gear ready for tonight's session. I had the little jenny purring away all day; its exhaust was buried about two feet down. Its regular note could hardly be heard.

21st March, 1944

It was about ten when we climbed up the rickety ladder. We found two IOC sepoys had already cleaned up the place and were polishing the different instruments – about time too!

We took it in shifts to wear the headphones – not a blasted signal for us. We heard Indian music, and plenty of dance bands, mixed in with the signals that filled the air. We really had to concentrate to pick out our signal from the background noise.

During the watch, a sepoy on duty below our hut reported hearing the jenny running rough, as if a bearing was seizing up. I told him to switch it off straight away. We'd have to use the reserve power left in the accumulators, hoping it would last to the end of the watch.

We stayed till four and heard no call sign, and as the dawn was breaking over the horizon down below, we shut down. Later on, when I got the jenny going again, we'd try to contact Chittagong and explain the situation.

Returning to the bungalow, we found Cyril had prepared chapattis and rice, together with mugs of the local

Zophan beer. It was made from fermenting rice and was a very potent liquid. After a few mugs, one begins to be unsteady or giggly. After the meal and drink, we both flopped down on our charpoys and pulled the mosquito nets over, to rest for a couple of hours.

After a snack at midday, I made my way up to the post to repair the jenny. The first job was to lift it out of the two-foot trench in which we had buried it to muffle the exhaust.

On stripping the generator, I found one end bearing was truly dry and scored. I'd have to clean it and try to take the high marks down by going over with old emery paper. Luckily, I had some tucked away in my tool kit.

Packing the bearing with graphite and reassembling the unit took about three hours. It gave me great satisfaction to hear the jenny purring away again.

So by dusk, all systems were go, much to the relief of Doug. It would have been disastrous if we were cut off from Chittagong.

We reported down at the depot that we were on the air again. Captain Scott was there, tipping back a mug of coffee, while checking various items. He had found two good chairs hidden away, and suggested we should have them before anyone else took a liking to them; so we carried them off back to our quarters. They would be useful on the verandah.

As we were preparing to clean ourselves up for the evening, a sepoy arrived carrying a large cloth bag full of tomatoes. Apparently, while they were out hunting, they found a plot of wild ones, larger than our domestic ones, and well ripened: we'd have some for supper.

Doug still ambled about, suffering from a swollen right knee. I couldn't tell whether it was poison from a bite, or had been twisted at some time; it certainly looked nasty. He needed to treat it with embrocation and we had some in the issue medical pack. I was still feeling a bit weak – the blasted malaria was still hanging about.

Cyril fried the tomatoes with eggs and beans. It made quite a good meal, washed down by the local beer; the tomatoes were very tasty.

It was very close and humid. The sweat was running off me in buckets. I believe a storm was building up; when it broke all hell was let loose. We would be warned, for all the inhabitants down below suddenly became quiet.

Looking down, I could see dark clouds gathering, swirling and rotating. Doug and I strolled outside to check any stores that might require securing down. The storm came with terrible claps of thunder; our bungalow shook, and then the rain came. I have never ever witnessed such a deluge. We passed through monsoons on the way up here – but this! It was deafening! We just stood there, ready for anything to happen. The main deluge lasted about ten minutes, and when it did ease, the rain on the roof still blotted out all other sounds.

Peering through the gaps in the bamboo wall, I looked down into the village to see what damage had been done, and could see a number of native huts battered to the ground. It must have been terrifying; when it died down we must give what help we could. The rain soon became just a trickle, and as we crept out to assess the damage, the full extent of it was there to see.

Our lean-to had gone, and parts of it were strewn all over the compound. Small sheds were flattened, and there was debris everywhere. It would take some time to rebuild.

Cyril suggested that he should go up to the post to check for damage. We decided that Doug and I should inspect there, while Cyril was to mobilise labour and get some clearing up done here.

On arrival at the post we were thankful that no damage had been done. Two sepoys on duty had gone through a terrifying experience. They had stayed up there throughout the storm, just in case a signal had been sent.

Indeed the whole structure was as sound as before; no part of it had moved. We could be satisfied that however much it moved during spells of duty, it certainly wouldn't fall down!

In the meantime, the chief had sent up some jungle fruit – yams, potatoes and other root vegetables, and so on. Perhaps we might receive a signal tonight concerning the whereabouts of our porter corps.

We were at our stations by eleven. The two sepoys on duty had it all under control; everything was in place, with the coffee keeping hot on the warm Primus. Actually, we needn't have come up tonight; it was just that we both wanted to contact Chittagong to inform them of the terrible storm we had just come through, and of course, ask about our supplies.

We spent two hours listening to hundreds of call signs, but not one was for us; so we decided to hand over the rest of the watch to the sepoys, and make tracks to our quarters to get what rest we could before daylight.

On arrival, we found our charpoys all ready with mosquito nets in place. Soon we both had flopped out, sweating and hoping the blasted mosquitoes would keep away.

I must have dozed off; it was the bright sun shining through gaps in bamboo walls that woke me.

I saw that I had collected a few more mosquito bites – my arms were swelling and beginning to itch. I would have to rub ointment in before the itching got unbearable. The bites certainly wouldn't help my recovery from malaria.

Doug was hobbling about, but he said the knee was much better; I hoped so, for the next signal would be for us to break camp and make our way up towards Lunglei. From there we would follow the trail up the high ridge towards Ijal.

After a wash down under the repaired lean-to, I joined Doug sitting outside on the verandah, where it was slightly cooler, to discuss out future plans. He, like me, was beginning to get restless. The sooner the signal came through, the better.

We received no news and no response to our signal for supplies. I suppose they thought we'd got them; little did they realise how short of essentials we were.

Cyril had prepared a meal of eggs and rice, together with coffee. Afterwards we strolled up to the post. I wanted to check the generator's bearings to see if they were running true; it was a great relief to find they were not overheating.

On our way back to our quarters, we were met by a native carrying two large cockerels, making signs that they were for us. While we were in the throes of waving our arms about, Cyril came along to explain the native wanted us to have them, as he felt safe with us being there!

On arrival at the bungalow, we were confronted by about a dozen natives squatting in a circle, obviously awaiting our return. They were all chattering and laughing – especially when I tried to speak their lingo! If only I'd been allowed a camera!

All of them were big strapping chaps – six feet tall, wearing just a strip of animal skin over their loins. They had long black hair down to their waists, with bamboo sticks through their noses and ears, and on some, through their lips.

Cyril said they were there to help us in any way, doing odd jobs around the compound. Cutting away undergrowth and shrubs that grew so quickly around was a job that often needed doing.

When they were given the word to go ahead, they were all smiles, especially when I handed out five of our ration cigarettes to each one of them. Off they went, laughing and chattering away. Later, I could hear them singing and the sound of their machete-type curved knives as they cut down the thickly growing shrubs.

The air was very humid, with no breeze at all, making Doug and me sweat like the devil; we'd have to cool off before starting duty tonight.

Cyril cooked one of the cockerels and made a very nice curry, together with some root vegetables. This made a good meal and there was enough left for two more.

We left the bungalow at about eight, and as we made our way along the ridge we could see far below the sun sinking behind the hills and valleys. With daylight fading quite fast, we were keen to reach the post before dark.

1st April, 1944

We spent the night glued to the headphones; we were looking forward to news of the location of the supply corps – they should be much nearer now; I thought perhaps we would have heard about them from nearby villagers.

We came away from the post at about four, leaving two sepoys on duty in case there was a signal. They'd come away at about eight, to be relieved by the day shift – all qualified technicians of the IOC. There were Bengalis and Pathans among them, as well as Indians.

On arrival at our bungalow, we were soon under our mosquito nets, hoping to have a few hours rest before Cyril started to prepare breakfast, and treat us to his Indian songs – a sort of wailing!

Doug was still suffering from stomach pains, together with a swollen knee; he had applied several native potions, massaging and exercising the knee most of the time.

After coffee and biscuits, I made my way down to the village and depot to ask Captain Bartlett if there was any chance of rations before ours turned up? He explained that they were very short, but he would muster up a small parcel. He would want it returned when ours arrived, which I promised to do. He did let me have a bottle of Rosa rum, and said he'd be up later to help us drink it!

During the afternoon, the Indian Major arrived up here. As he was a liaison chap, he very much wanted to be with us on a night's duty. Then perhaps he could decipher a few signals; it would be interesting to see if he could pick up some that the Indian Observer Corps sepoys were unable to decipher.

He explained to us that his spell of duty had expired, and that he would be off in the morning, and make his way up the ridge to report to the District Commissioner at Lunglei. From there he would probably be made to report to Headquarters at Ijal.

Anyway, he wanted us to be at his basha that evening, as he was giving a farewell bash, and had invited a few others to attend. I reckoned it would be quite a session – especially for him, as he had acquired quite a number of friends. I reminded him of his spell up in the post that night and he promised not to drink too much!

The evening passed quite well. Doug and I managed to make ourselves presentable, with clean shirts and trousers. The basha was full. There were about sixteen officers, all glad to let their hair down, and swap yarns, including a few that were close to the knuckle!

It was about ten thirty when we decided we should report up at the post. The Major was ready; besides from being unusually talkative, he appeared to be looking forward to the venture.

By the time we had climbed up to the ridge on our way to the post, the Major seemed a trifle out of breath. He hadn't reckoned on the distance, and when he attempted to climb the rickety bamboo ladder, it was touch and go!

It appeared that the Major had been informed at Chittagong that there were two BORs maintaining wireless posts situated somewhere in the Chin and Lushai Hills along the Burmese border, but at the moment, they had no idea where exactly our position was.

Waking up at about eight the next day, I decided to go down to the depot to say cheerio to our friend before he left, but on arrival at his basha, I saw that he had made an early start: the basha was empty.

On the way back, I strolled through the village, acknowledging the toothless grins from the women as they squatted down, working their makeshift bamboo looms to weave gaily coloured *poens* or shirts. There weren't many men about, I suppose they were out hunting for food – wild boar, small monkeys, wild cockerel, snakes, and any other animal that took their fancy.

Doug was still suffering stomach pains and felt sick at times, but he was still cheerful. His knee seemed much better, and he said the sickness would go off if he was careful what he ate; I hoped so.

In our small medicine box, there were still plenty of bicarb tablets, along with other pills; if they didn't work, I'd ask the chief if he could recommend any of his potions! I was thinking of the liquid the chief of Mullianphui made me drink to cure my dysentery; perhaps it was not known in this village.

I decided to visit the chief to ask him if he knew of any potions that would help Doug, but on arrival at his basha I learned that he had gone hunting for the day; there was only one native left to guard the place.

I had brought Cyril with me, because of the language difficulty, and through him I asked the native for permission for me to have a look round inside. I was rewarded with a huge grin and the waving of arms, indicating that we could enter.

The floor was made of bamboo mesh and covered quite a large area, and as we made our was across it, it gave slightly, giving the feeling of walking on cushions. In the centre was a sturdy tree trunk, running up the whole middle of the basha; it must have been at least three feet in diameter.

Where it protruded through the roof, a large gap was left to allow smoke to pass out; no light was provided, other than when the bamboo shutters were removed at the entrance.

The skins of various animals were scattered about the floor, making it obvious where people slept. We didn't stop long as the guard chap was looking a bit uneasy. I thought we had better go, so after bowing to thank him, Cyril and I made our way down the ladder. We made sure the guard would tell the chief of our visit.

On arrival back to our bungalow, I found Doug looking much better, and able to walk more steadily. When I told him about our search for medicine, he seemed his old self again.

By the time I'd had a good wash, Cyril had prepared a meal; judging by the smell, it was curry. After the meal, we would have to prepare for duty up in the post.

5th April, 1944

We were up in our hut in the treetops. We arrived up there at about ten, together with a sepoy to look after our needs. Soon after our arrival, he was brewing cha on the Primus stove, and opening a tin of issue biscuits.

The duty was a waste of time; we listened intently for our call sign amongst the babble of others, but I'm sure we were forgotten that night.

We came off duty at about five, leaving our sepoy friend to clear up and close the transmitters, and finally lock everything up securely, checking all the locks before leaving.

Dawn was breaking as we walked along the ridge. On reaching our bungalow, we both had coffee before crawling under our nets to have a couple of hours' kip before breakfast.

I was woken by the melodious singing of Cyril. The kitchen lean-to was next to my bamboo wall, and I could hear every movement; perhaps it was just as well, as I would have overslept.

Doug was already up; I could hear him moving about, so it seemed as if his leg was much better. Over breakfast he confirmed it – most of the pain and swelling had eased. I suggested he rested a day or two before putting weight on it.

While Doug took things easy, I said I'd go down to the supply depot to have a word with Oliver, and ask if he could let us have something – a bag of rice, or flour, or even tins of bully!

As I walked down the narrow trail to the village, the foliage became rather dense, with the overhanging branches taking up most of the light. Besides this, moisture from the branches made getting a firm foothold very difficult.

All the time I was being followed by a pack of small rhesus monkeys screeching and making a hell of a din just above my head. When I stopped to look at them, they just sat there, gibbering and spitting at me. I didn't think they would attack, so I decided to walk on.

I arrived at the supply depot and made my way to where Oliver had his basha. It was built high up, resting in the fork of a tree, and to reach it one had to climb up about twenty feet on a bamboo lash-up ladder, with every step making it sway.

At the top, you stepped on to a wide verandah, which surrounded the basha, with the main entrance facing you. There was no door, just a bamboo panel you pushed sideways to open.

As I approached, the door slid open and his Lushai woman beckoned me to enter. She made signs for me to follow her towards a corner where Oliver lay stretched out on his charpoy, shaking and shivering: a clear dose of malaria.

We shook hands, and I asked, 'How long have you been in this state?' He said, 'The worst is over. Bloody glad to see you. Sorry to be like this.' I said, 'Is there anything I can do?'

6th April, 1944

I knew as well as Oliver that the malaria would take its course; he seemed to have passed the high temperature stage, and would now have to wait for the shivering to subside, before eating to gain strength.

His Lushai woman knew how to look after a person recovering from malaria, for the illness was widespread among the villages. She had doped him up with quinine – where she obtained it was nobody's business, though I believe it was drawn from a certain tree.

I stayed with Oliver for about two hours; I don't believe he wanted me to go, but I gave some excuse and said if he wanted help in any way to send a runner up. I returned to our bungalow to find Doug much better. He was more cheerful and most of his pain was on the wane, while he was behaving more like his old self.

After a lunch of fruit and rice, we both decided to have a nap. It was quite oppressive; the little breeze of the morning had by now subsided, leaving a playground where all the insects could dive-bomb, building up a continuous humming sound. By now we'd got accustomed to it.

Cyril came into my room with the news that four white men in shirts and shorts had been sighted near our camp. I hurried down to see the chief to ask for some strong warriors to join me in searching for these chaps.

He immediately produced four ferocious looking natives, six feet tall, with all the bamboo ornaments in place and wearing little else. They carried bamboo spears, with short *kukri*-type knives tucked in their twine belts, and they were headhunters to boot!

We made off, following the trail leading down into the deep foliage, and entered the jungle. The four natives were leading, with me and Cyril bringing up the rear. Doug wanted to come, but I persuaded him to stay behind, and give his leg a rest.

I carried my Sten gun. This was the first time I'd used it. The magazine was full and all ready to use; I hoped it wouldn't be necessary, but at the same time it would show my authority.

We must have covered three miles deep into the jungle in the direction where the four men were last located. Our native guides looked at the ground and overhanging branches for clues, sometimes we would stand quite still to listen – all to no avail.

After about four hours, we decided to return. The sun was sinking fast, and we didn't want to be roaming about down there after sunset; so we backtracked along the trail to reach our village before losing light.

Our guides grinned from ear to ear and then returned to their homes.

On my arrival back at the bungalow, Doug was pleased to see me. He'd thought it was a bit dangerous to have gone, but as I told him, it was quite a challenge. While I washed and changed, Cyril cooked some chicken and rice, and by the time the meal was over, I was beginning to feel very stiff. Doug suggested that we delegate sepoys to take our watch, but I said perhaps there would be a message for us, so we both decided to go on duty.

There was the usual keenness on our part for news. We took it in turns to decipher all the signals that sounded quite like ours – there were a lot. By four we gave up and prepared to return to our quarters.

On the way, we were able to observe the wonderful dawn and the sheet of beautiful colours that filled the sky, reflected in the jungle far below.

After reaching our basha, we were both soon stretched out on our charpoys, with our mosquito nets over us, hoping to catch a few hours' sleep.

The wailing tone of Cyril's chanting woke me up. As I said before, his lean-to kitchen abutted the bamboo partition that separated us; I could even smell the different dishes that were being cooked, so I know as near as dammit what we'd be served up with.

I only managed a couple of hours' sleep before the sound of, 'Cha, Sahib!' There stood Cyril, offering me a large mug of cha and then opening the shutters. I enquired about Doug's health, to be told that he would like to rest. His leg was much better; give it a day, and he hoped to be back to normal with all systems working.

After a breakfast of eggs and rice, I decided to visit Oliver again, and found him much better and more cheerful. Even his Lushai woman smiled on seeing me again, and offered me a mug of rum! She had swept over the bamboo mesh floor and tided up all round. I suspect Oliver got her going in case other people paid a visit.

Before I left, he asked me to call in at the depot and ask for a certain sepoy to visit him. It appeared that the chap did all the hair cutting for the depot. Had I known, he could have done mine before Doug had hacked it off!

Later, after cutting Oliver's hair, the sepoy reported back to me that Oliver sahib and his woman would visit us in the evening, if that was all right. I replied to say that we'd be very pleased to see them. Was he well enough to walk? Obviously he wanted to try.

The rest of the afternoon was spent making the place shipshape, while Cyril prepared a chicken curry, with fruit to follow.

At about seven they arrived, Oliver saying how good it was to get out. I must say he looked much stronger, while his woman looked nice in a clean white blouse and gaily coloured *poen*. Cyril had laid the table on the wide verandah; it was all very nice.

Oliver brought along a couple of bottles of rum, so as the evening wore on, conversation flowed freely. He told us tales of incidents and experiences arising from dealings with these reformed headhunters.

He was employed by the Bengali government, in liaison with the British to keep the supply route open for all requirements. This was a difficult task, as one would imagine, bearing in mind the treacherous Karanphuli River. Apart from that, there were some not so friendly tribes that lived on the banks.

It was nice to have company and swap yarns in such unusual surroundings. It was not quite so humid and we could hear all the different species giving vent to strange noises. Our oil lamps attracted hordes of mosquitoes, but as we had long sleeves and trousers on, it was our heads and necks we had to cover with cream.

Between us we drank one bottle of Rosa rum. I don't believe they were in a hurry to leave, for it was about eleven when I said we'd have to go on duty.

They assured us that they were quite safe walking home, the Lushai woman showing by gestures what she would do if in any trouble. I could see her point, but to make sure of their safety, I told Cyril to escort them most of the way. I suspect they were grateful.

We'd both had our share of drinks, and the walk along the ridge would I hoped, clear our heads. On reaching the post, we both felt much better, and climbing the ladder wasn't such an ordeal after all.

Two sepoys were on duty, both with no news. Plenty of signals filled the air, but ours was not among them. I really believed HQ had forgotten us. Before we left, the sepoys made cha and chapattis; the latter were most tasty, the best we'd had so far. It would save making a meal on returning to our quarters.

When we did arrive back, we found some post had been sent up from the depot: three letters and a copy of the *Free Press*! I spent the rest of the morning devouring every word. It was very difficult for Audrey to manage on such a low income, and having Nicky as well – what a upheaval this war caused!

I'd have to write back straight away, then perhaps I'd catch the native runner before he returned on his long journey to Chittagong. It was over three hundred miles. I guessed he would be going back the next day; I would have to make enquiries at the depot.

The weather was terrible. It was raining very heavily, while the air hung humid. My body was covered in sores, together with mosquito bites, which I'd smothered with grease. While writing, I looked at the water rushing down between the natives' huts. They dug channels diverting the water from entering their homes; a precaution they must have arrived at many years before.

There was so much to put down on paper – how much I missed home, with Audrey and Nicky! I lay awake during the night seeing images of how they were coping. On the air during the night I picked out English-speaking Bengali stations which gave news of bomber raids over London, and prayed that none were dropping over my area.

I wrote to Whiteleaf as well, telling them of my unusual walkabout. It was difficult to describe it all without using actual names, but there it is, we had to be careful. Cyril offered to run down to the depot to catch the despatch runner before he set off. Away he went, and returned to say my letters were in safe hands, and the runner would put them with the official letters for the next post.

9th April, 1944

About mid-morning, we decided to walk down to the depot and enquire if there was any news of our supplies, only to find that Captains Scott and Robinson were out on inspection in the surrounding villages. Our friend Oliver was there, sprawled across a bamboo settee, and was very pleased to see us; he was only too glad to talk to white chaps.

We stayed with him for about an hour, and left for home. Making our way through the village, we met Cyril playing with the children, running round and round and shrieking with laughter – it was good to see that they got on well.

Calling Cyril over, I asked him to take us to the chief, if he would act as interpreter, just to have a chat.

On reaching the large basha, Cyril climbed up the short ladder on to the wide verandah, but before he could knock on the bamboo shutter, it was opened by a huge native asking what our business was.

Speaking in Lushai, Cyril explained who we were and said would like to speak to the chief. At this, the guard put his hands together to greet us, while at the same time making signs that he would enquire if the chief could see us.

After a minute or two, we were beckoned in. It took quite a time to get used to the semi-darkness. There were no windows as such, just slits between bamboo branches, allowing just enough light to see what one was stepping on! As I said before, shrunken heads were on display on narrow shelves, letting one know it wasn't so long ago that they took heads on important occasions! Cyril stated that it was only a few years ago.

After talking to the chief, Cyril quoted him as saying that while on a hunting party, they had got wind of a small Jap patrol. They had actually sighted them moving along a trail on the slopes of the hill opposite; thankfully it would seem they were moving away, but to make sure, they were kept under observation till out of our range of hills.

It was not long before the chief told his minder to fetch his hubble-bubble pipe. The smoke went over the water to provide a cool and mellow taste – ugh!

As we were leaving, the chief suggested that we have the post camouflaged, and he would send natives up to help: a wise precaution. We had been through this exercise before.

By nightfall, the post was indistinguishable from nearby foliage and trees; the natives were quick and thorough. This meant no signals tonight – just the time HQ would try to reach us, I guessed. The chief sent out scouts to be posted within a radius of three miles; if there were any Japs about, they wouldn't have a chance of not being located.

Again, as we'd done before, all movements were strictly cut. The villagers behaved as they did previously – all the men were in the jungle, leaving the women squatting at the entrance of their bamboo shelters.

11th April, 1944

We sat up most of the night, taking turns of about two hours' duty watch on watch. It wasn't exactly dark outside; we could distinguish different landmarks, so our scouts could note any movements. All we had to do was sit tight.

There was little air; the humidity and closeness hung everywhere, and the sweat ran freely over us, which didn't help prevent the sores from itching. I could have scratched the blasted skin off, but instead we applied plenty of the calamine powder that we'd found in our medicine supply.

Heavy clouds were hanging overhead, and given the overbearing heat, we were certainly in for a severe storm. It was all so uncanny: all the different calls from the inhabitants of the jungle had faded away. Usually at this time the air would be filled with a cacophony from all of them.

The wind had risen to a high, whining gale. We were all waiting for the thunder and lightning, and when it did come, all hell was let loose.

Torrential rain poured down. The noise was deafening, and I thought the roof of the bungalow would cave in. It was certainly straining under the load, giving creaks and groans as the bamboo lashings moved with the whole structure.

The storm lasted for about an hour, with us huddled under what protection we could find. When it did abate we emerged on to the verandah to inspect the damage.

Along one side of the verandah, a large branch had fallen on the protective railing, completely breaking it down. It had been swept away into the undergrowth below. Thankfully, the roof and structure weren't visually damaged – we should be thankful for that – but all around was debris from trees and bashas.

Cyril had been down to the village to assess the damage, and found that most of the natives' huts had escaped the high winds, though some were completely flattened. The main damage was from flooding; some huts were two to three feet under water. It was a pitiful sight to see the owners wading through it, trying to retrieve what household goods they could find.

The sky by now had cleared; the tail end of the storm could be seen moving away fast, as the wind was still very strong. Perhaps it was just as well, for it would help to dry out the huts more quickly.

The natives formed a band of people to go around and assist those who needed help. I must say the spirit of the majority was quite amazing. As they went around, laughter and singing filled the air. I'm quite sure this attitude lifted everyone's spirits, for as the water retracted, they sorted out the sodden household goods, cleaned them and put them on high ground to dry out.

While Doug and I started up the ridge to see what damage had been done to the post, Cyril started to sort out the debris of pots and pans, trying to collect utensils in which to cook a meal. Just before the storm broke, a native had arrived with a gift of two chickens, so it would be curry and rice – how we suffered!

On reaching the post, we were thankful to see it still upright. The tall trees, being close by, must have acted as a shield and windbreaker. Even the bamboo hut was still in position.

Scattered around were piles of branches. It would take us quite a while to clear the approach to the ladder, so rather than looking at it, we both began lugging the branches away.

Very soon natives appeared to assist us, so amid chants and laughter, a wide path was cleared. They waved their arms to indicate that they would clear the whole lot up later, and with that they disappeared along different trails, to go hunting and so on.

As we climbed the bamboo ladder, we found quite a few rungs were adrift. The twine around the joints had stretched, and it would have to be put right before being used often. I'd ask Cyril to find a native who was fit for the job.

In our little hut itself, we found nearly all the gear had been dislodged, but was not damaged. However, everything needed battening down again, so for the next few hours we both strengthened all the fixtures – a job that we couldn't finish, as the daylight was fading fast. We'd have to pack up, and return again tomorrow.

Back at the bungalow we decided to have a rest. We'd both been lugging heavy branches in the cleaning process, and my joints were beginning to ache! Cyril had made more curry and rice, and here we were again – sitting out on the verandah, going over the day's events. I made one of my large rolled cigars – a leaf about ten inches across. It was green when picked, but after lying out under the sun for a few hours, it was ready to smoke, after being rolled with bamboo twine.

We both were expecting our bobijee back from visiting his child bride, but up to now there was no news. We hoped he'd return. I guessed he would eventually, as he only got paid as our bobijee when we gave him a chit to present at the DC's HQ at Lunglei.

I forgot to mention that I'd fostered a little dog – black and white – which recently followed us in our walkabouts. I would say it was a terrier; it was about that shape and size. It was an intelligent little dog, and never let us out of sight.

I decided to stroll through the village to check the trail and see if it was still passable after the storm. I started off about ten, complete with walking stick, with the little dog following.

Owing to the storm, the trail had become very slippery – at times I had to hold on to the overhanging branches to keep upright, and after a short distance I realised it would take at least three to four days to dry out.

On retracing my steps, I became aware that my little dog was missing. Standing there waiting for it to reappear, I could hear squealing and the sound of swishing leaves. I walked back and found the little dog running round and in circles, obviously in great pain, its paws clawing at its nose.

I had quite a game catching him, especially as he was wriggling about all the time. Eventually, as I hurried back to the village, he seemed to quieten down.

On arriving back, I made straight for the chief's basha only to find he was out on a hunting trip, leaving a native in charge. By making signs and holding the dog for the chap to inspect, I got him to understand. He immediately entered the basha, and returned holding a leaf containing a small brown powder.

While I held the dog he pulled back its nostrils and pushed some of the powder in. Immediately the dog started to sneeze – and out came a large leech!

I couldn't describe the relief the little chap felt – continually barking and wagging his tail, jumping up at me excitedly.

The storms were still hovering about. Far down in the valley the clouds were heavy and still rumbling, so for today we stayed put. As the danger of the Japs had receded, we gave instructions to have the camouflage over the post removed, a job that would take a dozen natives most of the afternoon to do.

When they had cleared all the trees away, it would be about five – just the right time for us to test the equipment, together with two sepoys, in readiness to locate our call sign.

As the light was beginning to fade, we set out to walk the short distance along the ridge, and found our usual trail washed out. The natives had made a new one through the undergrowth – an improvement, as it was more direct and therefore shorter.

While Doug climbed the ladder, I inspected our charging unit. It had been located underground, buried about two or three feet down, so that when it was working, the exhaust was muffled to deaden the sound. After checking all connections for dampness, I wound the starting rope round the pulley and gave a great heave.

Lo and behold, it started straight away! It was purring as if it had been shut down only yesterday – what a relief! Letting it run, I made my way up the ladder to see how the transmitters were.

Doug and Cyril were busy checking them and were both satisfied that in operation they would be all right. Before leaving, I shut down the jenny; it was nice to know it had escaped the storm. I'd expected the dugout to be full of water.

The main thing was that when we operated that night we would be able to contact HQ about our moving up further towards Lunglei, to await instructions from there.

Doug was still suffering from a painful stomach. He couldn't keep his food down, and I thought he looked thinner. I hoped it wasn't anything serious.

Leaving the post until later, we made our way back to our bungalow to have a meal before going on duty. On arrival we found a sepoy was waiting with a message from Captain McCall. He would like to meet us, and asked if we would have dinner and a chat. We accepted, but explained that we had to be on duty at about ten.

After a quick wash and change of clothing into clean shirts and trousers, we made our way down to the depot, to enquire where the Captain was billeted.

When we reached the depot, a sepoy was waiting to escort us to our new-found acquaintance in a basha recently occupied by an IOC major, or perhaps someone from the supply corps.

We were welcomed at the entrance by a lean chap, tall in stature, with dark hair and small wisp of hair on his upper lip, who offered us his hand in welcome. 'Pleased to meet you, chaps – drink?' he said, by way of greeting.

He explained that he had heard of the two BORs and their roving commission, and thought they might be interesting to talk to.

It appeared that he too owned a tea plantation towards the Assam–Burmese border. As he knew the lingo, he was called up to enter the liaison corps, and was then posted to the supply corps at this jungle dump.

After a few rums, we felt more at ease, and were chatting away about all subjects, especially about home. Though he had a Scottish name, he was actually born in India. His father had started the plantation at the turn of the century and in fact was still alive and well, running the place with his wife and a few faithful employees.

During our conversation, he expressed the wish that he would like a chap like me to look after the maintenance work on his plantation; a house and car would go with the job. I believe he was serious, but as I explained, a lot of events could happen during a war; no one knew where he'd land up. I took his home address in England as a matter of courtesy, but doubted if it would come to anything.

By ten, we were well away. We would have liked to stay longer, but we promised the two sepoys on duty that we would join them later, in the hope that a signal from HQ had been received.

Thanking the Major for an interesting evening, we made our way up through the village towards the ridge beyond. It was a bit scary picking our way between the native huts, hoping not to disturb them. They were still a bit ferocious at times – especially at night!

The sepoys were glad to see us. They had made chapattis and coffee in the hope that we would turn up; we had to leave the chapattis, as we were full up from eating earlier.

They hadn't received any signal up to now. As Doug took over, we both felt a bit despondent. We were hoping we'd get some message, but as the dawn approached it was obviously not tonight, Josephine!

We followed the usual procedure. We shut down at about five, then left the post in the capable hands of the sepoys, to clear up and to lock up.

To make sure the batteries were up to capacity, I left the jenny running; the sepoys would check them before tonight's stint.

It was after breakfast, when we were sitting out on the verandah discussing plans for the day, that we heard quite a commotion outside, with Cyril announcing the arrival of a small platoon of Pathan IOCs, with the officer in command enquiring who to report to.

As he approached us, I was aware he was a great disciplinarian. He was dressed to perfection – he thought perhaps he was to meet the DC or someone of that rank.

His shirt and shorts were spotless, while campaign medals spoke for his many actions against aggression. His hand reached forward, and he made us both feel friendly towards him. I noticed, too, that he had two pips showing, giving him the rank of jemadar, or lieutenant, while we both were in shorts and showing no rank.

I could see he was a bit mystified, so we explained our mission to him; after which he did say that before leaving Chittagong HQ, they had spoken of two BORs maintaining wireless posts up in this range of hills, and that, he was very pleased to have met us.

A clearing just off our basha gave plenty of space for his small platoon to camp for the night, while he was most welcome to join us here in the bungalow. I told Cyril to put a charpoy in our small stockroom.

During the morning, he was busy organising the camp for his platoon. I must say they made little noise – no shouting or banging about. If they hadn't called in here first, we wouldn't have known about them.

He had lunch with his men, and after we'd had ours, he strolled over to ask us to show him a small part of the trail leading down into the jungle.

Doug's leg by now had got much better, and as he said, it would give some exercise and perhaps ease the joints.

We set off, taking with us two sepoys carrying *dahs* (long curved knives) as protection, and in case we had to make our way through the undergrowth – a wise precaution, for as it turned out we often had to hack our way along.

By the time we had got back to our bungalow, the Jemadar had become quite friendly. We respected each other's views, and were getting on quite well; he was still puzzled by our rank, as we wore shorts and old bush shirts.

As he would be moving up the ridge first thing at sunrise, we invited him for nosh that evening, and he seemed very grateful. We said we'd see him at about seven.

About mid-afternoon, a sepoy arrived with a message from Captain Scott to say that he had received news from villages along the trail that a captain sahib and a small platoon had been sighted, making their way in this direction. He wasn't expecting anyone, so he presumed they would be for us.

Anyway, they were a good day's slog away, so it would be in the morning some time when they arrived up here.

Tonight we were having a meal with our friend the Jemadar. It couldn't be too late, as we'd have to be on duty in the hope there was news for us.

In the meantime, Cyril and a help from the village were cleaning the whole place up, washing and scrubbing the bamboo floors and walls. It had never been done before! It would serve a twofold purpose, as the basha would be ready for the other platoon in the morning – that's if they were heading this way.

The evening meal went off quite well – vegetable curry and rice. It was a good job we didn't serve meat, for after all he was a Sikh officer, not Pathan. When he arrived for the meal, he came dressed in all his regalia – all in white, with a turban adorned with the star of his religion.

He had a twinkle in his eye, and gave a grin as he shook hands. Doug and I were wearing just trousers and shirt; with no medals or rank; he was still mystified.

We made the excuse that we were on duty later on. We should have told him no dress, but we were both most impressed by his presentation. It certainly gave colour to the evening.

The meal was very enjoyable. There were plenty of events to chat about. He wanted to know of London, and of course, Buckingham Palace; perhaps one day he would be able to visit all the famous places.

16th April, 1944

I do believe the Jemadar enjoyed last night's meal, especially after a few tipples of Rosa rum, together with the local beer.

He certainly let himself go, pulling our legs, making jokes and laughing all the time. He did remark that it was a long time since he had enjoyed good free and easy company; most times it was a staff dinner consisting mainly of junior officers creeping round their superiors, trying to impress in some way.

The party broke up at about ten. We had promised to be at the post between ten and eleven so we had to move. He wanted to come along, but was put off by our explaining there wasn't much room. I think he got the message.

It was the usual drill: listening for our call sign amongst hundreds of others that filled the air – weird signals that surely baffled many.

It was dawn when we were relieved, and were treated to the same glorious sight down in the valleys, with all the different colours spreading over the jungle treetops.

On arrival at the bungalow, and entering our rooms, we found the whole place was full of mosquitoes. There were swarms; I've never seen so many forming such a cloud.

Also on the walls were dozens of geckos darting like lightning to devour the mosquitoes if they dared to settle. It was very interesting to watch the gecko catching the insects. One moment it was motionless, then its long tongue shot out to catch its prey. It was quite common to see these lizards motionless on the bamboo walls; they did a good job.

Cyril had managed to erect our nets without trapping any mosquitoes, so apart from hearing the continuous dive-bombing outside, we managed to snatch a few hours' rest.

I woke up feeling a bit weak. Sliding off the charpoy I felt very groggy, and the usual symptoms of malaria started – shivering and perspiring at the same time.

Doug came in to see how I felt, and it was plain to see that I was in for another dose. Telling me to rest, he said he would search for some quinine. I said there was a drop left, but where the hell I put it, I couldn't recollect.

Luckily it was found, and after taking a stiff dose, I rested for a while, only to wake up shivering and sweating uncontrollably – here we go again!

For two days I shivered and shook, with Doug and Cyril keeping me under close watch. I don't know how high my temperature went, for at times I couldn't stop shaking and shivering; sometimes I dozed off during the night, while during the day someone was at my charpoy side, occasionally changing my sweat sodden sheets. On the third day I awoke feeling much quieter.

18th April, 1944

The shivering had gone, and my temperature dropped; I didn't feel so hot. I lay there for a while, listening for the sound of others moving about. At last Cyril came in to check, and was very surprised to see the change in me.

After making coffee, he helped to hold me while I got off the charpoy in an attempt to stand. We were both laughing, as I hobbled feebly about the room, bent double!

Gradually my strength returned, and by midday my dose of malaria was clearly disappearing, though I was still feeling weak. I had to take it easy and at the same time build myself up.

Doug came in and was pleasantly surprised at my quick recovery, and thankful I was nearly my old self. We even had coffee and eggs out on the verandah.

We both looked forward to moving on. The inactivity and lack of a challenge in not making our way farther up the ridge, was not for us. We wanted to probe up towards the higher range of the Chin Hills, where we were told, a few observation posts were being worked.

The sores on my body were now getting less irritating, and I was not perspiring so much; the borax powder certainly helped to quell the incessant urge to scratch.

After a light lunch of chapattis and rice, we both were sitting out on the verandah, when Cyril said a native out hunting had seen an officer sahib on his way up here, leading a small platoon of soldiers. They were about a half hour's trek away.

We presumed it must be Captain Wade, and proceeded to tidy the place up. We had barely finished when Cyril shouted, 'Here they come, Sahib!'

Leading the party was a tall military chap, complete with the correct moustache and bearing, dressed lightly in an open shirt and knee-length shorts.

His pips of rank were overlapped by his collar. He came forward with his hand outstretched, and his first words were, 'I'm bloody glad to reach you at last!'

I could see he was surprised that we showed no rank; it didn't make any difference to the way our conversation went once we were inside the bungalow.

While Cyril was busy in the kitchen, we found a nice comfortable chair for him, and thrust a large mug of rum in his hands. For that I could see he was very thankful, and said if there was room here he would like to rest for a few days.

He said Chittagong had warned him of the conditions here, but at that moment they hadn't a clue as to our whereabouts; they would try to contact us during the next few nights – what a tale! We'd been glued to our receivers in the hope of a call from them.

In fact, he was attached to the 14th Army, and was up here to report back to HQ on the location of Jap movements – if any.

Before going on duty, we had a long conversation regarding our way of life up here, mixing with the natives and learning about their basic way of life – their religion and beliefs and so on.

During our talk, I got the impression that the Captain was a bit of a disciplinarian, and didn't exactly approve of our trust and mixing among the natives.

Then we enlightened him about their belief in the British Raja and said how the hunting parties used the village chief's basha as a resting point in the hunt. I told him, too, of pictures of the royal family in frames above the chief's chair. There could be no doubt of their loyalty.

All this would be confirmed by his fellow officers when he went down to the supply depot on the following morning. My impression was they would size him up straight away, and fill him in accordingly.

He said he would also like to meet the chief. For that, I suggested he dressed casually; after the meeting, we could go down to the depot to introduce him to the other chaps.

The day had been spent in conversation, and by now dusk was falling fast. Soon it would be time for Doug and me to prepare for another spell up in the observation hut. Wade wanted to come with us, but as I explained, there was little room. Perhaps later…? Not bloody likely! We both agreed we didn't want him nosing about; he'd be full of suggestions which would put our routine to question.

Tonight the weather was kind to us. There was not much wind, with the temperature a little close, but bearable. The sepoy on duty had just placed mugs of coffee in front of us, when Doug waved his arm, indicating to us to keep quiet. Obviously he had contacted Chittagong, and was deciphering their signal.

They had assumed that Captain Wade had found us, and that he would give us all assistance in dismantling the post, and would accompany us in our move farther up towards Lunglei. There the DC (District Commissioner) would give us further instructions as to what trail or direction we should take.

We now had quite a busy workload: dismantling the post and collecting all our gear for packing into different lots of about 90 lbs for each bearer to carry. There would also be the task of mustering a porter corps. This was a job for our friend, the chief. He would be surprised at our moving; we had enjoyed a liaison and friendship which would take a long time to erase.

It was just before dawn when we finally stopped listening for signals. Now it was time for us to start dismantling the whole unit, marking and getting the gear in readiness for packing into crates.

Leaving just two sepoys to start the job, we made our way down to our bungalow along the ridge. It was a short walk we had done so many times. Once, it was a chore taken for granted; now, as the job ahead began to sink in, we both gazed at all the familiar landmarks so that they'd be imprinted on our memories at all times.

On the way down, we found a narrow trail that led to the extreme edge of the highest point of this ridge, and looking down into the valley we could see a herd of elephants feeding among the trees in a small meadow.

I hadn't heard of them being hunted; the natives just keep out of their way. They are smaller than their African cousins, but quite as ferocious when cornered. It was the first time we had sighted them so close. The natives had made signs to us that they were there; now we could say we'd had a good look at some.

We had been warned, too, of tiger traps that were set up in various parts off the beaten trail. A deep trench was dug, and covered over by bamboo branches in such a way that it was very difficult to detect. For this reason, we tended to keep to the well-known trails.

During my travels between villages, I often walked through clearings full of beautiful and exotic flowers, with orchids growing in a carpet of wild species that created a blaze of colour.

High up in the surrounding trees were packs of rhesus monkeys – a small species- that delighted in darting about ahead and screeching at movements below; no wonder travellers were so easily located by the villagers nearby.

On one of my walkabouts, I came face to face with a small hunting party. There were four of them, fitted out with all the usual weapons – bamboo spears, long curved knives and long bows slung over their shoulders, with the arrows kept in skin pouches.

All I had was my walking stick! Luckily I recognised one and called out the welcome, '*Collome*!' They stood aside to let me proceed, and as I passed they looked down at me from their six feet odd. They were jabbering away in light-hearted tones; I think they quite enjoyed my discomfort. As I walked away, I turned round to wave farewell, but they just stood there watching me: was I glad to get out of their sight!

I arrived back at the bungalow to find Doug and Cyril wondering where the devil I'd got to. When I explained, they thought I must be mad. Cyril said next time I should take a native, or one of them. This little episode happened about fortnight ago; I don't believe it was mentioned before.

As we made our way downwards along the ridge, we were met by sepoys in charge of natives on their way up to start dismantling the tall observation post and the basha below it. So this would be our last duty stroll down to the depot. I wondered what our next assignment would bring.

On arrival at the bungalow, we were overjoyed to find the post had arrived. Cyril said a runner from the depot had delivered it about an hour ago.

I flopped down on my charpoy to see who had written; there were three – from Audrey, Mother and the bank. I read and reread the one from Audrey; my thoughts were of home all the time – what a situation! Here I was stuck up in the Lushai Hills away from civilisation, while Audrey and Nicky were so far away in England. My thoughts were with them always.

19th April, 1944

In my mother's letter she spoke of her anxiety as she wondered where I was. She wished me all the best of health, and looked forward to my return. She did say that Father's garage had been converted into a small munitions factory, and been taken over by Broom and Wade; they were working non-stop, day and night.

An orderly from Captain McCall asked us to report at his basha as soon as possible. First we would have a rest on our charpoys before seeing him, as I didn't think it could be anything important.

On contacting the Captain, he said the Lister water pump had packed in. Did we have any knowledge of their working?

I asked him to show me where it was. I could see immediately that the leather seal round the rim was worn and hard. It would be quite a job for me to dismantle the plant; at the same time, I asked the sepoys to hunt around for strips of leather suitable for making a seal.

By the time I had dismantled the pump, a large piece of hide had been found. It was quite pliable, just the job. The native who found it said it came off a small deer caught yesterday by a hunting party. I was lucky to have it, as it would have been burnt to get rid of it.

Soon I had the pump assembled, keeping my fingers crossed that my newly fitted seal would serve its purpose by not letting the water return.

Cheers all round, and fresh water for all. For the last few days it had been foul, but now the pump flywheel was rotating at a steady pace. The sepoy in charge of the pumping station seemed quite a reliable chap; he said he had noticed lately the output in volume had been gradually going down, and had reported it to his sergeant – but that's as far as it got.

Doug and I decided to move further up the ridge the day after tomorrow. For the last few days we'd gradually packed small loads not required for our immediate use.

All the post's equipment – transmitters, receiving gear and all the assembly parts, were ready for the IOC to collect and to take down to HQ to be stored. I wondered when, if ever, they'd be used again.

Our next commitment was to visit the chief and inform him of our move. I didn't think the old boy would be pleased; he regarded our job in locating Jap movements a great safeguard. He would have to position more guards round the village.

I forgot to mention that our bobijee arrived back, all smiles and very cheerful, thanking us for giving him the time off. The village where his young bride lived was quite safe, situated in a remote part of the northern Lushai jungle.

The day was been spent gathering and checking what gear we'd want on our travels. The chief had promised us five stalwart porters to arrive in the morning.

21st April, 1944

I woke up to the knowledge that this was to be our last day here, and I felt quite morbid – though not in the deep sense. I suppose we had made this village our base for so long that we had both got quite used to the inhabitants and their primitive way of life.

Doug was already moving about. That was nice to hear; it suggested that he was better; I hoped his stomach had settled down at last. The bobijee came in with coffee, and to say all the kitchen had been packed away. Only our basic requirements were left out – a few utensils that we would need today.

After a light breakfast, I left Doug to continue the packing, while I made my way down to the village and the depot. I had to arrange with the chief to have five stalwart porters to be at our bungalow before dawn, so that we could be off as early as possible.

He was most helpful, and promised they would be there. He was quite sorry that we must leave, and hoped we would meet him again on our return journey. As I made my way to the depot, I looked back at the village and could see the chief and his staff out side on the verandah watching me as I made my way to the depot. I waved, and they waved back.

After leaving the chief and his party, I collected Doug and made my way down to the depot to enquire if Captain McCall would be able to spare two sepoys to act as further cover on our trek up towards Lunglei.

We found the Captain in his small office, surrounded by stacks of boxes and papers, busily searching for the right paper. He seemed pleased to see us; perhaps it was a good break for him, for he immediately produced the Rosa rum and poured out generous tots.

After listening to our request, he stated that he had just the men who would look forward to accompany us, and straight away sent his clerk to find them. Within ten minutes they stood before us – two intelligent chaps, their uniform spotless, erect in their bearing, just right for the job. I asked them if they could be ready for first thing in the morning, before dawn, and they both said they'd be there.

We stayed with the Captain for about two hours. He said he would miss us, not only for our transmitting, but for having two white chaps to converse with. He said we must say goodbye to the other officers in charge, and we said that was our next port of call.

By the time we had made our farewells to Captains Scott and Robinson, and dug out Oliver from his Lushai live-in the light was fading fast, and it was nearly dark when we reached our bungalow.

On returning to the camp after a short walk, I found Doug checking the sepoys who would be responsible in looking after our bungalow and its contents while we were away, though on reflection I doubted if we would return this way.

The rest of the day was been spent in final checks for our early start. We were both feeling a little weak; I knew my malaria was still with me, while Doug staggered about as if he was drunk, but we were both determined to get away.

Our plan was to make for Lunglei, and from there towards a place called Rangamati and Ijal, a distance of about three hundred miles. We would have to have a damned good try, as there were four observation posts dotted about in the hills around, placed in villages that were well off the beaten track.

I still felt a bit shaky. We'd make it early to bed, as we had all our gear packed and ready for an early start. The weather was in our favour – clear skies and a slight wind. We hoped it would last.

The bobijee had prepared a serving of chapattis and rice, perfectly cooked, together with a deep brown soup. It was our last meal sitting out on the verandah. We'd got quite attached to the bungalow; I wondered if our next billet would be as good.

Before retiring, I'd had a nice tot of rum together with a mepacrine tablet. Doug had already retired to his room; it was only about eight, but it would give us both time to have a final check round. I wandered around the compound noting all the various changes Doug and I had made during our stay here.

The whole campsite seemed much larger, owing to the amount of undergrowth we had removed. Now the ground was covered in thick bladed grass and made an open site that would appeal to any passing traveller.

I was woken by the usual chatter just outside my bedroom shutter. High-pitched voices were engaged in a crescendo of arguments, their owners all trying to pick the best of jobs. By the time I emerged, all had been sorted out.

Doug was ready, so after a last check round, we started off, with my party leading and Doug at the rear. I had the bobijee and three of the tall Lushai guides – if only a camera had been was permitted! Villagers watched as we took to the winding trail leading down into the jungle below.

Our first day's call would be Ridge Camp, a distance of about eight miles. I guessed it would take all day to reach there, as the trail we were using was narrow and in parts overgrown – giving my porters plenty of opportunities to demonstrate their skill in cutting a way through the undergrowth. They seemed quite happy at the job, singing and laughing most of the time.

Watching them using their long curved dahs in such an easy way, I shuddered to think what injuries they could inflict!

We made steady progress, picking the best footholds along the narrow trail, at the same time keeping a sharp lookout for snakes that lay hidden amongst the undergrowth. After about three miles, I found a nice clearing for a rest.

As we followed the twisting trail, schools of our friends the small baboons and rhesus monkeys were always overhead, chattering away, apparently delighted that they could follow our every movement.

Rounding a corner of the hillside, one of the porters in my leading party gave a joyous shout and pointed towards the next range of hills. Very faintly, we could see an assembly of bamboo huts dotted amongst the dense foliage. The bobijee said it could be Ridge Camp, and it would take about three hours to reach. If so, we'd have to follow this trail down into the dark undergrowth, making more work, as we would have to cut our way for another two miles. Then we'd reach the trail that would lead us out of the oppressive and stifling jungle.

The sweat was pouring off all of us. The porters didn't seem to care – I suppose they were immune to all skin allergies. Theirs must be thick!

It took another two hours to reach Thiga Ridge. Viewing it from our approach as we did, it had seemed only a half a mile away: how optimistic we were!

On our arrival, we were met by a tall Sikh officer, Captain Shukal, whom I straightaway recognised, as he'd been one of the party which Doug and I attended.

After a few pleasantries, in which he said he was very glad to meet up with us again, he gave instructions to an orderly to arrange where my porters were to billet. First, however, he told us to dump our loads in the dāk bungalow.

It was built on the same layout as all the others – two bedrooms, a sitting room, with the lean-to kitchen at the rear, and of course a verandah to circle the building. One side overlooked the valley, far down between the distant hills: a view that will always be with me.

After a good wash down, and a change into clean clothes, we both felt much better, and look forward to our bobijee's cooking. Wonders of wonders, a bottle of Rosa rum was sent up with the compliments of our Sikh Captain friend; we'd sleep well tonight! He also sent us an invitation to have tiffin at about twelve in the morning.

I didn't sleep at all well. The atmosphere was so overpoweringly close and hot. What with the mosquitoes dive-bombing and trying to get under my net, it was a great relief to see the rays of the morning sun slanting across the walls of the basha.

The bobijee brought in the coffee, and said he didn't think Doug Sahib was well; he looked very pale. I went round to see for myself and sure enough, the poor old chap looked like chalk. He complained of stomach pains, but said they would go off. After telling him to rest, I rummaged amongst the few medical packages that were left and unearthed a small packet of bicarbonate – what a find!

I gave him a dose, and told him to stay in bed for the morning. I would go down and explain the situation to our friend; perhaps he could help with some medicine.

On meeting Captain Shukal later, I told him of Doug's tummy trouble. He straightaway told his medical orderly to go up to our bungalow and diagnose the complaint.

Ridge Camp

22nd April, 1944

After a few rums, we were quite friendly. It appears he was a café owner in Calcutta and was called up and given a commission straightaway. I told him my father owned a garage, and was now working on munitions. He seemed quite surprised that Doug and I were given the responsibility of inspecting and servicing the wireless posts over such a wide area, a job in which we had to use our own initiative and drive.

The medical orderly returned to report on his examination of Doug. He was mystified, and the only antidote he could prescribe was bicarb. As we were short, he would send a supply up to catch us before leaving.

After quite an enjoyable session, I managed to drag myself away at about three, and by the time I had climbed up to our basha, I felt whacked.

I looked into Doug's room and found him fast asleep – a good thing. He hadn't had much sleep lately, and it would help him recover.

As our observation post had been dismantled, I checked with the IOC that it had all been crated up and sent down to HQ at Demagri. They assured me that it all had been done, and it took fourteen porters to carry the load. They should be halfway there now, as they had left here two days ago.

Returning to our bungalow, I found Doug sitting out on the verandah, looking quite cheerful. He told me the pain in his stomach had virtually gone – he put it down to the orderly's powder.

We then discussed when we could move out. Doug was for tomorrow morning, but I said he should get a little stronger, and we decided on the day after tomorrow; it would give us more time to check everything – a full day.

The bobijee had prepared a nice chicken curry – complete with chapattis for our last evening, and we sat out on the verandah. While eating, we could gaze down to the forest and hills far below stretching well out of our sight.

Making sure that all our gear was at hand for first thing in the morning, we decided to turn in, leaving the bobijee to clear up the few remaining bits and pieces before lights out.

I had a fairly good night; I felt a bit shaky, but hoped it would wear off after coffee. Our two sepoys arrived, both looking very smart; I told them to check the loads and to see if the porters had turned up. If so, we would all be ready to make a start.

The dawn was by now just breaking. Far below, a tip of the morning sun could be seen rising above the jungle. Soon all the inhabitants would be awake to fill the air with different cries, and another day of challenges would begin. After a last look round, we were off. Our winding trail led across small open cultivated plots of land, in which rice and other vegetables could be seen growing.

Leading the column was one sepoy with a porter. Doug and I were next, with the rest bringing up the rear. The porters bent to offset the load, at the same time chanting and singing their favourite songs. I believe the idea was that it would keep all the inquisitive animals off – I hoped so!

As we slowly made our way down the winding trail, we often had to use our dahs to cut down the overhanging foliage, as it grew so densely.

On some stretches of the trail we found it most difficult to keep upright. The dew from overhanging foliage had made it very slippery, and we had to hang on to branches to keep on our feet.

After about two hours, we had to call a halt. We were beginning to curse quite a lot, and I thought a rest would be in order. We were lucky, because soon afterwards a clearing was spotted ahead. It was quite a large open space in which some orange and grapefruit could be seen growing; perhaps some might be right for picking.

Wood was gathered, and a large fire was soon burning, with the water pot held by a metal tripod in the centre, all ready to make a welcome coffee. While we were waiting for the coffee, the bobijee was busy making chapattis and preparing some rice.

By the time we had eaten, the sun began to sink, and Doug and I decided that as we had found a favourable stop, we might as well bed down there for the night.

The decision was gratefully received by the rest of the party; it would be a good rest, and give us strength to make an early start.

More wood was gathered to keep the fire alight during the night. At the same time, Doug and I found a level plot on which to prepare our sleeping space, not far from the fire.

A roster of two-hour watches during the night was drawn up, just in case any animal or inquisitive native might be around. My spell was from two to four, so I'd have a few hours in which to doze off.

I had scooped out some earth to make my bed more bearable, and had laid small leafy branches to offset the lumps. I looked over to where Doug was lying: not a movement. And, apart from the wood crackling on the fire, not a sound from our camp could be heard.

Around us in the jungle, all the night creatures kept up a cacophony of shrill noises – high shrieks, mingled with deep grunts from others foraging in the undergrowth. I hoped the guard was keeping a sharp lookout for any that might charge this way.

As soon as I dropped off, my shoulder was being shaken by one of the porters, to indicate that it was my turn for guard duty. There was a pot of coffee by the fire, so it wasn't going to be too bad after all.

The time would be about two, on a jet-black night; the stars were obscured by a blanket of mist. While I was keeping the fire stoked up, I had to step over a few bodies to pick up firewood. They didn't seem to mind!

Sitting on a large tree trunk surrounded by the sleeping natives, my thoughts were of home – if only they could see me now! My only concern was that Audrey and Nicky were well and out of danger, especially from those blasted flying bombs. Glancing up through the gaps in the trees, I became aware of the coming of the dawn. Shafts of light were beginning to fill the sky – another day had begun.

27th April, 1944

After a breakfast of fried eggs and rice, our next job was to restore the campsite to its original state, eliminating all traces of our overnight stop – a job that took about an hour. We swept the ground to remove all waste that might have fallen. We had saved some branches on making camp, so by the time they were strewn about in their original places, passing travellers wouldn't see any difference – especially Jap scouts.

We were all ready to move on. With many grunts and groans, as the porters heaved their loads on to their backs. Once there, the weight seemed less as the legs took most of the strain, especially when they were moving along the trail.

As we progressed, the air felt noticeably cooler, due to the gradual upward gradient of the trail. Glancing down the hillside, I could see pockets of mist or vapour swirling around below, so we must be climbing all the time.

Though the air was cooler, we were all sweating. It was simply running down our backs, thanks I suppose to the uneven trail, and having to chop our way through parts of the deep undergrowth. This was borne out by the deep scratches on our bodies.

Rounding a bend, a porter at my side gave a shout, and pointed to the next range of hills, where we could see, high on the summit, a cluster of bamboo huts. 'Lunglei!' he said.

As our destination was about four miles away, we decided to have a stop. We knew that it would take the rest of the day to reach there, and a mug of coffee would be most welcome. We were lucky enough to find a clearing from which Lunglei could be clearly seen; we wondered if anyone there had spotted us.

After an hour's rest, and feeling fairly refreshed, we set off on our last leg, with the sepoys starting up a sing-song to boost our morale.

Cyril Sirren, who had joined us for our trek to Lunglei said I must have been mad to have taken this job on, and as we slogged on, he referred me when speaking to the others as the *pugla* (mad) sahib.

We had to take another rest; our final destination seemed so near – and yet so far! The mug of coffee, and a short rest, made us all feel better. As we moved on, the chattering and the chanting started up again, stronger this time, with the knowledge that we hadn't so far to go.

It was about ten minutes later that we spotted the observation tower, with bamboo bashas surrounding the base. As we got closer, several IOC sepoys came running to greet us.

Pathans, I think they were, wearing turbans smaller than the Sikhs. There were about six of them, headed by a sergeant, who on approaching was looking for our rank. He did the best thing by saluting and shaking our hands. Cyril Sirren drew him to one side to explain why no rank was worn.

Lunglei

27th April, 1944

After the initial introductions, we were shown our quarters – a wing of a large dāk bungalow, consisting of sitting room, two single bedrooms, with a shower room connecting. Our bobijee was given a room nearby, alongside the adjoining kitchen.

The bobijee was quite pleased with his kitchen. To have a concrete and stone building to work in was quite a change from sagging bamboo walls.

We both slept well. Our charpoys were very comfortable – better made, and larger than before. I believe we would have slept all the morning, but for the bobijee's high-pitched call of, 'Cha, Sahib,' and his report on how different the conditions were.

Our shower room was a bit basic – no hot water, of course – but by the time we had showered, the sun was nearly at its height, clearing all the remaining mist to give another close and hot day.

Just after breakfast, Captain Wade called to enquire if we wanted anything, and to suggest we paid a visit to the MO, just to have a check; perhaps it would be to our advantage.

I had been told that Captain Wade was a liaison officer with the 14th Army, visiting areas ahead of a forthcoming push; hence his interest in us two chaps roaming about inspecting out of the way wireless posts.

It was decided that we would visit the post and send a signal to Chittagong informing them of our whereabouts before seeing the MO.

On arrival at the post, we introduced ourselves to the duty Pathan sepoys and requested them to contact HQ and inform them of our position.

They explained it wouldn't be till after seven, and we said it wasn't imperative – just to let them know where we were.

Looking over the post, we noted how much better it was kept, compared with our past experience. All the equipment was in first-class condition; but then, they had got much more room. Surrounding the post were trees and shrubs, giving seclusion on all sides.

Leaving the post, we made our way down from the ridge into the HQ, to enquire where we could find the MO. Entering the compound, we were struck by how all the bamboo bashas were arranged: a maze of entrances were built along a twisting trail that wound its way past each basha.

We found the small medical unit, identifiable by the red cross fixed to the bamboo wall. On entering, I was quite surprised at the cleanliness and display of medical supplies. An orderly came forward to ask us to sit on the cane chairs while he informed the MO of our arrival.

Coming forward to meet us was a Bengali doctor. He was about five feet ten, with a moustache and all the jauntiness a man could muster. His hand was outstretched to welcome us.

I believe he had been told of our exploits by Captain Wade, and asked to give us a good check over. We were with him for a couple of hours and were examined thoroughly.

28th April, 1944

I guessed that the MO was a bit concerned about Doug's stomach. He gave him pills, and told him to report the slightest pain and to rest for a few days to which Doug readily consented! Anyway, we both were looking forward to a prearranged rest.

I had lost a few pounds, and at times felt quite weak. It takes quite a time to build up one's strength after a dose of malaria. I still had bouts of shivering, but after taking a mepacrine tablet, my resistance returned.

At lunch Doug said he felt much better, and said he would come with me on my walk down to the village in the afternoon. I said I would see Captain Wade first to have a chat about things in general.

On arrival at his office, we found him flopped out in an old bamboo armchair, looking pale and weak, but glad we had come for a talk about things.

He said he'd be all right; he was as stubborn as a mule. I suggested he saw the MO, and he gruffly remarked, 'If it gets worse.' I thought, Yes, mate, you have a lot to learn yet.

We stayed with him till sunset, and got rid of a bottle of rum between us, so we were feeling much better by the time we left.

On the way back to our bungalow we both agreed that we had broken the ice and that we could converse more easily when meeting again.

By the time of our arrival back at the bungalow, I began to feel a bit shaky and weak. I hoped it was not another attack; I had lost quite a bit of weight. I would have to take a mepacrine tonight; together with a tot of rum, it that usually sent me off to sleep.

The bobijee put his head round the corner to say good-night, while we decided to sit out on the verandah to have a chat and a tot of rum.

As usual the night was still, broken only by the croaking of numerous bull frogs and the shrill cries from the animals that roamed the night. I had a few rums and decided to turn in.

The bobijee's 'Cha, Sahib,' woke me. I must have slept well. I couldn't remember waking up during the night, though the heat was very oppressive. It must have been the rum.

I really had to write home. It was my turn, so in the morning, I got my head down and reassured everyone at home that all was well at my end. The entire morning was taken up writing three letters; I hoped they would be deciphered!

I'd try to catch the native runner before he made the long journey down to the junction at the river depot. There, he would transfer his mailbag to a canoe, which would be easy to manoeuvre when shooting the many rapids. It would take him two to three days to reach this point, then there'd be the hazardous and dangerous trip down to Demagri.

At this point the mail would be transferred to a *kisti*, which in turn would eventually reach Chittagong.

29th April, 1944

On awakening, my first thoughts were of Doug, but on checking his room before breakfast, I was pleasantly surprised to find him up and moving about. He told me that most of the pain had gone, and he was feeling much better.

After breakfast, a sepoy arrived up here at about ten to ask would I see Captain Wade as soon as possible.

On arrival at the depot, I found Captain Wade clambering about on the roof of his office and shouting down that he was looking for a break in his telephone line; so far none had been found.

Together with two sepoys, I made a recce of the surrounding trees in which the line passed through. We must have penetrated deep into the jungle for about a half a mile radius, only to find the line still intact and disappearing into the foliage.

I decided to report back at the depot to collect more tools and sandwiches, and make a fresh search in the afternoon.

Back at the bungalow, Doug was wondering where the devil I had got to. Nobody knew I had decided to search for a break in the line.

After lunch, I set off again. Taking Cyril Sirren and another sepoy as company, we set off in a different direction, with the intention of making a more direct approach to the line near the point where I had left off in the morning.

On taking this short cut, we didn't realise how dense the undergrowth would be. Luckily, Cyril and his friend carried long dahs, which were just the job for clearing the way as we pushed forward.

Cyril gave us the first hopeful sign that we were on the right track. Pointing up into the treetops, he showed where our telephone line was definitely sagging; so it would seem there must be a break further on.

During our search, a school of rhesus monkeys had attached themselves to us. There were fifty at least, screaming and gibbering and watching our every move.

By now, the sweat was pouring all over me; I frequently had to clear my eyes. My one hope was that my sores wouldn't start again.

As we pushed farther forward, it was obvious the break had to be near, and sure enough, one end could be seen hanging down over the trail, resting amongst shrubs far down the hillside. While I was looking up into the tall trees, I saw the offending break.

Cyril offered to slide down the steep hillside and retrieve one end of the cable, while his mate climbed up into a tree to disentangle the main lead.

It didn't take long to repair the break – I had a few cleats in my repair kit – and after hauling the cable to its original position, the sepoy shimmied down to report that the communication line was repaired.

We were about to leave, when, one of the sepoys called out, '*Asti! Asti!*' meaning 'Careful!' He thought someone was coming this way.

Concealed behind tall foliage, we waited for the approach of the strangers, friend or foe?

We heard their voices first, jabbering away and high-pitched, including a few giggles. Then they came into view. Both were about six feet or more tall, with long black hair woven into pigtails that reached down to their waists. They were wearing only a small skin to cover their loins. Their lips, noses and ears displayed large bamboo ornaments.

They stood transfixed, their eyes darting from one person to another, their spears held rigidly at their sides. It was one of our porters calling out in the local lingo who broke the tension; immediately they were all jabbering away, arms waving to express their point.

Eventually an understanding was reached. There were smiles all round, then they touched their foreheads in respect and stood aside for to us to pass. Phew! Afterwards I wondered what would have happened if Doug and I had been on our own.

In passing, they were asked what village they came from. They replied, from northern Lushai, bordering the Naga Hills – three days on the trail from here.

We watched them till they were out of sight. Then, our next job was to retrieve the ends of the broken cable for repair and put the line back high up in the tallest tree. Looking up at the height, I realised how careful we must be. We had mended the break, but how the hell could we put the cable in line?

It was Cyril who volunteered; I must admit he was slightly built, so after a few encouraging hints, he set off climbing with the repaired line slung over his shoulder.

The main job was keeping the line free from being entangled in branches as he climbed. So far all was clear, he was doing quite well. Having reached about three-quarters of the way up, he looked down at us and gave us a reassuring wave.

At last he reached the point at which the cable was to be anchored. It took him quite half an hour, and we began to wonder if he had encountered any snags. But at last he could be seen to be coming down, very slowly, as the descent always seems more perilous, to be warmly congratulated by all.

We had no testing gear to check with Lunglei if the line was now operative, so we all hoped for good news on our return.

We were both relieved that we'd found the break and were able to make a good repair. It gave us both a little uplift – after all, the depot would have been isolated without any line of communication; the whole supply route would have been cut.

Before leaving, we swept and roughened up the patch where we had been working, replacing fallen branches, making the place look the same as when we found it.

We must have taken the wrong trail, for after two hours the hills and foliage around us didn't seem familiar; so much so that I called a halt. Doug and I had to decide which trail to follow.

It was Cyril who made the decision. He maintained that by the wear and the beaten foliage, this was the one we should follow – which I suppose was sensible.

As we pushed forward, it became evident to us that we hadn't been this way before. None of the trail could be recognised and we seemed to be getting deeper into the jungle.

Doug said as we had come so far, we'd have to push on to see where it led to, but we might as well have a rest and make coffee.

We found a clearing amongst the tall grass and collected wood to make the fire. The rest and coffee was most welcome. We camouflaged our brief stay by the usual practice of roughing up the grass and covering the ground with dead branches.

I didn't think this trail had been used lately. In parts, the undergrowth completely covered it, and it was hard work for two porters using their long dahs to cut a passage through.

Eventually, the trail widened, giving us an open space in which we could see the sky above – what a relief!

After a few more yards in the open, we halted to take our bearings. We gazed down at the jungle far below, spreading its way over hills and valleys; we could see for hundreds of miles.

Just ahead, on the next range, a number of bamboo buildings could be seen: Lunglei. It was about three miles away and if all went well, we should reach there before sunset.

As we approached the outskirts, a sepoy could be seen making his way towards us. He had the news that they were in contact with Chittagong by phone, and would we, as soon as possible, have a word with Captain Wade.

After a wash and change of clothes, Doug and I presented ourselves at his office to be met by quite a jovial

Captain Wade. He was all smiles, and asked if we would like a rum. I believe the repairing of the line meant a lot to him. Without a telephone line, he had to rely on weekly runners and wait days for a reply.

During our conversation, it was evident he was fed up here. He was pressing for a relief, hence his being grateful for the line repair.

In his next report he would inform HQ of our valuable exploit. Whether it would go any further, I doubted. He also invited us for a meal at about seven, for more talk of home and a few rums.

The remainder of the day was spent resting. I noticed Doug looked a little better – quite the opposite to how he felt. His stomach felt very sore, with rumbling and shooting pains. It wasn't at all nice; we would have to see the MO.

1st May, 1944

We spent quite an interesting evening with the Captain. I'd thought on my first contact he seemed a bit bullish and cocky, but during our conversation he was certainly most charming, laughing a lot and showed an interest in our travels.

By the time we had consumed a bottle of Rosa rum we were well away, exchanging jokes and various yarns until midnight, when it was time to stagger up to our bungalow.

Approaching it, we could see lights in one or two rooms, and were surprised to see the bobijee sitting out on the verandah waiting up for our return. He explained that it was a dangerous time to be out; there were all sorts of natives roaming about.

He had made our charpoys up, with mosquito nets, so it wasn't long before we both were stretched out listening to our friends dive-bombing us, trying to get through the mesh.

I think our cable repairing jaunt must have contributed to the stiffness in my limbs. As I eased myself off the charpoy the next morning, all my moveable parts seemed seized up. I staggered round the room bent double, just at the moment the bobijee came in with coffee.

He was most concerned, saying he would fetch the MO, but I said that wasn't necessary, I'd work it off in time – I hope! I must say, I've never experienced such immobility. But I wouldn't give in; gradually the pain began to ease off and I began to stand up straight. At this moment Doug came in to have a giggle at seeing me doing my exercise. Funnily enough, he was feeling much better.

By the time I washed and had breakfast, most of the stiffness had eased, so I decided to take a steady amble down to find the doctor.

The observation post was located just off the trail, so I called in to enquire if any messages had been received. As I approached, the Havildar (sergeant) in charge came down the ladder to greet me with outstretched hand, and to say how it was nice to meet up again.

He assumed that Chittagong was sending fewer messages as the Japs were believed to be sending patrols out in this area.

Scouts from villages within a radius of ten miles had been sent out; so far there was no contact. The scouts blended into the deep undergrowth so thoroughly that it should be the Japs who felt uneasy.

The Sergeant informed me that the MO wouldn't be at his basha till the afternoon, as he visited around the village in the morning, and suggested that we would be welcome to a meal here.

Thanking him, we made our way down to a small bamboo basha, which served as a comfortable hut. The inside was fitted out for sleeping and eating.

As it was nearing tiffin time, the Sergeant suggested we eat, then the afternoon would be free to consult the MO.

I must say the curry was very good: wildfowl with yams and root vegetables fresh from the jungle, washed down with plenty of the local rice beer. They made us most welcome.

By noon we were most comfortable – well fed and watered – and decided to stagger down to our basha to rest before seeking out the doctor.

After a short rest – enough to pull ourselves together – our first job was to find out where he was to be found. The Sergeant suggested I visit his small surgery, while he asked amongst the villagers.

It was my luck to meet him in between the closely built native bashas. He had just been attending a hopeless case involving gangrene, an awful condition that is most revolting; the stench is horrible.

He was most pleased to meet me. He asked me down to his hut, offered me a rum, and said, 'How can I help you?'

I explained to him about the bouts of pain Doug was experiencing. When he had time, would he diagnose the trouble? After a few rums, it was decided that he would make his way up to our bungalow to attend to Doug, while I and the Sergeant made our way up a steep grassy incline towards the supply depot.

The air was much fresher at this altitude and the plants were greener, making the whole area look like the English countryside. We seemed to have entered another planet; trees were displaying thick green foliage and it all seemed rather unreal.

It appeared that the Sergeant had been here before, for he knew where the supply depot was. Meanwhile, I set off to find the District Commissioner's office.

On arrival at the office, I was informed that the Commissioner had started early this morning on a duty inspection of the main villages in this area, and would be away for two to three days.

He was aware of our journey up here, and had left instructions to his second in command to assist us in any way possible.

Captain Barka, the Commissioner's aide, turned out to be quite a nice chap. He was glad to meet us, and was most eager to hear of our experiences. I informed him of Doug's trouble and hinted it would be at least a week before we could resume our inspection of IOC posts farther up the ridge.

He assured me that when my list of supplies was ready, he would have it made up straight away.

His main worry was the Japs; he hoped they would be diverted in their push down the Chin Hills towards Lunglei. All the villages within a radius of twenty miles had scouts posted in various hideouts in the jungle.

At his office, I was introduced to a Mr Carter, who was in charge of all Christian missionary work in that part of the hills. He said he'd be grateful if we called at his place on our way up.

4th May, 1944

I hadn't much time to prepare myself for Captain Wade's evening get-together. I managed to have a good wash; luckily the *dhobi* wallah had recently washed my trousers and shirts, so in a short time I was ready.

I looked in at Doug; he seemed more comfortable and said he would have a walk round the basha for exercise. Most of the stomach pains had eased. He said, 'Don't drink too much – wish I was fit enough to attend. See you later!'

On the way down, I was met by an IOC orderly who'd been sent up by Captain Wade to accompany me to the basha in which the get-together was being held.

On my arrival, Captain Wade came forward to introduce me to the other members of the party. They were all IOC staff officers, most interested to hear of our travels.

I explained the absence of my companion, at which they all seemed concerned, and said they hoped to meet him later. They had heard of Doug through the MO.

Skin colour and rank were forgotten – we all were isolated in this stinking dump, miles from civilised regions.

The Rosa rum and local rice beer were flowing freely, and within a couple of hours they all wanted to hear my reminiscences of our main cities – especially London.

It was past midnight when the singing had to stop. We'd had quite a good get-together, had all met each other and learnt each other's location and job.

A sepoy was detailed to accompany me back to my quarters. At this time of night, natives would be prowling about, bent on thieving or whatever.

On entering the bungalow, I was surprised to find the bobijee, half asleep, waiting up for me. He was glad to hear that an escort had seen me back.

My charpoy, complete with mosquito net, was made up, so within half an hour I lay stretched out, dozing and listening to the drone of the mosquitoes trying to penetrate the net.

I suppose it was the rum, for I soon dropped off, and was woken by the bobijee's, 'Cha, Sahib!' The chap was standing at the foot of my charpoy, grinning.

I enquired how Doug was, and was told that he was much better last evening. I hoped that when his cha was taken in we'd find the improvement continuing.

I soon slipped off my charpoy to go round to see how Doug was, to be met by quite a different chap: the colour had returned to his cheeks, his bearing was upright and he looked quite cheerful.

Of course, he wanted to hear about the get-together. I told him of their concern, and that they all hoped to meet him later.

Now that he felt much stronger, he suggested we strolled down to have a chat with Captain Wade, to express his disappointment at missing the party.

On arrival at the Captain's basha, we found he had a duty of inspection to make and had left early, so that was that. After telling the Sergeant in charge to inform the Captain of our visit, we slowly made our way back up towards our bungalow.

5th May, 1944

By the time we had got to the bungalow, it was evident that Doug was feeling the strain. On the way up, we had to rest; he was quite cheerful and tried to make light of his weakness, but was most relieved when the bungalow was reached.

This morning, on looking through the shutters, I could see all the mist had lifted, and far down into the valley the dense jungle was awakening.

I'd have to arrange with Doug about our next move up the range. We hadn't checked at the observation post lately, and there might be a signal waiting. Doug came in while I was clearing up, to say the bobijee had prepared breakfast, and asked what we would do today? He said his tummy was much better – thank goodness for that.

During a light breakfast of coffee and rice, I suggested we stroll up to the observation post to check the equipment and see if a message was waiting. We both agreed it was about time we made a move along the ridge towards Ijal, whether we would ever reach there I couldn't say. Captain Wade pointed out that there were posts manned by the IOC in this area.

We arrived at the post to find the two sepoys on duty busy clearing up and getting things tidy. There was a strong smell of curry being cooked for their midday meal; otherwise, the small hut was being kept clean and neat.

They were pleased to see us. During their night's duty there was no word from HQ. Neither of them had heard a signal; the air had been filled with codes being broadcast in numerous tongues. We had to be very alert in order to decipher any signals meant for us.

While we were checking the transmitter, a meal of chapattis and rice was being prepared; it would save our bobijee from cooking. A sepoy arrived with a message from a Miss Oliver. She, with the help of a companion, ran the missionary school, which was built by the side of the trail about two miles up.

She was asking us if we would have tea, and said she would love to have a chat about topical happenings. We asked if tomorrow would be convenient, as we had a get-together this evening. We said we hoped to meet them, and so on.

Before leaving the post, we sat down to a nice meal of chapattis and rice; the sepoys made both of us most welcome.

6th May, 1944

This evening we had a get together at our bungalow. We asked about eight people from the supply depot – all IOC, including liaison officers.

We asked the bobijee to prepare a large chicken curry and chapattis, together with plenty of *Zophan* rice beer. We had a couple of bottles of Rosa rum, and our guests would bring bottles with them – it all helped.

The bobijee had done a good job. The tables were nicely laid out, with chairs dotted about; Doug and I had to wash and make ourselves presentable.

They all turned up, casually dressed in open shirts and long trousers, showing no rank. I do believe they wanted to be as informal as possible, and let their hair down in a friendly get-together – or was it because we held no rank?

What the hell! In this sweaty hole, etiquette seemed out of order; we all had to help each other to liven up our time stuck out here.

It was all very magical: the temperature had dropped to a pleasant level, the air was filled with scents from all the wild plants growing in the undergrowth, and added to this was the chorus of bullfrogs and other midnight marauders.

The bungalow was dimly lit, with shutters to prevent us being seen from far down below in the jungle.

The party broke up at midnight. I believe they were all pleased to get together, to talk shop and discuss working plans for the future. Doug and I gave accounts of our river journey on the way up here, and spoke of the different villages we had to kip down in for the night. We recalled several stinking holes with rats running over us, where we were fully aware we could easily be robbed and knocked off.

I believe the boat wallahs told each village chief where we stopped that we were up here to locate the Japs and signal their positions back to base. Who did the chiefs want? The cruel Japs or the present administration?

Our friends were most interested in our account of the journey up here – how did we get the job?

When they had all gone, we sat out on the verandah having a cool off with a nice rum, and discussed further movements before crawling under our nets to escape the hordes of mosquitoes. There were many geckos clinging to the walls, waiting for mosquitoes to settle near. Then they'd devour them, quick as a flash.

In the morning after breakfast, we decided to pay the post a visit. Perhaps there'd be a signal intended for us. But we heard that a porter corps was on the way up here with supplies for the depot here at Lunglei: good news, as we'd need a fair amount for our trek up the trail to Ijal.

I asked the Sergeant in charge to instruct the IOC to keep a sharp lookout for signs of the approach of the porter corps.

7th May, 1944

We returned to our bungalow to wash and put on clean clothes to prepare for our tea at the missionary. We were looking forward to it.

On arrival at the small settlement, we were surprised to see what a compact bamboo built compound it was. Just by the main bungalow stood the church. Thick bamboo logs were the main foundation, while interwoven panels formed the walls to a height of about forty to fifty feet.

There were no windows; light was introduced by means of tall apertures let into the bamboo panels. The altar and vestry were underneath a huge painting of Our Lord, giving the small church a tranquil sense of reverence.

The seating capacity would be about fifty. We were told all seats were taken every Sunday, mainly all women dressed in gaily coloured attire, all giving of their best in singing God's praises.

For them it was also a meeting where they could gossip and discuss family matters, together with all the children, who ran about screaming. It was indeed a lively get-together every Sunday.

The two ladies then asked us into their small bungalow, which was a short distance from the church by way of a path through masses of flowers of all colours. I thought then, what a wonderful setting it was up here, high up on these hills, so far away from civilisation.

Inside the bungalow it was typically English, with chintz curtains and a display of ornaments and pictures of home, giving a sense of cosiness.

They both were very pleased to have company and introduced themselves as a Miss Oliver and Miss Jenkins. Straightaway they wanted all our news of home.

During our conversation, a young Lushai girl brought in trays of delicious home-made cakes and arranged them neatly within our reach. I noticed Doug had got his eyes on them! It was all out of this world: tea was brewing in a large china teapot, and it was a real home from home.

Children were playing outside, all attired in clean frocks – so different from the poor little half-starved *chikos* we had encountered on our travels. What a wonderful job these two ladies were doing.

Conversation covered all the events happening at home, and sadly it was soon time for us to return to our duties; but not until after we both had thanked them for a lovely afternoon. We both assured them that it had been most memorable; as I write this it is still fresh, although now so many years ago.

On arriving back at our bungalow, we were told that the IOCs on duty had received a signal that our food convoy would be arriving up here some time tomorrow afternoon. In that case, we had to clear a space for accommodation, and collect wood for fires.

The bobijee had prepared chapattis and rice for the evening meal, and afterwards we decided to stroll up to the post to inspect and await any messages that might come through.

8th May, 1944

Climbing up the rickety ladder to enter the small bamboo hut, we found two Pathan IOCs on duty, both very pleased to see us. They immediately gave us chairs, and offered to make tea.

After checking over the equipment, we decided to do a spell of duty overnight and told the sepoys they could have the night off, but must return early in the morning. We were shown where the tea and rations were kept; both seemed pleased to have the night off, and after thanking us, away they went.

Doug and I settled down to make ourselves comfortable. While he donned the headphones, I checked all connections and wiring. I took a good look at the two tall glass containers, in which the walls of the cells had to be checked for corrosion; though as these were practically new, it would be quite a long time before they started to flake.

We took turns to listening for our call sign, and had nearly given up hope. Then, during Doug's stint, he suddenly called across to me, 'Got it!

'Two BORs to proceed towards Ijal on inspection of three IOC posts set up within a distance of forty-five to fifty miles. Make all porters and provisions ready within two days – good luck.'

It was such a relief to know that Chittagong had us still in their wavelength. With the porters arriving tomorrow, we would be able to prepare a stock of provisions for the trek.

The two sepoys came to take over at about five, and straight away made breakfast for us, during which we told them of the signal and that we would be moving up the ridge.

Our first duty was to inform the Sergeant in charge of our movements, thank him for all the help he had given us, and to hope on our return down this way we would meet again.

Making our way back to our bungalow, we discussed our plans: how many porters we'd need, what provisions, and what was the route to the nearest village.

While Doug compiled a list of provisions we would want for our next venture, I made my way down to the village hoping to contact the chief; he sometimes spent the day forming a hunting party.

Luckily, he was at his large basha, holding a meeting with a few elders. On seeing me approaching, he came forward to greet me, his toothless smile stretching from ear to ear. At the same time, he gave orders to one of his women to fetch a container of the local rice beer, together with two wooden mugs.

When we told him we were moving on, he expressed regret by pulling a long face; whether this was sincere or not, we couldn't tell. But I must say, he had been very helpful to us.

On my request for three reliable porters, he at once knew who to pick, and sent one of his men to fetch them in.

9th May, 1944

When the three chosen porters arrived, I was confronted by tall ferocious headhunters. As usual, they wore very little – the usual bamboo ornaments through nose and ears, with just a small loincloth covering the vital parts. Their bodies were covered by dyes made from jungle berries.

They were carrying bamboo spears, and machetes slung from leather skin belts round their waists; I felt sorry for those who opposed them in conflict.

I must say, it was a great comfort to know that whatever dangers we might encounter, they would deal with it effectively.

The chief told them to report to us at dawn. At this, they gave us a slight bow and joined their hands, and returned to their homes to prepare for the morning.

We stayed with the chief for quite a while, drinking his rice beer, and we thanked him for all the help he had given us. He replied that he felt safe, knowing we had wireless communication with the nearest HQ. We explained that the post would still be in operation – the IOC would be in charge; but he said he hadn't the same trust in them as he had in us. We thought that was quite a compliment.

At last we had to say our farewells. His whole entourage came out to see us off – four dusky women, and six warriors or headhunters – and we said we hoped to visit them again on our return from higher up the ridge.

Returning to our bungalow, we found that Cyril and the bobijee had sorted out our rations and packed them neatly away ready for the morning. He'd made a list of everything.

Checking the list, I found he had left out the most important thing – medicine. He had forgotten the small box containing mepacrine and pamaquin, the most important drugs for fighting off malaria.

Besides our native guides, Cyril and our bobijee would also make up the party, so in all there would be seven of us.

I sent a runner to the depot asking a few IOC associates to have a nosh this evening; I hoped Captain Wade and fellow officers would be able to come; it would be our last bash for quite a time.

The bobijee prepared a huge chicken curry, together with a large earthenware bowl of the rice beer. I had managed to save a bottle of Rosa rum, and perhaps those who were able to attend would bring a bottle or two.

We were pleasantly surprised when quite a few turned up. There was Captain Wade with four others – two Indian army officers and two sergeants – all ready to wish us well for tomorrow.

The evening went off very well; the curry was served on huge chapattis, and plenty of beer and rum was consumed. Conversation filled the warm evening air, and we could have been at home; it all was very friendly.

The party broke up after midnight, with everyone wishing us two BORs the best of luck in our journey towards Ijal.

10th May, 1944

The faithful bobijee came in with coffee before sunrise, and said he had left the bamboo lean-to kitchen completely bare and had swept it out.

After a cold shave and wash down, I slipped on shorts and an open shirt to join Doug for our last breakfast on the verandah here at Lunglei – not knowing whether we'd be coming down this range of hills on our return.

Cyril arrived to say our three porter-cum-guides were sitting on their haunches ready to be off, but before we left I had to wave farewell to my friends down in the village.

This didn't take long, as they were all standing outside their huts to watch us depart.

After this duty, we were ready to move. The porters were loaded up with provisions slung on their backs, leaning forward to spread the weight. They were quite happy to be employed in a venture such as ours.

Doug and I led the way, the porters went next with Cyril, and two sepoys and the bobijee brought up the rear.

The trail we were following wound through tall elephant grass as high as our shoulders. Sometimes we came to open spaces and were able to look down at the jungle far below, which we were making for.

While keeping up a steady pace, the three porters chanted a Lushai ditty, over and over again, I can still remember the monotonous tune.

I called a halt after about two hours; Doug suggested we should rest and have coffee. The open space we arrived at had a covering of short grass, making it comfortable for us to lie down and ease our aching joints.

While the coffee was brewing, I wandered off the trail to explore around. I was amazed at all the different flowers and foliage – there must have been orchids there of collectable value; their blooms and scents were everywhere.

Banana trees abounded, and on the ground covered by grass were lots of pineapples, nicely ripe and all ready for picking.

Gathering quite a few, I made my way back to where I had left the rest of my party, and found them wondering where I had got to; but when they saw the pineapples, all hands were reaching out for them.

The bobijee had cooked rice and made coffee, so for the next half-hour we were all busy eating and taking a short rest, before clearing up the camp and getting ready to push on.

By now we were descending to meet the edge of the jungle. As we entered, the light became thin, and visibility was poor, owing to a haze of different vapours rising from the carpet of exotic plants that covered the ground.

The air was also filled with swarms of mosquitoes and other insects swirling around.

As we pressed on, deeper into the jungle, one of our native guides stopped to speak to the bobijee; it appeared he thought we were following the wrong trail.

11th May, 1944

We were debating whether to push on or backtrack, when one of the guides put his finger to his lips – a signal for quiet. He made gestures that someone was coming this way.

Standing close together, we awaited the approach round the corner of whoever it might be. A tall native rounded the bend, and at the sight of us he froze on the spot, defensive and frightened.

The bobijee called out a welcome, in Lushai, at which the native seemed to relax, and answered in the same tongue. It seemed that he was out hunting, and it was a great shock for him, on rounding the bend, to come face to face with a military party. At the same time, he was thankful we weren't Japs.

When the bobijee explained to him who we were, he seemed more at ease, and began to jabber away more easily, explaining that his village was quite near, and we would have to pass through it to join our rightful trail.

Becoming more friendly, he offered to direct us to his village and put us on the right path. This we accepted, and proceeded to follow him.

The trail became more overgrown as we made our way. I said to Doug, 'I hope our trust in our friend is not misjudged.' However, the porters seemed to have no such fears. As we made our way, and picked out our footholds, we had to keep a sharp lookout for snakes hiding under the foliage – especially the dreaded krait. One bite from him, and you collapsed within seconds!

Eventually, we arrived at open ground, leaving the dark shadows behind. Here we found fruit trees of all kinds. What a difference! The air was much cleaner, with no hordes of mosquitoes. There were oranges, grapefruit, and bananas, mixed with tobacco and other trees – we had found Utopia!

Our new friend pointed across to where we could see bamboo huts clustered – his village. As we entered, the usual cries of children greeted us as they laughed and danced around, or stared at us with open mouths.

We were asked to stop awhile and have a meal, but we said as the day was passing, we would rather push on, and thanked him for all his help.

By now most of the village had gathered to see us. Some of the older and more suspicious were eyeing us over. Looking at some of them, I got the expression that they would kill first and ask questions afterwards.

I believe our friend must have had some authority, for as we made our way towards the outskirts of the village, he spoke sharply to the young men who were looking very aggressive. We were most relieved to get well away and on to our right trail.

It was much wider and obviously well used, giving us enough space to walk alongside. The porters seemed more cheerful, so perhaps the meeting with the native out hunting had been to our advantage.

14th May, 1944

We'd been slogging away for about two hours, carried forward by the monotonous chanting of the porters, and the midday sun began to intensify the heat. Sweat was pouring off us, so we decided to call a halt at the next clearing.

We must have covered at least four miles – not bad under those conditions – and when a suitable clearing was found, we thankfully flopped down to rest and make coffee and eat.

The bobijee and porters got a fire going, and hung the water pot over it from a tripod. Soon they were busy making chapattis and putting the rice on to boil.

Doug and I were checking what supplies there were while waiting for the meal. During this time we noticed how the light seemed to be fading. I said to Doug, 'By the time we've had a meal, it will be dusk.'

As our clearing seemed to be free of deep undergrowth and trees, we decided to stop there for the night. I didn't think we would find a better site.

After a meal of large chapattis and rice, we set about planning our sleeping places, cutting away the thick roots to reach the soil, then covering it with large leaves to make the ground as soft as possible.

We sat around the fire till about midnight, and I made a rota of two-hour watches, to keep the fire going, and look out for any inquisitive prowlers. I was thinking of the looks on the faces of natives in the village we had just passed through.

My stint was to be three to five, so at least I'd see the dawn. I don't think any of us slept; the noise of the jungle creatures made sleep impossible, and the porters were jabbering away in low voices. I spent most of the night thinking of home.

We could hear movement around us – grunts and squeals – mainly from wild boar; they can make life unpleasant if you meet them face to face. I must have dropped off, for I felt my shoulder being shaken, and heard a voice saying, 'Sahib! Sahib!' Then I saw the face of the bobijee above me.

It was my turn to keep watch. Looking at the others lying huddled around the fire, I couldn't help thinking what a place it was to be in. Soon, through gaps in the treetops, I could see the sky just beginning to show signs of the dawn.

As the jungle dwellers woke, weird cries welcomed the new day. Animals and birds all seemed to try to better each other. I could hear movement not far away, prompting me to put more wood on the fire; in the process, sparks rose high in the air to frighten intruders away.

By now, one or two of the party were beginning to stir; the Lushai guides were sitting up, grinning across at me. When I looked to where Doug was lying, I saw he was stirring and beginning to sit up.

By now it was getting light. The bobijee had put the *pani* pot over the fire, so soon we'd have coffee. I felt very stiff, I would have to exercise.

15th May, 1944

After coffee and issue biscuits, all hands worked to clear the camp-site, collecting branches to sweep the ground and laying undergrowth to cover our tracks.

At last we were all ready to move off. The next village we were making for was called Hawlong, at a distance of about sixteen miles; I didn't reckon we'd make it today.

My limbs feel terribly stiff. As for Doug, I could see he was feeling the strain; he said he felt fine, but the jauntiness was missing. I suspected his stomach was still painful – we'd have to make more rest stops.

The trail we were following was about five feet wide, allowing plenty of movement. The porters were still chanting away as we picked our way along, keeping our eyes on the ground. Snakes hid there, and when we found them we flicked them off with our bamboo sticks. I had only come across one or two so far.

At times, as we followed the trail, gaps in the foliage allowed us to see ranges of hills stretching far away, with valleys of jungle in between.

We were halfway up the hillside; at this height, the air was quite cool, making a change from the clammy and close conditions we had been suffering. At one stage, on looking down just off our trail I could see a few banana trees, and wondered if they had any ripe for picking.

One of the porters volunteered to go down, and after a short while, returned from climbing up the steep incline bearing a large branch of bananas. They were green, but they'd ripen when kept. Stripping the branch, we found room for them in our packs; they would be edible later.

Across the valley, I could just make out a few huts and pointed them out to one of the porters, who immediately became excited, throwing his arms in the air, and turned to the others, pointing over the valley.

I estimated they were about eight miles away, and doubted if we'd reach there today; half-way perhaps, then we'd have to camp and rest before the last lap.

We now had to look out for a clearing to rest, and make coffee in before the last slog before nightfall. We came to the ideal spot – open with thick grass; I presumed the ground was getting more fertile as we descended.

I believe the party was glad to rest; I could see Doug was – he was looking a bit weary. We all flopped down in the grass before making coffee.

We rested there for about an hour, then loaded up to make our final trek for Hawlong. It was about midday, and very humid, the going wasn't so bad, though my feet were feeling very sore – blisters, I reckoned.

The Lushai porters started chanting again; I must say they always seemed cheerful and they certainly kept the morale of the party up.

The trail we were following went gently on a down gradient. We were leaving tall jungle trees and entering undergrowth mixed with tall elephant grass. Passing through this, we emerged on to a wide open approach to the village of Hawlong, and the usual inquisitive children came running out to greet us.

Hawlong

16th May, 1944

By the time we had arrived at the chief's hut at the far end of the village, native heads were peering from behind bamboo shutters, while our porters were telling them that we were friends trying to locate the dreaded Japs.

Assembled at the entrance to the chief's basha were members of his bodyguard – tall headhunters, all looking most ferocious, carrying spears and knives. From this group the chief stepped forward. He was a heavily built man, dressed in ornaments from previous battles, with plumage on his head taken from exotic birds.

We left it to the bobijee to do the talking, and he spoke in a loud voice, explaining our presence, and asking for the use of a basha and room for our porters to camp down for the night.

As they talked, the tension seemed to ease, with the chief jabbering away to his guards; I presume he was telling them to get our request seen to.

In the meantime, women came forward with trays on which earthenware mugs of the local beer were presented – a sign at least that we were getting more friendly.

The whole atmosphere was still tense; Doug and I just didn't feel at ease. Eventually, we made signs that we would take a rest, and asked if a suitable basha had been found for us.

While our bobijee and the chief were discussing arrangements for our stay, quite a crowd had collected. The children stared at us with wide open eyes, while others ran around shouting and laughing. The women stared too. I realised they probably hadn't seen white people before.

Making our way from the chief's basha, we were led through the maze of huts to the outskirts of the village where it did seem more agreeable. The air was clean, away from the stench of the settlement.

We were shown a fairly large basha. Evidently it hadn't been used for ages, for the bamboo walls were overgrown with grass and the doorway was wide open. One could guess the state inside.

The floor was covered in animal dung, and the stench was awful. I immediately sent one of the porters to ask the chief for the hut to be cleaned out and new flooring to be laid. Half an hour later natives came carrying branch brushes and mesh flooring.

I must say they worked hard; within two hours it was thoroughly cleaned out, but the stink still remained. We'd have to put up with it for one night.

The porters prepared their spaces just outside, so in any event we were well guarded. This left plenty of room for us five, consisting of Doug and myself, the two sepoys (Cyril and his mate) and the bobijee.

In no time, a fire was built and pots were on tripods in readiness for coffee and rice. The smoke from the fire smothered some of the smells, but the bobijee did mention that rats would be running about during the night!

17th May, 1944

I felt much better after a meal of rice and coffee. Our bed spaces were all set out, and soon we'd try to sleep; the ground was a bit uneven, but we were getting used to it by now.

I must have dozed off, but I was awakened by the squealing of rats as they ran around the floor. Some even scampered over me; my reaction was to grab a bamboo stick to ward them off. By now, we were all awake, chasing the blasted vermin away and taking quite a while to do it.

Cyril and his mate were really enjoying it, shouting and laughing as they chased the rats away, leaving Doug and me exhausted. We were lucky not to have been bitten.

By now the porters from outside were awake, and asking what all the commotion was for. When told, they advised us to have a small fire lit in the centre of the hut.

Having lit the fire, we settled down again, only to be choked by the fumes: what a night! I was glad when the light of dawn appeared, and I could survey the state of all our kit. In our chase of the rats, the contents of our kitbags were strewn about; so before making coffee, we had to clear it all up.

I didn't think the chief was concerned about us, so the quicker we got away the better. A few children had gathered around, but none of the elders; anyway, I felt we were not exactly welcome. Remembering some of the inhospitable glares we encountered on our arrival, I thought the sooner we got going the better.

Moving around was now most painful, and I could hardly put my feet to the ground. On examination I found the soles were once again covered in blisters. When Doug saw them he suggested resting today and moving tomorrow. Then the bobijee said he would go into the village to obtain a special sort of grease which would harden the skin.

After a short while, he returned with the good news that a native had a small container in which he kept a little of the ointment for medical use.

After bartering a little rice, he was able to return with the stuff. Like most medicines, it was dark in colour; but on applying it, I could feel its effects – the soles felt terribly chilled. The bobijee said it would take quite a short time to harden the skin.

While the rest of our group was clearing up, and packing our loads, I sat on a tree stump, resting. Now and again I put some weight on my feet, and was amazed to find most of the soreness was disappearing, and the skin was hardening. By the time all was ready to move off, I could hobble along with little pain.

18th May, 1944

We said farewell to the few natives who had helped us; there was no sight of the chief. We made our way out, taking the trail from the village that we were told would put us in the direction of Rangamati, which lay at a distance of about thirty miles.

Moving along at a steady pace, I found to my relief that my feet were beginning to give less pain; I must say the grease that the natives supplied for my feet certainly cured the blisters.

As we moved deeper into the undergrowth, the temperature rose and the sweat began to pour off us. I could feel the signs of the itching of prickly heat, not to mention the leeches that had fallen on my neck and arms.

Doug and the others were having the same trouble, so it was decided to make for a clearing where we'd rest and eliminate these awful parasites.

We had by now covered about three miles, which in those conditions, wasn't at all bad. We were grateful at last to emerge from a stretch of overhanging foliage into a clearing with a carpet of green grass. We immediately flopped down, without even unloading!

We lay there for a few moments before getting up to make a fire and put the water pot over to make the coffee.

Cyril helped by taking my shirt off, and revealed about six leeches busy sucking blood from different points. He immediately lit a cigarette and commenced to apply it to them, watching them curl up and fall off – ugh! They were ballooned up with blood.

After that, we all had our sores dusted with calamine powder. Now for a rest and some coffee. I soon felt better – the porters were even chanting some weird native song; we'd just have to wait a little while before moving on.

We enjoyed moving in fresh air, with no overhanging foliage, and looking ahead I could see a range of hills stretching away into the distance. Who knows, Rangamati might be down there.

As we moved along, I was grateful for the brown paste the natives had given me. It certainly did the trick. They concocted medicines from plants and trees to cure all their ailments.

We had been moving along at a steady pace, and must have covered at least eight miles. From the grunts and blowing of the porters, I guessed it was time to stop and rest.

It must have been mid-afternoon. We were still passing through open ground, and it wasn't long before a suitable spot was arrived at, much to the delight of the porters. Soon the coffee and rice were being prepared, while we rested our aching limbs.

We must have dozed off, for when I awoke it was to find the sun sinking down over the valley far below. Doug was awake, sitting by the fire, with the rest of our party laying sprawled about half asleep.

Going over to Doug, I suggested we must stop here for the night; obviously, the porters and our two NCOs were fagged out. We'd rest here and make our final push for Rangamati in the morning.

On awakening, everyone was relieved to know we would stay for the night. The porters collected more wood for the fire, while at the same time provisions were taken from our supply packs and made ready.

As we were in the open, with little cover from trees, it was decided to keep guard, in two-hour shifts, just in case humans or animals came too near.

My duty was from two to four, which I liked, for then I would welcome the dawn. It was wonderful to see all the colours of the heavens displayed with the sunrise.

Meanwhile, the bobijee was preparing chapattis over the fire, with rice boiling in a large pot; during the night we could all help ourselves when in need.

I was woken by Cyril, shaking my shoulder and grinning broadly. 'Your turn, Sahib!' The fire was well lit, giving a reassuring glow all around. I crept over to help myself to coffee, careful not to disturb the sleepers, and returned to my patch.

Quite near me, shrill cries from the inhabitants of the jungle broke the night, and I heard movements too. I was thankful for the slow arrival of the dawn.

By the time the rest of the party had stirred, the sun was in full yellow glow, rising above the hills far below and piercing through the mist that shrouded the valley.

In no time, the fires were built and alight, cooking rice and coffee – the latter smelling especially appetising.

Clearing up the site didn't take long; we did our usual brushing over with branches, disguising our overnight stay. The fact that we were nearing our destination didn't eliminate the possibility of Jap scouts.

Soon we were all ready to start off again. The packs were loaded on to the broad backs of the porters, with much grunting and laughter. We had by now formed quite a respect for each other; I would trust these chaps on any journey.

As we pushed on, the width of the trail increased as the overhanging foliage had been cut back, giving more light and less humidity. The swarms of mosquitoes had gone, and surely we were nearing Rangamati.

We were in the open now. Not far away down in the valley, clusters of bamboo huts could be seen. I hoped they were the object of our journey.

I could see, as we plodded on, that it was obvious that we needed to take a rest. Then one of the porters suddenly shouted, pointing towards a timber built building ahead – obviously a dāk bungalow!

Rangamati

20th May, 1944

By the time we had reached the dāk bungalow, a reception party of natives had assembled. At the head stood a tall chap, wearing a tiger skin over his shoulder and little else but a pair of army shorts!

The sight of our party must have aroused much interest – two IOCs, three tall Lushai headhunters as porters, the bobijee in white to his ankles, while Doug and I were dressed only in shorts and loose shirts, showing no rank.

Our bobijee approached the headman to explain who we were, and asked for the dāk bungalow to be opened. In the course of their conversation, quite a crowd of children had gathered.

Eventually, an elderly native spoke to the bobijee, saying he was appointed by the DC to look after and keep tidy the bungalow and its surrounds. Handing over the keys, he asked if there was anything he could do to help; his bamboo basha was at the rear, and he would be at our call at all times.

While Doug entered the bungalow to inspect it, I instructed the bobijee to arrange a site for the porters and IOCs to camp down nearby.

Within a short while it was all resolved. As the surrounding area was clear and partly level, the rest of the party erected tents to form a small circle, and set about collecting firewood.

After making sure they were all right, I returned to explore the bungalow, and found to Doug lounging in a large bamboo chair on the verandah. 'Have a rest!' he said.

The bobijee had found a bottle of the local beer, so before anything else we both were enjoying a mug or two. On checking the accommodation, I found it to be quite spacious: two large bedrooms, a sitting room overlooking the valley way below, with a kitchen and storeroom at the rear.

In each bedroom there were two charpoys, complete with mosquito nets, and bamboo chairs, with a table in the centre.

There was no glass in the window frames, but rolls of bamboo slats instead, if cover was required. Outside there were shutters, which provided adequate protection against bad weather.

With a verandah and rails built all round, the whole bungalow stood three feet off the ground, supported by numerous thick tree trunks.

The sun was slowly sinking down behind the hills below and the daylight was fading. I began to wonder what we had for lighting, when the bobijee came in with three oil lamps that he'd found in the store, plus a barrel of kerosene.

While he was preparing a meal, Doug and I strolled round the back to see how our party was managing. They had the tents up, with each one allocated just as they wanted.

The Lushai porters preferred to sleep in the open; at least they'd be on guard! We were assured they were quite happy; they were about to light a fire for cooking.

21st May, 1944

I must have been tired out last night – I forgot to drop my mosquito net, and upon awaking, I found my shoulders were covered with bites, all beginning to swell.

Feeling a bit feverish, I swallowed a couple of mepacrine tablets, hoping to keep the fever down; but I was sure I'd have a shaky turn.

The bobijee came in with the coffee, and asked us for a month's leave. He had to travel all the way back to Mullianphui village to visit his family, who were suffering illness at the time.

In the meantime, he had found a replacement cook. He also was a Lushai, a long-standing friend, in whom he had complete trust – woe betide him if he betrayed his trust! He would bring him along tomorrow, in the morning.

Before washing, I went into Doug's room to enquire if he was all right, only to find him looking pale and complaining of pains in his stomach.

After giving him a dose of bicarb, I told him to rest for the day; after all, we had both had a long trek over difficult trails, and he was not the strongest of chaps.

His open window gave him spectacular views, way down over the hills and jungles, stretching hundreds of miles into the distance. I believe the memories of those spectacular sights will remain with us forever.

We both decided to stay there as long as possible. Doug was feeling weak; I also had a touch of the shaky do – malaria was still in my system. I felt poorly, and sweated all the time, but was able to keep going.

Our new bobijee seemed passable; he was all out to please. His coffee this morning tasted quite good; we had yet to sample the cooking.

He spoke little English, but had a cheerful outlook, which helped a lot in getting some problems sorted.

I decided to check our stores. I found the small lean-to quite in order, what stores there were all being neatly stacked. The floor had been swept and the bobijee was chanting away while moving items. I decided to check the stock from the list made when it was delivered.

A small sack of rice and one of salt was missing. I couldn't accuse our new bobijee, as it could have been taken when we arrived here. Salt was very much needed, as plenty was taken to strengthen the system against weak blood and loss through sweating. Salt was also a good bartering agent.

While I was in the process of making a small inventory of the goods in stock, Doug came in. He was looking a bit pale, but spoke quite cheerfully, saying he felt much better; he asked how much had we in stock.

Our new bobijee appeared to have his job well in hand – his only trouble was, that he marked all items in Lushai!

After a light lunch of rice and biscuits, I had a short rest, then decided to see if Doug would like to walk with me to inspect our worksite. We had enlisted about a dozen natives to make a large clearing on the crest of the hill not far from the dāk bungalow.

The idea was to erect an observation post and a small basha – this would take less than a week – in the meantime, we'd have to send an IOC sepoy with one of the Lushai porters back to Lunglei to arrange the bringing up of equipment to supply the post.

Doug made a list of all that was required. It would take, I judged, another two porters for the load, but they would have to arrange it at that end.

The site we had chosen was at the top of the range overlooking the Lushai and Chin Hills – an ideal position for receiving signals.

The height of the post was to be about twenty feet, and it would be entirely built of bamboo, lashed together by strong thongs of bamboo skin.

The whole job would only take three to four days. The natives, once they knew what to do, would work together, chanting and laughing as they laboured, the sound of their songs echoing far and wide.

I spent the afternoon with them, making signs showing what was wanted; I could already see the foundations of our new observation post. Doug went back early to rest.

As the light was fading, I made my way to the dāk bungalow, hoping Doug was feeling better. As for myself, I still felt very weak, but the shaking had subsided, and I was sweating less.

On arrival at the dāk, I found Doug sitting out on the verandah, looking much healthier, and saying he felt much better; the pains in his stomach had almost gone.

I went to my room and found it had been transformed. The charpoy and table and chair had been shifted, giving me more room to move around, while the bamboo mats had been shaken out and the floor swept clean.

Added to all this was the smell of cooking – something good, I hoped. Joining Doug on the verandah, I asked what was in the pot. He said, 'Wait till you see the cook!'

Our cook came from the kitchen to say the meal was ready. We noticed he had changed into a clean shirt and *poen* or native skirt.

He had cooked a marvellous meal of roasted wildfowl, together with *kolebeha* and yams – root vegetables that grew in the jungle – and fried rice. After this we had a mug of the local rice beer.

I remarked to Doug that his cooking was better than our bobijee's; but then he was not responsible for all the duties the bobijee had to perform.

After our meal, we sat out on the verandah to let the food digest. I enjoyed one of my 'cigars' – a tobacco leaf picked from one of the trees around. I spread the leaf on the roof to dry out, then rolled it and bound it with bamboo string. Some were quite long – eight to ten inches.

We talked of further plans. It would be two or three weeks before the equipment for the post arrived. In the meantime, Doug would be able to get his strength back, and try to get rid of that stomach pain.

I missed our bobijee; he spoke English as well as Urdu and Lushai. Our new chap was very capable, but could only manage a few English words, and of course, '*Tekai*, Sahib,' and '*Acha*.' The rest of the conversation was done by signs.

I must say, he was always very cheerful, and did all he could to please. The dāk bungalow was kept spotless, whereas our bobijee was a bit slap-happy.

The days slipped by. I often wandered down into the sprawling market in Rangamati; it was mostly stalls of fruit and cloth. I didn't meet any white chaps, not even the odd trader.

All people with any knowledge of the language and details of the district had been called up to assist the military in mapping out all trails that the Japs might find.

In the market, a little English was spoken. I stopped at one or two stalls where I thought the holder looked intelligent enough to make conversation. Then I probed a little, making hints about the whereabouts of the Japs.

I'd been advised to be careful in making such enquiries. These markets were rife with shady informers, working for the side which paid the most; but at the same time, very reliable news was obtained by reading the signals put out by the drums from village to village.

On returning to the bungalow, I found three letters on the table – two from Audrey and the third from my mother.

Doug said a runner had taken three days to deliver them from Lunglei – a distance of thirty miles.

I decided to have a meal first before digesting every word in the letters. Doug too, had two from home, so after chapattis and rice, we retired to our charpoys.

It was quite late by the time I had read and reread the letters; there was so much to take in. While doing this, I was home again.

26th May, 1944

It was past midnight when I at last crawled under my mosquito net. I'd have to write in return first thing in the morning. I'd have to delay the return of the runner to Lunglei – he must not return without my letters.

The Lushai cook woke me at about seven, holding the usual mug of coffee. I straight away sent him down to the village to tell the runner not to go back till he had my letters. It wouldn't take me long to scribble a few lines; at least I could explain in them how isolated I was up here. I intended to write more fully at a later date.

I had about an hour to write my two letters. I hoped Audrey and Whiteleaf would be able to decipher the scribble. The runner arrived to collect them – a tall Lushai, dressed in khaki shirt and shorts. Round his waist was a belt with pouches holding a *kukri* and other knives.

Speaking broken English, he explained the many hazardous trails he had to pass through. Many villages he had to avoid, as they couldn't be trusted. It would take him approximately three days at ten or so miles a day. All the time he had to keep clear of Jap patrols, by listening and reading the constant beating of drums. These sent messages around villages all along the Naga and Chin range of hills.

The Japs must have been frustrated on reaching their villages, when they found the local headhunters tracking their every movement. The drums would then signal when all was clear, and the men could return to their homes. They all hated the Japs; stories of their atrocities were well known. That's why they thought our observations ports were a safeguard, as they maintained a connection with various army units; so we were both respected.

In the meantime, our temporary cook had made a marvellous cake – a mixture of currants and wild fruit, together with five eggs! He had made a deep recess in the bank at the rear of the bungalow, large enough to contain the base for a fire, with a biscuit tin perched above acting as an oven.

Doug's health improved. The pains in his stomach went and he had more colour in his cheeks; the rest here had restored some of his strength.

In the afternoon I decided to visit the local chief. Living near Rangamati, he had learnt a little English; perhaps he had learnt of Jap movements.

On arrival at his large basha, I found him squatting on the bamboo floor, being attended to by four giggling women. On seeing me approach, they retired to the other end of the large chamber.

An earthenware jug was placed by our side, together with two mugs. I could see it contained a pure white liquid – rice beer, or as they called it, *Zophan*. I enquired about Jap movements, and he confirmed there were none within his territory.

26th May, 1944

Using broken English, gestures and waving arms, we were able to understand each other. He made signs which told that in the past many sahibs had passed this way on hunting parties.

As we talked, I was taking sips of the rice beer. Little did I realise how potent it was, till I got off my haunches and prepared to make my farewells. He noticed I was a bit unsteady, and offered to order a native to walk back to the bungalow with me; but I made him understand I'd be all right.

By the time I had reached the bungalow, my legs felt a bit wobbly. Doug was waiting out on the verandah, very anxious about my safety. When I told him where I had been, and about drinking rice beer with the chief, he said it was a bit risky.

After a mug of strong coffee, my head felt much clearer, and I told Doug the chief's opinion was that there were no movements of any Jap patrols in the area. If he did get a whisper, he'd let us know.

The sun had sunk low down below the jungle, and dusk was fast closing in. I went round to the lean-to for a wash, and used the rest of the evening to sit out and plan the following day's events with Doug.

He told me that the observation post was built and ready for the installation of the transmission equipment when it arrived – it wouldn't be long now – a few days, perhaps.

The rest had certainly done him good; he had more colour, and he had put some weight on. He said the pain in his stomach had gone – let's hope it stayed this way.

We sat up till quite late; it was much cooler now, and there were fewer mosquitoes – a change from the stifling nights when it was impossible to sleep, with sweat pouring off one all the time.

It was past midnight when we crawled under our nets, to listen to all the weird calls from the jungle before dropping off.

I had a good night's sleep and woke up feeling much better. The Lushai cook came in holding a mug of coffee, and told me Doug Sahib was up and had gone to stretch his legs.

27th May, 1944

After a long day on a medical call in the village, armed with bandages and iodine, I arrived back at our bungalow as the sun was sinking down low over the valley. Now was the time for the hordes of mosquitoes to fill the air, and for us to rub cream over our skin and cover up.

After I had washed and told Doug of my afternoon's mission, it was nearing mealtime, and the smell of chicken being roasted came through from the lean-to. The medical work had been well rewarded by a gift of two fowls for the pot.

After the meal, we talked of further plans, though our position was static until the equipment arrived and was installed and working. The lookout post had already been erected, together with a small basha nearby.

We sat out on the verandah till past midnight. I was enjoying one of my hand-made cigars, with Doug nattering away about what our next move would be. This would be determined when eventually we contacted Chittagong.

For three or four days the routine was the same. We passed the time taking walks down to the village, trying to converse with the natives, amid much laughter. Some stared at me with mouths wide open, but they were all well behaved.

One day, Doug seemed a little weaker, and complained of stomach pains. I wondered if he had contracted a dose of dysentery, as I had some months ago.

If I sent a runner down to Lunglei for a doctor, it would take weeks; then again, if the observation post was operational, it would be easy to signal for action.

After much thought, I wondered if by chance the chief of the nearby village had any knowledge of the medicine that cured my dysentery.

1st June, 1944

Taking the cook as translator, we made our way down into the village to seek out our friend. We were fortunate enough to find him sitting out on his verandah, surrounded by giggling young women, who on our approach disappeared into the basha.

On learning the purpose of our visit, he said he also had the medicine, and would instruct his medicine man to let us have a small quantity. As we waited for it, his women brought forward earthenware mugs of rice beer and chapattis – during which, I noticed, their eyes were all on my tall Lushai cook. He chatted away all the time, making the most of his presence and quite enjoying it all.

Along came the medicine man – an old, bent figure. I immediately thought of the weird ceremonies he must have performed in the past – some quite gruesome, I should imagine.

His toothless mouth was muttering as he presented us with a small earthenware cup, in which a small amount of dark brown fluid just covered the base. Looking at it, I recognised it as identical to the stuff that had cured my dysentery.

After making my thanks and farewells through my interpreter, the cook, I wrapped the cup in a large green leaf, and holding it tight, made my way back to the bungalow.

It was midday by the time I returned to seek out Doug. I found him still resting on his charpoy, looking a bit frail, saying the rumbling pain was less frequent; but I noticed he was still a very bad colour.

He looked paler still on seeing the thick brown liquid, but I told him it seemed to be the same stuff as I had taken.

Sitting up, he did manage to swallow it, grimacing at the awful taste. 'Try anything,' he said. Telling him to rest for the day, I returned to my room to wash and see what the cook had prepared for me.

During my quest, the wife of the native I had tended had delivered a large wild cockerel, already plucked and cleaned, saying her husband's cut was healing fast, and thanking me for my medicine.

I must say, it was nice to have a few days' stock of cooked fowl, and to be able to have a snack when we got a bit peckish. In fact, for lunch I just cut a lump of chicken to eat with a few ration biscuits, after which I snatched a few minutes on the charpoy. It was just after midday, with the temperature well over a hundred degrees.

I must have dozed off for a couple of hours, for on waking, I found the sun had sunk low down over the hills below. I found my first thoughts were of Doug; on going round to his room, I was surprised to find it empty, and was told by the cook that Doug Sahib had gone for a walk!

I hurried out to find him, and eventually caught up with him not far away, sitting on a tree stump. He was looking quite cheerful.

6th June, 1944

Doug agreed that the concoction certainly did the trick. He still felt a bit shaky, but all the pains had gone.

Strolling back to the bungalow, we were met by our cook, who informed us that our transmitter equipment was nearing us; a runner had come ahead to say it would arrive in the morning.

After more chicken and rice, our first job was to go along to the site to make sure all was ready for the equipment to be installed.

Doug by now seemed his old self, and the colour had returned to his cheeks; perhaps the news of action will have bucked him up.

At the site, Doug nipped up the bamboo ladder leading to the little hut quite easily. It made me think these natives must get all the potions they needed from the jungle plants – recipes that had been handed down through the ages.

The little observation hut had been put together quite sturdily. No nails were used. The four eight-inch thick bamboo poles were lashed together with the cross-beams by thongs made of bamboo. When these had dried, they would have lasting strength.

After climbing down, we stood back to survey the site. With tall trees surrounding, it would be difficult to see from way down in the forest below.

Making our way back, I suddenly remembered our Lushai cook warning me of tigers that had been seen in this area. I didn't mention it to Doug; I'd tell him when we returned.

On one of my recent strolls to the base, it had been apparent that an animal was in the undergrowth. I was aware of movement in the branches that covered the leaves and dead wood that lay thickly on the ground. All I had for protection was my bamboo walking stick.

Striding on, I thought, What the hell! It will, or it won't! The latter was the case, for as I pushed on the sounds grew fainter, giving me the opportunity to stand still for a while and listen. Thankfully, whatever it was it had taken another route.

On my return to the bungalow from my walk, I found Doug very worried, as I had been gone for quite a long time. After telling him of my experience, he made me promise to take my Sten gun, and not to go out alone.

Tomorrow we were expecting the arrival of the transmitter, together with the jenny and batteries. Then our time would be taken up with the installation of these and getting the post operational.

We were both looking forward to start-up again. It would be interesting to exchange signals with Chittagong and hear of the whereabouts of the Japs.

The post itself was all ready – benches, tables, and chairs had all been built in bamboo by the local natives. I believe they all wondered why this funny looking basha was built so high in the tree.

By the time we sat down for a meal, the sun had sunk low down over the hills below, heralding the time for swarms of mosquitoes to come out in search of blood.

7th June, 1944

At mid-morning, the equipment arrived, escorted by four Sepoys, all well armed. The units were slung on stout bamboo poles and were carried by four stalwart natives.

One of the Sepoys was Cyril Sirren, who had left us on arrival at Rangamati. On seeing me, he gave a loud shout of welcome, and seemed overjoyed at meeting up again.

The rest of the day was spent lugging the equipment up the ladder and fixing it firmly to the floor. By evening we were all ready to wash and looking forward to a good meal.

After the meal, Cyril said movements at Lunglei were about the same. The DC had returned from Lushai outposts inspection; it appeared that the Lushai Brigade had flushed out a Jap patrol and destroyed it, capturing valuable information on troop movements.

Passing down the trail and enquiring at villages on the way, Cyril had learnt that there were no Japs in the surrounding area – information that was most welcome.

After the meal, discussions were had concerning where they would all sleep. The four sepoys stayed up in the post, while the natives seemed quite happy to rough it on the ground underneath. They would act as sentinels, in case any natives got inquisitive about who the new arrivals were.

By the time we got through a bottle of the local rice beer, laughing all the time at our previous encounters, it was past midnight and time to get down for the night.

I was woken early – it must have been about four – by a commotion outside. A crowd of natives were jabbering away, all apparently excited at some incident.

When the cook came in with the coffee, he explained that apparently a tiger had killed in the area and dragged the carcass quite a distance to the outskirts of the jungle.

After washing and eating a few biscuits, I told Doug I'd take the cook along and follow the trail as far as possible. His reply was, 'Don't be such a bloody fool!' I assured him that I wouldn't take risks and would carry my Sten gun.

Of course, it was all a waste of time. We did follow the blood trail, but as the undergrowth got very dense, it was obvious we would be in danger. Much to my Lushai friend's relief, I said, 'Let's go back.'

On our return, we made our way through the village at midday. Most of the women were attending to the cooking of rice in cast-iron pots held over the fires by tripods made of metal rods. How they were obtained was a puzzle, it must have been when the tiger safaris were held.

Some of the women were operating crude looms made out of bamboo sticks, secured by thongs of the bark. They all seemed very secure as the cloth was being woven. The women squatted down about four feet from the loom, nimbly threading different patterns. I stood there for quite a while watching, and to my surprise an elderly woman offered as a gift, a *poen*, or a native skirt, which I gratefully accepted.

Having received the *poen* I had to drink an earthenware mug of the local rice beer, with much giggling from all; by the time I reached the bungalow, my head was rather light.

8th June, 1944

Doug had news that the sepoy on duty at the post had decoded a signal to read instructions for us to proceed further up the ridge towards Howlong, a distance of about thirty miles.

Our sepoy knew that an observation post was already established there; we were to inspect and report on conditions. HQ hadn't heard from them for quite a while.

We both decided not to make a hasty preparation in moving. We would give it at least three days; perhaps further signals would give us definite and more detailed instructions.

This afternoon the heavens opened up: torrential rain obliterated the village, washing away all trails and tracks. Heavy volumes of water made deep gulleys between the bamboo bashas, but as the huts were protected by deep channels dug previously, most of them remained dry.

The roof of our verandah, on inspection a few weeks ago, seemed a bit rough, but at least no water came through this time; in any case we'd be away in a few days.

The rest of the day was spent inspecting equipment and food stocks. As for Doug, he seemed much stronger – more like his old self.

The rain eased off. Looking from our verandah, I could see all signs of tracks had been washed away. I hoped the sun would bake the ground, making it possible for the villagers to forge new tracks.

After a meal of curried chicken and rice, we sat out on the verandah for a while before deciding to check our IOC friends up in the observation post; perhaps more information had been signalled.

It was about eight at the time we set off. I had my Sten gun slung over my shoulder, just in case. Visibility was quite good, with no cloud, and a reddish glow covering the sky.

On our arrival at the post, the two sepoys on duty told us we had been under observation most of the way here – they could observe our movements as we made our way through the undergrowth – hence coffee was awaiting us!

As the time for locating our signal from among numerous others wasn't until later, chapattis were made and cooked on a flat metal plate on the Primus stove.

Both sepoys spoke fairly good English, so until the time for duty, we were chatting away. They mostly wanted to know about London and all the principal cities, especially Buckingham Palace. I then described all the bombing, with people living underground to escape; it was difficult to explain the tube railway.

9th June, 1944

I sat up late last night, writing letters to Audrey and Whiteleaf. I found it difficult to put into words my emotions – they were in my thoughts at all times.

I would have to ask one of the sepoys to find a trustworthy native to make the journey to Lunglei, a distance of about thirty miles.

The runner would have to pass through many villages, or try to give them a wide berth, as we did on our way down; some were friendly, but others viewed strangers with deep suspicion. They would sooner put a spear through you and ask questions afterwards.

I gave him a chit to the value of ten rupees, which would be honoured by the DC's office on his arrival – safe, I hoped.

The heavy rain stopped by dawn, leaving a cloudless sky; my main concern was for my runner, as the trails must be flooded and very slippery. After a few days, I'd try to signal Lunglei to confirm his safe arrival.

We spent the day collecting and packing provisions and utensils that we would want on our trek further up the ridge. We decided to make a start the day after tomorrow – it would give time for the trails to dry.

Doug seemed much better. He was more cheerful, and stronger – a boost that would give us both the strength to push on.

One more day to go. As we sat out on the verandah we both felt a little loath to leave. We had made many friends among the villagers and some have given us much help in many situations; some of these were most ugly.

By this time, we could rest assured that they regarded the observation post as a sentinel in guarding them against the dreaded Japs; they had heard of the terrible atrocities inflicted on villagers.

Of the four IOC sepoys left in charge, we both knew while feeling in awe of the actual post, they would certainly not in any way provoke the working.

I thought perhaps there might be a signal tonight, but as no sepoy reported anything, we decided to turn in for the night: one more day to go.

The morning broke with the usual din of the birds. Looking through the slits in the bamboo wall down into the jungle valley below, I could see the mist was slowly lifting. The sunlight pierced through, creating a most humid atmosphere deep under the roof of the jungle.

Oh well! This was the day. The cook made coffee and bowls of rice for us, all ready out on the verandah. Our rooms were cleared; the charpoys were stacked against the wall, and it all seemed so empty.

As well as the two Lushai villagers as porters, we'd have two sepoys as a precaution against any eventuality. This gave us four Sten guns in all, though up to now there had been no need to use them.

11th June, 1944

We were all packed and ready to push off. I had a last look back at the bungalow as we made our way along the twisting trail leading down the hillside, passing isolated native huts; a few villagers clasped their hands together in farewell.

The two Lushai porters were leading and Doug and I were in the centre, with the sepoys bringing up the rear. The trail made a gradual descent at every turn; now and again, glimpses of the jungle were caught as we made our way through the thick undergrowth.

The trail was at times very slippery. Often we had to cling on to overhanging branches, at the same time looking out for leeches. As soon as they dropped on our clothing, we had to brush them off before they started their blood-sucking ritual – at the same time they were very difficult to remove once they began.

About halfway down we came upon a nice flat clearing, just the place for a rest and coffee. After all, we'd struggled to keep a foothold on the slippery trail for the last two hours, and we deserved a rest.

Firewood was gathered, and in no time the water was boiling for coffee. As we rested, birds of every colour flew around filling the air with songs, while a few grunts could also be heard, perhaps from wild pigs. Our two porters knew of all the sounds; they were grinning from ear to ear, gesticulating and making funny faces.

Before starting off again, we cleared the site and covered it over with old branches; we never knew where the Jap patrols might be working.

It became evident that we wouldn't make Howlong before night. The slippery trail had slowed us, so we decided to push on for an hour or two before stopping for a midday meal, which would take at least a couple of hours to prepare; and then we'd rest.

The humid heat was becoming oppressive. Perspiration simply poured off us – my shirt and shorts were saturated. The danger was leeches; we wouldn't know if we had collected any till we stopped and stripped our clothes off. They just clung on and sucked blood.

The sun was now at its peak and the sooner we found some shady cover the better it would be. We were all stumbling and cursing, and Doug looked all in.

When at last we reached the shade, we found lush grass, combined with a cool breeze, and we all flopped down, relieving ourselves of our packs.

It became evident that by the time we had eaten and rested, packing up and pushing on farther wouldn't achieve much progress, so we decided to make this our camp for the night.

A space was soon cleared to build the fire, with arrangements made for our sleeping. Soon the sun had slowly begun to sink and the light was fading. It was time to light the fire, and start cooking the rice and chapattis.

I thought after the meal that it was rather rash to build a fire at such an exposed spot – it surely could be seen from below.

We then decided to make a guard rota of two-hourly stints, keeping the fire as slow as possible. I thought that by now we should have been visited by inquisitive natives; those we had met on the way here said there were certainly no Japs within a twenty mile radius. Besides, the drum signals would have started.

I had scooped out a shallow bed space and spread soft undergrowth branches to make it as comfortable as possible. Then I settled down to await my stint of guard duty, from two until four; then Doug would take over.

I must have dozed off, as I was awakened by one of the sepoys saying Doug Sahib was still sleeping, and he would take over to give Doug more rest. I showed my appreciation at his thoughtfulness, and decided to put some more wood on the fire. By now the dawn was breaking, heralded by the chorus of birds from far down in the jungle.

The camp was soon awake. Doug thanked the sepoy who stood in for him, at the same time saying he felt much better for the rest. After a breakfast of rice and coffee, the camp was cleared up as at previous stops; after our treatment one could hardly have detected that it had been used by people.

We loaded up, ready to make the last trek down the hillside towards Howlong. The mist down below was slowly clearing, and by the time we reached the jungle, it would give us shade from the overpowering heat; but at the same time, the exhausting humidity and leeches had to be reckoned with.

One thing in our favour was that the trail by now had become reasonably dry. Most of the way had involved a battle to keep upright. We all felt better being able to walk without hanging on to overhead branches.

The trail also became much wider and was not so uneven, due probably to increased use by villagers trading between one place and the next.

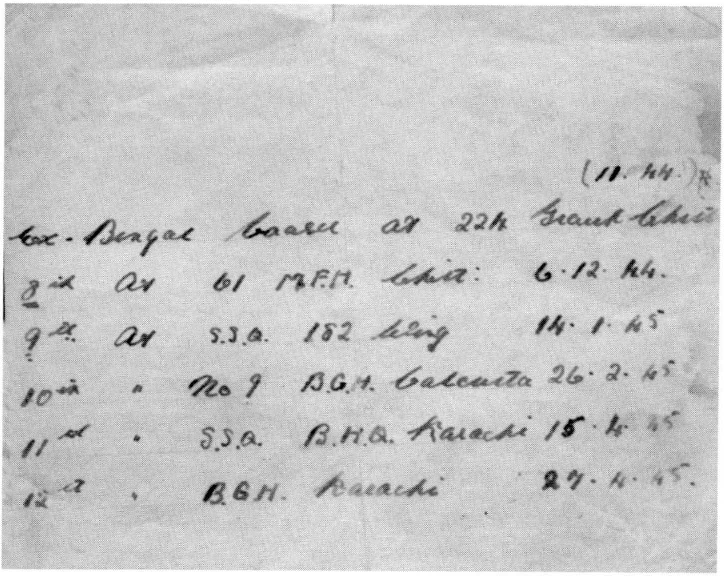

(11.44.)

ex-Bengal [illegible] at 224 [illegible]

8th at 61 M.F.H. [illegible]: 6.12.44.

9th at S.S.Q. 182 Wing 14.1.45

10th " No 9 B.G.H. Calcutta 26.2.45

11th " S.S.Q. B.H.Q. Karachi 15.4.45

12th " B.G.H. Karachi 27.4.45.

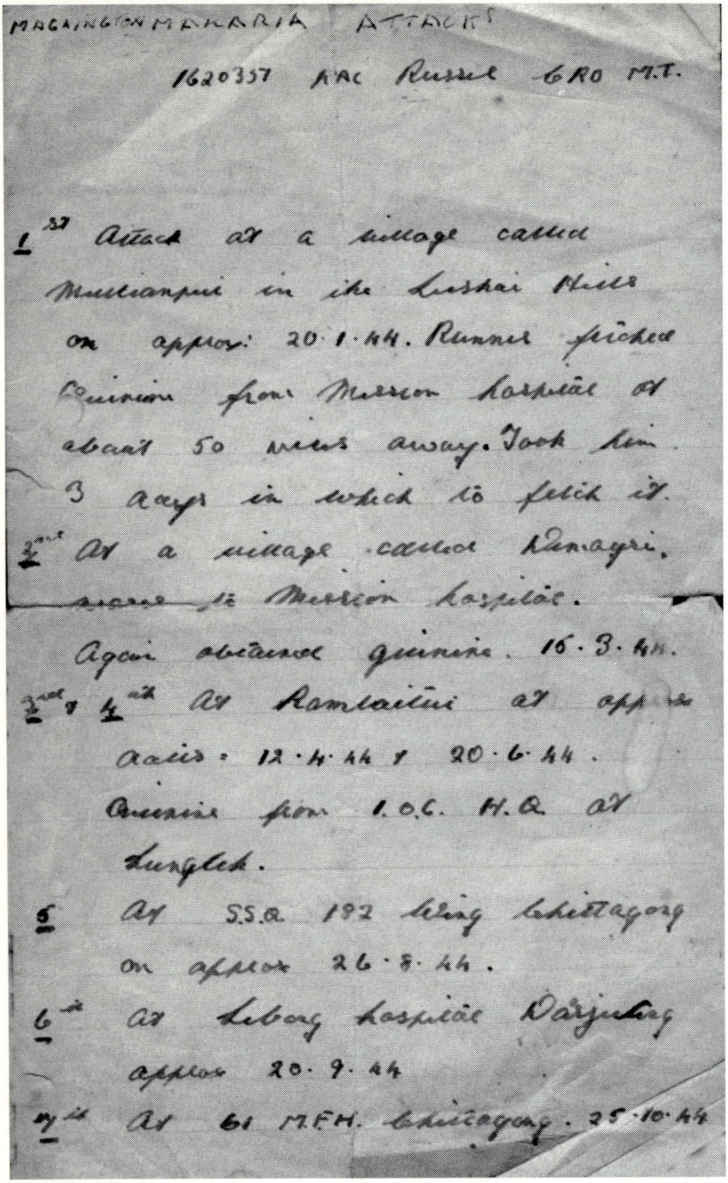

MAGAINGTON MALARIA ATTACKS

1620357 RAC Russell 6RO M.T.

1st Attack at a village called Mualcanpui in the Lushai Hills on approx: 20.1.44. Runner fetched Quinine from Mission hospital at about 50 miles away. Took him 3 days in which to fetch it.

2nd At a village called Demagri. near to Mission hospital.

Again obtained quinine. 16.3.44.

3rd & 4th At Ramlaitui at approx dates: 12.4.44 & 20.6.44.

Quinine from I.O.C. H.Q. at Lunglei.

5 At S.S.Q. 182 Wing Chittagong on approx 26.8.44.

6th At Lebong hospital Darjeeling approx 20.9.44

7th At 61 M.F.H. Chittagong. 25.10.44

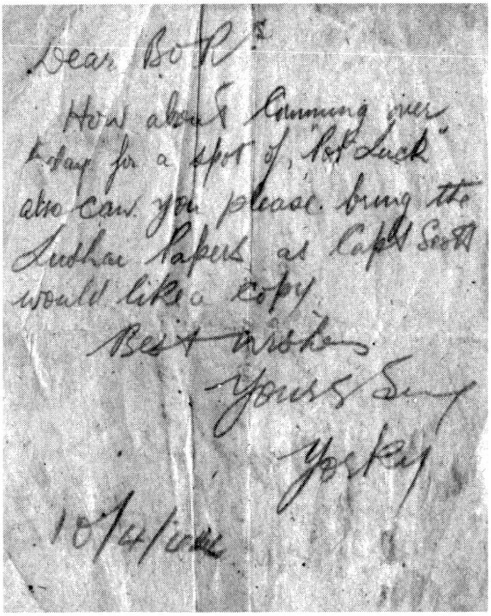

Dear Bob,

How about Cumming over today for a spot of "Pot Luck" also can you please bring the Sudhar Papers as Capt Scott would like a copy.

Best wishes.

Yours Sincy

Yorkey

10/4/44

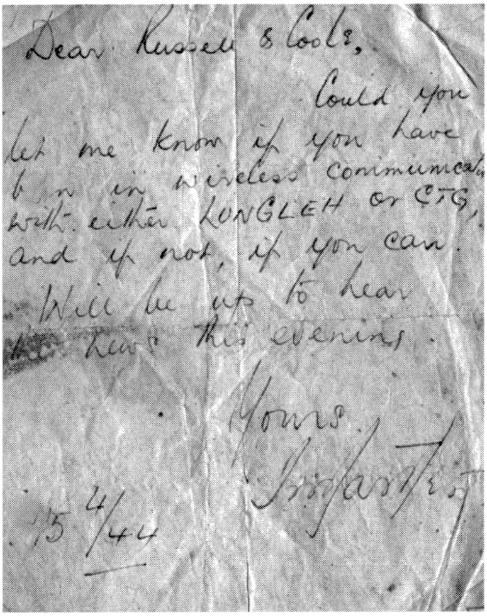

Dear Russell & Cools,

Could you let me know if you have been in wireless communicat with either LONGLEH or CTG, and if not, if you can.

Will be up to hear here this evening.

Yours.

[illegible]

15/4/44

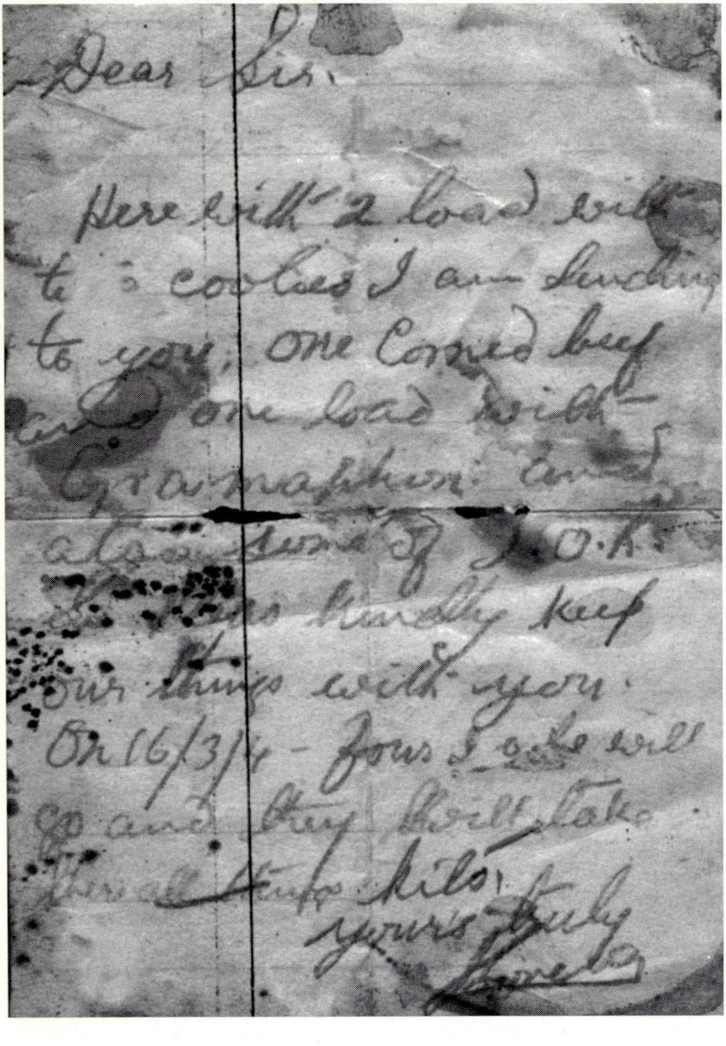

Dear Sir,

Herewith 2 load with [illegible] coolies I am sending to you, one Corned beef and one load with Gramaphon and also sums of I.O.U.s [illegible] can hardly keep our things with you. On 16/3/[illegible] - fours [illegible] will go and they will take these [illegible] kits.

yours truly

[illegible]

Howlong

14th June, 1944

Through a gap in the foliage, we had a glimpse of Howlong – bamboo huts sprawling amongst the trees – but we couldn't locate the dāk bungalow.

We still had about a mile to go. The sun was just over its peak, so perhaps the humidity down there would lessen by the time of our arrival.

By the time we had reached the outskirts, news of our approach had been spread, for children came running towards us, waving their arms and shrieking and laughing, and making circles round us in welcome.

Towards us came a havildar (sergeant) of the IOC in spotless uniform. He was about to salute, but I signalled not to. Doug and I put our hands forward, which he heartily shook, at the same time expressing his pleasure at our meeting – he had received signals of our roving commission.

To the Havildar, it was obvious the state we were in. What clothes we were wearing showed all the signs of rough going. My shirt and shorts were in tatters; Doug's were the same, while he could hardly stand, and was leaning against one of the sepoys for support.

Orders were given to natives standing by to take the loads from our porters as we made our way round the outskirts of the village up a slight incline leading away from the settlement.

We could see the dāk bungalow ahead, sitting on the brow of the hill. It had the usual design of roof and verandah, but one outstanding feature that stood out was the carpet of flowers surrounding the unit.

As we approached, a figure stepped out to greet us, dressed in a spotless white shirt and multicoloured *poen*. He was a youthful figure, his hands held together in salutation. He was grinning from ear to ear, and seemed very pleased to meet us.

While the porters and IOCs were being shown their quarters, Doug and I flopped down in bamboo chairs along the verandah, our new bobijee putting out a wooden bowl of the local rice beer together with earthenware mugs for us.

After sampling the beer and resting, we were shown round the bungalow. It was the same as the others, with two bedrooms and a sitting room leading to a lean-to kitchen, From the open shutters acting as windows in the sitting room, we were rewarded with a marvellous view of the Chin and Naga Hills, stretching far to the horizon. As I looked down, I wondered what sort of lives the primitive people led – were there still headhunters down there?

We were eager to rest and eat, and we both had not washed. Also, we both had nasty sores and blisters to attend to. At the moment I was staggering on the heels of my feet. After washing, I would have to apply some of the local ointment gently over them.

By now it was past midday, and our main desire was to flop on to our charpoys and rest, to rid our bodies' aches and pains. Doug looked all in; my hope was that a rest would restore his strength – he had lost a lot of weight.

After a half-hour's rest, I staggered round to Doug's room to see how he was, only to find him half asleep and shaking. Putting it down to a touch of malaria, I searched through our small supply of medicine and to my relief found some mepacrine tablets.

He managed to swallow two, then dropped off to sleep. I hoped they would do the trick. I felt a bit shaky myself; perhaps it would wear off. It was late in the afternoon, and the sun was slowly sinking down over the hills below. The mosquitoes were beginning to make their presence known, hordes of them were pouring through the shutters. I could see the geckos clinging on to the bamboo. They remain motionless, then catch the mosquitoes as they settle.

The bobijee asked if we were all right before he turned in, and said he hoped Doug Sahib would be better in the morning.

15th June, 1944

I had a restless night – my torso and back itched like hell, and the temptation to scratch was enormous. By the time the light of dawn arrived, I felt whacked. Washing was quite an effort; I just dabbed lightly, then covered myself with boracic powder. After putting on my shirt and trousers, I felt much better – the itching had nearly gone.

Doug was about the same, and he had treated the sores in the same way. We would both have to rest and hope the sores would heal.

After a lunch of chapattis and rice, we both felt much better, and decided to visit the post. It stood about a mile away. The trail led through undergrowth on a steep gradient up to the highest crest of this particular hill in the range.

Before reaching the post, we had to pass through a small village. On entering, we were met with smiles of welcome by the women squatting outside their huts, all weaving cloth from which to make blouses and *poens*.

We assumed our approach had been well noted by the lookouts. They were always watching the trail for possible strangers. As we passed through we saw there weren't many men around; we guessed they were all out hunting.

We also noted how many of the women suffered from swollen legs, with pus oozing through cracks in the skin, and their feet had the same disease. I presumed it was gonorrhoea. They just took it for granted; it was part of their way of life.

Making our way through the maze of bamboo huts, we came to a clearing in which stood a large bamboo built building, proudly showing the cross signifying a church. From within came the sounds of children singing.

We were both taken aback at this sudden appearance – a place of worship in the middle of headhunter territory; there must be a missionary installed hereabouts.

We decided to press on; to stop and make acquaintance would take time. If we returned this way we would certainly call in.

On reaching the observation post, we were welcomed by the IOC Sergeant in command, who expressed his pleasure at meeting us. He had heard of reports from different posts that we were in the vicinity. While we were talking, a sepoy came forward with a tray of drinks, which looked like the familiar *Zophan* rice beer.

During our conversation, the Bengali Sergeant gave the good news that all his equipment was in working order. Perhaps after a good night's rest we would give it all a good check over.

He also reported receiving a signal from HQ that we were in the vicinity. On arrival, would we stop here for a few days, as there would be further instructions to follow.

It was nearly midnight by the time we were shown our quarters – a compact basha just a few yards from the post, comprising of two bedrooms, sitting room and the usual lean-to serving as the kitchen.

Our Lushai cook was already in residence. He had laid out a table on the verandah with a bowl of the local beer, together with rice and biscuits.

It didn't take long before we both were under our mosquito nets stretched out on our charpoys, both thankful for a rest.

The following day was spent sorting our kit out in readiness for further movement. I thought it would be towards Ijal, a distance of about twenty-five miles. At least the trail would be more bearable, as more traffic used it.

We both took things easy. Doug looked much better; he had regained some colour to his cheeks, and was stronger when helping with various tasks.

The day passed quickly; by the time we had finished our evening meal, it was time to make our way up the trail towards the post. Before reaching it, we were met by an IOC sepoy, who by his manner seemed very glad to meet us.

Reporting that no signals had been received, he did say that a meal had been prepared for us – chicken curry – and we both said we looked forward to it. On reaching the post, we both remarked on its siting. It was largely obscured by trees, leaving a gap through which there was a clear sighting of the range of hills leading up towards Ijal. Beyond that was a distant blur that must be around Kohima.

Looking up at the flimsy bamboo ladder leading up to the hut, we were advised to climb up one at a time. I went first. As I ascended, the shutters of the hut were opened, to reveal the smiling Pathan Sergeant of the IOC stretching his hand forward to help me in.

As there wasn't room for all of my party, my cook and the two IOCs were shown to a basha not far away. The

Sergeant said they'd find it quite comfortable; it had its own kitchen.

The next half-hour was spent checking the equipment. Then the Sergeant and two sepoys retired to their basha, leaving us to take the watch.

It must have been after about two hours of concentration, listening to call signals in different codes, that we at last picked out ours.

Doug jotted it down – it only took a few seconds – we then ceased operating, just in case any Japs might be on patrol in the area.

The message confirmed the one received by the sepoys previously. We were to proceed up the ridge towards Ijal as soon as possible – a distance of about twenty-five miles.

17th June, 1944

At last we had confirmation of our further instructions. We would take a couple of days to prepare for the venture.

We returned to our bungalow; dawn was breaking and the sun could be seen rising up over the hills far below. The air was filled by a chorus of different cries from the inhabitants of the jungle.

Our Lushai cook had prepared a breakfast of fried eggs and rice, together with coffee. The rest of the morning was spent resting on our charpoys. All our thoughts were on organising food and equipment for the next slog.

After a small lunch, we again discussed our movements, and both decided that I would lead the way ahead with porters and equipment, while Doug cleared up the camp and followed on later.

My first job was to recruit five reliable natives from the nearby village. For this job, I would have to trust our Lushai cook's judgement.

Off he went down into the village, to return later accompanied by five tall natives. They were wearing little but the usual loincloth, and their bodies were adorned with bangles made of the bones of past victims.

These were worn piercing their nose, ears, and lips; they were typical headhunters. I believe it is still practised amongst isolated tribes. They stood staring at Doug and me, but soon appeared more friendly, clasping their hands together in salute.

After being instructed of their duties, they promised to report here at dawn the day after tomorrow, and sloped off down the trail back to the village.

The bobijee assured me that he would visit them frequently to make sure that they would be available for the dawn start.

One more day to go; Doug and I sat out on the verandah discussing our future plans. We agreed to link up at a village called Ramiaitui. This was about twenty miles away, over rather a rough trail, but by now we should be able to master any eventualities.

We both felt much fitter and stronger. Doug looked much better; his stomach pains had gone, the colour had returned to his cheeks, and his walking was much firmer.

By now the air was full of clouds of mosquitoes, twisting and diving round the light from the oil lamps. We both covered our arms and faces with cream; soon it would be time for us to turn in, crawl under our nets and try to get some sleep in the oppressive heat.

Just as we were about to say goodnight to each other, we both heard high-pitched voices outside. On opening the shutters, we were confronted by about a dozen natives running round and round shrieking at the top of their voices. It appeared a tiger had been spotted roaming round, and they were looking out for it. The vigil was kept up for about an hour – then silence.

19th June, 1944

I was awakened by the porters jabbering away while they sorted out the various individual loads. Each one was trying for the best. At last it seemed all was nearly ready.

I had coffee and biscuits with Doug. I was pleased to see he seemed his old self – quite cheerful. I said, 'Take care. We'll meet up in a few days' time.' It would take that long to recruit two IOCs to replace the two I was taking for liaison and for any encounters we might have on the way.

At last we were off, following the trail leading down into the jungle. Two of the porters were leading, while I and two sepoys followed, leaving the three porters and the bobijee at the rear.

As we made our way along the trail, my thoughts were of home. Whatever would they say if they knew of our operation, and could see us making our way through the jungle?

The porters were chanting a tribal song as we slowly moved forward, sometimes interspersed with raucous laughter; at least it would keep some animals at bay.

Following the tall porter, I couldn't but admire the physique of the man. He moved effortlessly, with all his joints working smoothly, carrying the 50 lb pack on his shoulders as if it wasn't there.

Overhead, high up on the branches in the dense foliage, were schools of rhesus monkeys, screeching and leaping from tree to tree. They followed us as we made our way along, picking our way and looking for footholds on the uneven track. There were no sounds of distant drums, so we assumed there were no Japs about.

We had been on the move for about two hours, and I could see the porters were beginning to stumble now and again, so I decided to look for a suitable clearing to rest and have coffee.

It was the leading porter who pointed ahead at a break in the foliage showing a nice green clearing. It was about fifty yards away, and the sight of it made the porters chant louder as we approached.

Very soon a fire was burning brightly in the centre of a dug out recess. There was a tripod over it, with a cast-iron pot full of water for our coffee. Soon we were sitting on our haunches around the fire devouring biscuits and coffee.

I was glad of the rest, as the sweat was beginning to irritate my sores. Now, as the irritation had eased, I would apply talcum powder.

We rested for about an hour. Then we set to, clearing up and obliterating the camp. Dead branches were laid over all traces of our brief stop there.

Starting off again, we moved off in single file as before, with the two porters leading, myself next with the two IOC porters and the bobijee at the rear.

It must have been after about an hour's trekking when the leading porters stopped suddenly and made signs for us to keep quiet, waving their arms to tell us to hide in the undergrowth.

After a few seconds, four natives came into view. They were tall, I should say well over six feet, and were fierce looking chaps, wearing all the ornaments of bamboo and ivory on different parts of their bodies.

One of our Lushai porters greeted them, and proceeded to explain who we were. After this they showed less tension, and even gave a small bow of the head. They carried spears of different lengths, while tucked in their hide belts were hunting knives of various sizes.

They were from the Naga Hills and were out hunting, looking for wild boar or cockerel, or any animals that would supplement their larder.

Our porter asked if they had any news of Jap patrols, at which the Nagas got excited and made plain their hatred towards them – all Nagas would kill them on sight.

During our conversation, they learned of our mission, and even began to laugh. We stood there for quite a while before moving off on our different ways.

While we were talking, one of my porters had slipped into the undergrowth and reappeared with his arms full of pineapples and bananas; so before moving on, we had to gorge ourselves, and took the chance to satisfy our thirst.

This stop for a rest had taken longer than I had foreseen. Judging by the position of the sun, the afternoon was well on the way, and I planned to reach Ramiaitui by nightfall.

The trail was beginning to get uneven and rough. I thought as we neared Ramiaitui that more use would have been made of it, as the only means of communication for trading natives.

I had no footwear now, as my sandals had fallen apart long ago. I'd been walking barefoot for the last hour and my soles were by now hardened, their thick skin immune to the rough ground.

Reaching a clearing to the left of the trail, we could see on the next ridge a cluster of bamboo huts on the crest of the hill. The leading porters at once shouted, 'Ramiaitui!' Heartened by the sight, we all felt much better, and pushed forward, hoping to reach there before dark.

The porters by now were beginning to flag. They were stumbling, and their chanting had reached a low point. I decided to send one porter ahead to prepare our arrival at the village.

As we approached the village, the sounds of children's laughter came nearer. To our astonishment, a crowd of them appeared, running towards us and waving their arms in welcome. Our porter must have put in a good word about us to the chief.

As we entered the trail leading through the huts, the inhabitants gazed up at us inquisitively – not aggressively, but accepting us. So far, so good.

Ramiaitui

21st June, 1944

The village was of the customary form – a cluster of huts around the main one in the centre. This was a well-built basha, quite large, with the usual verandah running completely around it.

As we neared, a deputation of the leading headmen came toward us. At the front was a tall native, attired in the usual regalia of bamboo and plumes that denoted authority, who paused to await our approach.

Turning to the bobijee, I said, 'You go forward to explain who we are, and say we will want accommodation.' As they conferred, it was obvious that the chief was very impressed. He nodded and seemed agreeable.

I and the two sepoys were shown to a large basha just off the centre of the village, with a lean-to attached, providing a kitchen and sleeping quarters for the bobijee. It was obvious that these lodges had been built especially for government hunting parties in the past.

Our two Lushai porters found lodgings in the village; they told the bobijee they would be looked after – I bet they would!

On entering the lodge, we found it was quite spacious. It had the usual amount of rooms, but was much larger than others before. The two sepoys took the rear room, while I had the one facing the village, with a verandah surrounding the lodge.

Just off my room was the lean-to with the kitchen where the bobijee was preparing a meal. I smelled the aromas of a curry. I would be glad to have a meal and stretch out on a charpoy. I must say I felt terribly weak; I hoped it wasn't another touch of malaria. I would take a mepacrine before settling down for the night.

I spent a terrible night, shivering and shaking, with the sweat pouring off me. By the time dawn arrived, I felt very weak. The arrival of the bobijee with coffee and his evident anxiety told me that I must pull myself together and try to shake the fever off.

Added to all this, I realised the monsoon season had started. The climate had become very heavy and close, and any day now torrential rain would obliterate sightings of the valley below. My hope was that when the rains did start, the roof would be able to stand the strain, as the previous few months of dry and hot weather had shrunk the overlappings and joints.

When the bobijee brought in the coffee, I asked him to see if there were any mepacrine tablets left. Luckily, a few tablets were found. I would have to signal for more as soon as a post was reached. In the meantime, I needed a change of sweat sodden bed sheets and clothing, then I would lie down and hope the mepacrine would work off this blasted shivering. Returning to my charpoy, I decided to take things a bit easy; the two sepoys could take over and make sure no marauders were hanging around.

22nd June, 1944

I must have dozed off for quite a while, for when I came to it was nearly dark. The noise of the monsoon rain was deafening, but the bamboo thatch all looked dry – I would say it had survived many onslaughts in the past.

Hearing the bobijee moving about in the lean-to, I called out for him to make coffee, to which he replied, 'Tekai, Sahib.' Within minutes he brought a large mugful, and asked about my fever.

After telling him I felt much better, I slipped off the charpoy, stood up and nearly flopped on to the floor! But for the steadying arm of the bobijee, I would have fallen.

Some time later, I had a surprise visit from the chief and two ferocious looking 'headhunters'. The bobijee showed them in, arranging stools along the wall; the chief sat on one, while the other two sat on the floor.

During the visit, the bobijee translated the exchanges. It appeared that word had reached the village of my fever, and could they help by giving me a potion to cure the sweating and shaking?

Smiling and making signs of thanks, I expressed my pleasure in their concern, and promised that no nasty Japs would endanger their village. At the same time, I asked if any signals had been sent by the drums within a radius of many miles; they replied, 'None.'

The bobijee translated that the chief welcomed my stay, and if there was anything I required, he would do all he could to help. All the time as they squatted there, their eyes were rolling round, noting all the different fittings and fixtures; perhaps they'd try to copy them for themselves.

My visitors left at midday, smiling and clasping their hands together in farewell. I must say they were most interesting, all dressed up for the visit. At least I could feel that I wasn't an unfriendly chap.

The bobijee asked if all was well, and I assured him I was very pleased with his translation. It was quite an experience meeting the chief; it will always remain in my memory.

It was getting much lighter and the low clouds had lifted. The torrential rain eased off, and it wasn't so humid, making us feel much better; but I was still very weak.

I asked the bobijee to go down into the village to buy a chicken, as I fancied a meal. I felt better, and stronger in myself.

While he was gone, I wrote to Audrey, hoping all was well at home; my thoughts were with her at all times. I couldn't explain to her my whereabouts in case the letter fell into the wrong hands.

The monsoon rain abated, and became just a drizzle. The air was very humid, making movements tedious; also, it invited clouds of our friends the mosquitoes. The rest of the evening was spent swatting the blasted things.

23rd June, 1944

I enjoyed a nice chicken curry last night. In fact I woke feeling much stronger and determined to pull myself together and try to move about.

Just after my light breakfast, a Pathan IOC sepoy arrived with the news that during the night's duty they had received a signal to say that Doug was on his way here. He was due to arrive about midday tomorrow, which meant I would have to get his room shipshape.

After the monsoon rains, Doug would be experiencing great difficulty in keeping to the trail. He would be slipping about, while all the time keeping a lookout for the dreaded krait snakes. They hid in the banks, and darted out if disturbed. Their deadly poison gave their victims only a very short time to live.

Looking down into the valley below, I saw the jungle was shrouded in mist, it must be extremely hard to make the trail in such heat, let alone find a dry patch to bed down for the night!

I just managed to stagger around the basha, noting that the bobijee had kept the outside quite tidy. All the paths were swept, and there was no litter left about. After the monsoon there must have been loads of debris to be cleaned up.

I was looking forward to seeing Doug again. Being on one's own was a bit monotonous, even if at times we differed on policy.

The afternoon passed quickly; all was now quiet. The high winds had abated, leaving the air humid and close. The bobijee remarked that more heavy winds were on the way – I hoped they'd not come before Doug arrived.

I spent the rest of the day making an inventory of all the stock left in the small store corner of the lean-to, finding it most depleted.

I retired to my charpoy at about eleven. Everything was peaceful now. Looking down to the village, I could see most of the cooking fires were out. Some were smouldering, leaving a blue haze that would slowly disperse; they'd be relit at dawn.

I had a much better night; I woke up a few times, but managed to nod off. Now I had to wait for Doug's arrival. I was sure we'd have plenty to talk about. This village was about three thousand feet up, so Doug would be on his knees.

The bobijee made a large cake for the occasion, using three eggs and plenty of fruit. Considering our oven consisted of a hole in the bank with a wood fire underneath a biscuit tin perched on a few strips of metal, this was no mean feat.

I had a small lunch of chicken and rice; I thought perhaps Doug might have made it by now, but then, I didn't know what conditions they'd encountered. The heat at this time of the day was most oppressive – no breeze, and the least exertion brought out sweat, let alone the blasted sores.

24th June, 1944

It was about five when a party could be heard approaching from some distance away. I heard the chanting of natives, with an occasional burst of laughter, and I stood outside peering down and trying to locate the trail, but the jungle was too dense.

It was minutes later when they emerged. The first to come into view were the tall figures of the two natives of the Lushai Brigade, with Doug and one IOC sepoy, and then two bearers carrying huge loads on their shoulders.

Our meeting again was quite an event. We were both glad to rendezvous. I could see he was at the end of his tether, and his face showed the strain. His loose shirt was stained with the juice of berries from the undergrowth, and there were a few leeches showing on his shoulders.

While I attended to Doug, the bobijee took the rest round to the back of the basha where a small hut was situated in a plot of land. It was just the place for the sepoy, with the bearers sleeping outside.

The first imperative task for Doug was for a change of clothing and a shower. In the process, I had to remove the leeches stuck to his shoulders by using salt. There were about a dozen of the filthy creatures and they were mostly full of blood.

While the bobijee was preparing a meal, Doug told how he had cleaned up the previous site with the help of some villagers. The chief came to see him off, and provided an escort for the first few miles.

As it was just after a dose of the monsoon rains, the trail was at times most difficult. To keep upright, they hung on to overhanging branches as they struggled forward. They'd been on the trail for three days.

Among the equipment he brought away was the transmitter, batteries, and jenny, plus a few fittings and tools – enough to start another post when required.

He spoke of the very anxious times he went through in keeping tabs on the porters. They were a mixed bunch – some were Lushai, while others were from villages around. During a check he noticed a sack of rice was missing, together with one of the porters; nobody noticed his going, they all remained silent.

We sat up late, going over different topics, and our future plans. How much further our duty lasted would be signalled to us; anyway, he would have to rest and regain strength. By midnight, after a good meal and a few mugs of the local rice beer, I could see the colour returning to his cheeks, and heard more confidence in his speech.

I saw him to his room; the bobijee had put up his mosquito net, so all he had to do was crawl under and try to rest.

I checked around before I spread down for the night – I said 'spread', which is the right word, as the atmosphere was most oppressive, with no movement of air. I lay under the mosquito net, sweating profusely, listening to my friends droning round and round as they tried to penetrate the net.

25th June, 1944

I was woken up by the bobijee offering the morning coffee, and my first thoughts were of Doug. I was pleased to hear he seemed much better, sitting up to drink his coffee, and apparently quite cheerful. I nipped round to his room after my drink.

We talked of our different experiences while separated. I did notice he was much thinner and I said, 'You will have to rest to build up your strength; don't move for a few days, and fatten up a bit.'

Over breakfast of eggs and rice, he did say that he had met Captain Wade at one of the posts. The Captain was on a tour of inspecting personnel of IOC, and it would be a few days before he reached up here, as the trail was washed away in places.

Leaving Doug to rest, I made my way down to the village in the hope of finding the chief at home. I wanted his advice about where a suitable spot could be found to erect an observation post, preferably on the highest ridge. Although he spoke a little English, I took the bobijee as an interpreter.

As I approached his basha, above the verandah, I could see the main shutters were drawn aside, so obviously I was in luck. Most of the time he would be out with a hunting party.

Just as I reached the bamboo ladder to climb up, a native woman appeared, and darted back inside, shrieking – immediately waking up the whole basha.

By the time we had reached the entrance, a small reception party had gathered. At the head stood the chief; at either side, tall warriors looked down at us, bristling with suspicion.

As I had met the chief before, he acknowledged me by extending his hand, a custom he must have acquired in meeting tiger hunting parties in the past.

Making signs that we should enter his basha, he invited us to squat on the ground, while his women brought in mugs of the local rice beer.

The bobijee explained to him my mission. After a confab with his aides, it became apparent that they were in agreement, thinking that when I had moved on, there would be a government post there which would keep the Japs away.

The chief gave instructions for two natives to lead us to the highest point of this range, and the bobijee indicated that it wasn't far away.

Threading our way through dense undergrowth, climbing at a steady pace, we eventually came to a large clump of trees, mainly bamboo. I looked down into the valley below and, it was obvious that this was the ideal base for our post.

Returning to the village, I told the bobijee to ask the chief to instruct natives to clear a site large enough to build an observation tower and a basha beneath it.

Back at our basha, I told Doug that a suitable spot had been found, and work would commence as from tomorrow. As soon as he was strong enough, we'd stagger up there so that he could to see the site.

26th June, 1944

The bobijee baked a lump of wild boar meat for supper last night. Most of the time afterwards, I had terrible stomach pains and wondered how Doug was faring; with his weak insides, he must have had a few rumblings.

Over breakfast, he said he had a few pains – so no more wild boar meat!

He was anxious to see where our new site was situated, and said he was strong enough to stagger up there.

We set off after breakfast, just taking it easy; as the incline was gradual, Doug seemed to manage. We stopped now and again to gaze down into the valley below at the jungle stretching for hundreds of miles.

As we approached the site, laughter and chanting could be heard, and as we got nearer natives could be seen chopping down the bamboo trees.

We were both surprised at the chief starting at once. I suppose building our tower gave the lazy natives an active purpose.

Doug agreed that it was a most suitable site. When the post was built, it would be obscured by a line of tall trees, and there was no way it would be seen from the jungle below.

They had already prepared a number of tree trunks. They were about twenty feet tall, with bases four to five feet in circumference. These would be the mainstay of the tower.

I understood from the bobijee that it would only take a few days for the post to be built. Then it was up to Doug and me to fit the equipment.

Faintly, I could hear the village drums being beaten. The sounds appeared miles away; the bobijee said they had located a Jap patrol, and were keeping close surveillance on their movements.

I immediately told the bobijee to instruct the natives to stop chanting and making any noise, and explain to them why we had have to work in silence for the rest of the day. At the same time we had to decipher the drum messages indicating all the Japs' positions.

To make sure no activity could be detected up there, I told the natives to stop the building for the day. The Japs had powerful binoculars, capable of detecting the slightest movement at a great distance.

As the workhorse were making their way down, Doug came limping up to see how the work was progressing, and immediately joined me as we made our way down to the village.

Arriving there, it was quite surprising to see it so quiet – no children were running about, and fires were put out to eliminate smoke – certainly the precautions had been acted on.

Overhead, thick clouds were gathering, indicating further heavy rain; that would deter the little bastards. Distant drums relayed the news that they had moved away.

27th June, 1944

By the time we had returned to our basha last night, it was nearly dark. Just below us, the village was still in darkness – a precaution in case there might be a stray Jap about.

As our basha was situated on a higher level, we also showed no lights; moving about in the dim glow of evening, we were groping our way around. We opened all the shutters to give us more light, but of course this let in swarms of mosquitoes.

We sat out on the verandah to have our supper of chicken curry and rice, washed down by a mug of the local rice beer. By this time the darkness had nearly fallen. It was time to crawl under our nets, and look forward to daylight.

I must have spent a good night, for it was the bobijee's, 'Coffee, Sahib!' that woke me. The sun was shining through the gaps in the bamboo walls, and a crescendo of song rose from all the birds, together with weird noises from the animals.

Sitting on the side of my charpoy, I became aware that I had been bitten by mosquitoes on my neck and shoulders – the swelling had started, together with the itching. I immediately covered the area with calamine lotion; the blasted things must have got under the net.

In the meantime, an IOC sepoy arrived to say one of his unit had a dose of malaria, and had I got tablets?

Telling the sepoy to wait, I pulled on a shirt and shorts, rummaged in my depleted medicine box and thankfully found quite a number of mepacrine tablets – more than I'd thought were there.

Telling the sepoy to lead the way, I passed through the village to reach a large basha over which flew the Indian flag; I never thought such a post existed, but I learnt later that it was for protection, covering a certain area.

The small unit consisted of a sergeant and four sepoys. Their duty was to patrol an area of about ten miles square; up to now, no movements of Japs had been reported.

Entering the basha, I was shown the sick sepoy, who was in the throes of shaking and shivering. I asked how long he had been in this condition and was told two days.

I immediately gave him two mepacrine, leaving four with the Sergeant and instructions to repeat the dose at four-hour intervals. I was sure it would bring down the fever.

Meanwhile, I was shown round the small compound. Bamboo fencing kept stray animals away, and there were small beds of flowers on display – it all looked so neat. Returning to the basha, I was surprised to find they had prepared a meal of rice and chapattis laid out on a table in the shade.

During the meal, the Sergeant and I became quite friendly. He was most interested to learn of our mission, he was a Bengali, and knew Chittagong.

28th June, 1944

Before leaving, I checked on the condition of the sick sepoy, only to find him sound asleep; at least the tablets had reduced his temperature.

As it was now semi-darkness, the Sergeant detailed a sepoy to escort me back to my basha, describing the area as still fraught with headhunters!

I explained to the Sergeant that if the malaria worsened, the sepoy would have to be carried by stretcher down the trail to Lunglei, a distance of about twenty miles. This would not be not a pleasant experience, as the trail was quite rough in places.

If need be, I would have to send a runner ahead to warn the field hospital of their coming; all this depended on the sepoy's recovery.

I arrived safely back at our basha last night; Doug was a bit worried. I gave him an account of my visit and said I hoped the sepoy would recover without making the journey to the field hospital.

During my stay with the IOC, I gave the Sergeant details of where we had a post erected and said that we would want some of his chaps to maintain it. He seemed most interested, and told me the small complement under his charge were at times finding no tasks with which to fill the passing days. He suggested perhaps he could come up with his personnel and show them the location.

Meanwhile, Doug had been busy fitting the transmitter and headphone equipment; it was my job to have a burrow dug just deep enough to install the jenny and the large batteries which supplied our power. All of this was buried, leaving the exhaust protruding some distance off.

We had a busy day, and by the time we had checked the various workings, daylight was fading. It was quite a relief to get back to our basha, have a wash and change of shirt and shorts, and sit out on the verandah and relax.

We expected the arrival of Captain Wade some time tomorrow. It meant we'd have to clean the place up and get the bobijee to do the same in the kitchen, though I must say he was most particular in all his duties.

Doug suggested, as it was a quiet night, that we should stroll up to the post to check a few instruments in readiness for the night's shift later. Telling the bobijee that we wouldn't be long, we set off in the dim light on the winding uphill trail. I remarked to Doug that we must be mad!

Between the gaps in the foliage there was quite a lot of light; then we entered the shadows and it was quite eerie. We could hear the movements of animals, and the grunt, snort or squeal of a wild boar, which could be quite dangerous.

By the time we had reached the clearing where the post was based, we both were thankful; it was silly to have started out.

After we had checked the different components, we heard voices approaching, with a cheerful welcome from the leader of three sepoys, all smartly turned out in their uniforms.

29th June, 1944

After making sure the sepoys were conversant with the equipment, we decided to return to our basha, but not before they insisted that one of them should escort us there. The sepoy who returned with us carried a Sten gun and spear.

It was quite late by the time we crawled under our mosquito nets, hoping that the sepoys would receive a signal from Chittagong about our further movements.

I was woken up by the bobijee with coffee, telling me that the time was nine o'clock! Looking out through the open shutters, I could see the sun rising quite high in the sky – we must have been worn out last night.

After a shave and wash down, we both felt much fresher. We were having a breakfast of rice and bananas when the bobijee informed us that Captain Wade had arrived up here with a small core of nine Pathan sepoys, and had found two vacant bashas on the edge of the village.

Knowing Wade, I expected he'd want to inspect our quarters and observation post, though he had no jurisdiction; we were RAF, while he, I believe, was a liaison officer attached to the 14th Army.

Apart from the military aspect, he realised that we were all stuck up in these hills doing a worthwhile job; rank was secondary if we intended to work as a team.

Just after lunch, a sepoy arrived up here to deliver a note from Captain Wade asking us to be ready at dawn to accompany him to inspect a village called Thenyaui. I replied we would be ready at about seven.

Why the bloody hell he wanted to slog ten miles to this out of the way primitive hole was beyond us. Apart from being miles off the main track, the location was well known as being headhunter country.

Tonight we would do our stint up in the post, but we'd have to shut down earlier to have a couple of hours' rest before Captain Wade and sepoys arrived.

It was after a light meal of rice and chapattis at about eight that we made our way up the trail leading to the post. We forgot to take the Sten gun, and would have to chance the danger – we had our stout walking sticks.

The usual grunts and queer noises from the undergrowth went with us as we made our way. We reached the post safely, to be met by a cheerful IOC sepoy at the bamboo ladder's foot.

We climbed up to the hut, and another sepoy helped us into the small quarters. Our first impression was how clean and well organised all the instruments were. Coffee was made while we exchanged notes. They hadn't received any signals for us; the air had been full of them, in many different codes, and they had to concentrate closely to decipher the different signals.

After the sepoys had left, we settled down in the bamboo chairs, hoping Chittagong hadn't forgotten us! There was no wind outside. Down in the valley, the forest below was covered in deep mist; at the same time it was very humid.

30th June, 1944

We spent a very quiet night waiting for our call sign to come through, listening to all the different codes and trying to decipher some, but they were all sent very quickly.

Plenty of music was being played. Orchestras and dance bands filling the air with monotonous regularity. Suddenly they'd stop and a short coded message would be flashed – very difficult to register. We had to be on the ball at all times.

At about four, our relief of two sepoys arrived, both looking half asleep, but to their credit they were correctly dressed, clean and smartly presented.

We returned to our basha to find the bobijee already up, and with coffee and chapattis ready – what a faithful friend! We decided to try to rest on our charpoys for a couple of hours before our friend Wade began his interrogation about our movements while up here. Personally, I failed to see what authority he had.

As liaison officer acting for the 14th Army, I suppose he would want all the locations of villages in this area. He thought that as we had travelled around these hills, we would have some information about the natives' customs and way of life.

At the moment, the valley below was deep in mist; we'd have to wait till it cleared before setting off to Thenyaui. That was probably why Wade was a bit late. There was no sense in starting now, walking into deep mist, not knowing the direction of the trail we were following.

Captain Wade arrived about ten, accompanied by two Pathan IOC sepoys, each carrying Sten guns – a wise precaution, as we had not communicated or made contact with these natives before.

He appeared more friendly and used rank less. As we were travelling in an area where headhunters were still practising their trade – in our favour – the drum telegraph would beat out our position along the trail.

During our preparations to move off, we ascertained that Thenyaui would be at least fifteen miles away. At our steady pace, it would take about two days. I hoped in that time we'd collect useful information that would be valuable in the future to the 14th Army, if they had to operate in this inhospitable terrain.

We discussed what trail to take, there being quite a few. The maps Captain Wade carried were roughly drawn from information he had collected from scouts who had previously been operating in this area.

The one we decided on looked quite fair. There were a few tricky negotiable sections through deep undergrowth; we'd have to tackle them as we encountered them.

With the two sepoys leading the way, we made our way down the khud-side into the oppressive heat of the jungle. It took at least two hours – the track at times was quite rough, and my companion, between comments, kept up a flow of cursing; but at the same time he was quite cheerful.

As we picked our way, the undergrowth on either side of the trail became more dense, while high above were packs of screaming rhesus monkeys, who followed us by leaping from tree to tree.

30th June, 1944

As we moved forward, exotic birds in a variety of colours were flying around. Now and again, a cockerel would dart across the trail, the sepoys giving chase, but usually not fast enough. It would be nice to have one for a meal later.

We had now covered quite a distance. The next thought in our minds was to find a suitable clearing for a rest. At the moment, we were making our way through deep undergrowth; neither side was suitable for making camp.

At last, one of the sepoys pointed ahead to where the sun could be seen through the foliage. Perhaps there might be a more open space in which we could camp.

As we pushed on, the dense covering made by the treetops gave way to a much clearer space. At last, with the blue sky above, the air became more bearable. The humid atmosphere which we had endured while slogging along had gone. We looked forward to finding a suitable site to rest and have coffee.

Suddenly, the leading sepoy shouted and pointed forward to where a clearing could be seen. It was quite large, and would give us ample space to kindle a fire and rest for a while.

In the clearing we found plenty of fruit trees – bananas, orange and grapefruit – while a few pineapples could be found amongst the tall grass. What more did we want?

A small clearing of grass was made in which to prepare our fire. We found plenty of kindling around and gathered it up. Soon the tripod was erected holding the billycan of water, while in the meantime we were all making comfortable spaces in which to sit.

I must say, Captain Wade helped at all times with these chores. He had quite a cheerful and friendly attitude – very different from the crusty chap I had known before.

After a snack of issue biscuits and coffee, removing all traces of our camp was the next task. We restored it to the condition we found it in by using branches to sweep over the vegetation and grass.

As we moved off, our friends the rhesus monkeys started up their high-pitched squeals, swinging from bough to bough high above us in the treetops. We cursed them, for they gave away our position to those who might be interested.

The trail had by now become more narrow, with a high bank one side and bamboo grass the other. We had to get into single file, at the same time keeping a sharp eye on the bank for the deadly krait snake: one bite would kill one in seconds.

Eventually, the trail led us into open ground. We found ourselves halfway up a steep incline on a hill, while below the dense jungle covered the terrain as far as the eye could see.

Looking down, we reckoned it would take us all the afternoon to reach our destination.

Thenyaui

1st July, 1944

Dusk was falling by the time our village was reached. We found it deserted – the inhabitants had scampered into their huts. No doubt they were peering at us through the slits in the bamboo walls.

We stood there, looking for movement, till at last a tall native approached, wearing little besides bamboo and ivory spikes sticking through his nose, lips, and ears, together with the usual loincloth.

As he spoke to our sepoy, more villagers came forward to stand and stare. They didn't seem all that friendly, but as the exchanges went on, the tension seemed to relax. Children began to play around, staring up at us with their big brown eyes.

At last we were accepted, and a faint smile even hovered around the lips of our contact. I presumed he was the head-man; we had yet to meet the chief. Now the introductions had been made, perhaps we would be led to the main basha.

Beckoning us to follow, the head-man led us through a maze of bamboo hovels to a large clearing. On the edge stood a large basha, around which was built the usual verandah, encircling the whole structure at about four feet off the ground.

It was obvious we were expected, for as we approached, the bamboo shutters were slid to one side, allowing a deputation of dignitaries to step forward and eye us with suspicion. The native at the head I presumed to be the chief.

He stood out among the others owing to his attire. His head and shoulders were covered in feathers from all the different birds of the jungle, while ornaments of bamboo were stuck through every spare piece of flesh.

Moving forward, our sepoys raised their arms in greeting, speaking (they hoped) in their correct language. It was evidently understood, for the chief stepped forward to bow with a short tilt of the head.

Captain Wade seemed tickled pink at all this ceremony. Glancing in his direction, I could see he was highly amused, especially at the natives' attire.

It was quite a lengthy conversation our sepoys were having, but at last it seemed we were accepted, for the rest of the elders came forward to greet us, smiling and showing all their broken teeth.

As the tension eased, our sepoys said we had been given a large basha which stood behind the chief's – not too close, I hoped.

A native came forward to show us the way. Immediately one looked at him, one thought of headhunters. He was a fierce looking chap – I shouldn't like to cross his path!

I must say they knew how to construct a basha. The one we were in was quite large. The rooms were clean, and there was the usual lean-to for cooking.

There were two bedrooms, each with bamboo charpoys. The rooms were far apart, so at least we'd have a little privacy. We both flopped down on the charpoys to rest before unpacking.

2nd July, 1944

It was quite late last night by the time we eventually retired to our charpoys. We had no mosquito nets, so I lay with my head half under my blanket. Happily, there weren't many mosquitoes around. I believe I must have dozed off for a couple of hours; then the voice of a sepoy woke me with the usual morning call, 'Cha, Sahib!' Captain Wade began to stir and grunted, 'Morning!'

We were now able to take a good look around. Plenty of grass and weeds were growing through the bamboo floor; the sepoy learnt that this basha had been built years ago for the use of hunting parties, but was rarely used.

After a breakfast of hard biscuits and coffee, we decided to visit the chief again, to get more friendly. We'd have to take with us our two sepoys as interpreters – and guards!

On arrival at the main basha, we were surprised to find all around was very quiet, with only a few *chikos* (children) about. Captain Wade sent one of the sepoys up the rickety ladder to make enquiries. When he reached the entrance, the shutters were opened revealing an interior full of all the inhabitants of the village.

At the appearance of us, the whole assembly stopped jabbering. It was the chief who broke the silence by standing up to greet us, clasping his hands and bowing slightly.

A discussion was held, during which it was announced to the gathering who we were and what our purpose was. This was greeted at first by silence, then by talking among themselves; soon this became a loud chatter and smiles, and we were accepted.

The interior of this large basha consisted of huge logs or tree trunks positioned between the walls at a height of about ten feet, all held up by sturdy tree trunks. The roof consisted of matted bamboo branches and leaves.

An opening of about five feet in diameter was left for the smoke to escape from the fires that were built in the centre. Surprisingly, as we squatted down to talk, the air was quite clear.

Women came forward with fruit and the local *Zophan* rice beer contained in wooden bowls. I caught the eye of Captain Wade as we drank; he was actually enjoying it all.

Our sepoy in the meantime was trying to explain to the chief why we were in his territory. It was obvious that he knew nothing of the Jap invasion and neither did the surrounding villages. We were deep in the jungle and away from civilisation.

As we got accustomed to our surroundings, trying to peer through the dim light, we became aware of shrunken heads placed on narrow ledges about four feet off the ground. The ledges ran most of the way round the interior of the basha.

When we had convinced the chief we were in his territory to help to keep the enemy away, he became less hostile; and in no time out came the hubble-bubble pipes.

We all took the pipe as it was offered to us. We tried not to cough, and our hosts were very amused when we nearly choked, but we did bring smoke up.

It was nearly midnight by the time we left to walk the short distance to our basha – weren't we glad to reach there! It wasn't long before we were stretched out on our charpoys.

3rd July, 1944

During breakfast the following morning, Captain Wade became more talkative. It appeared he had been a regular soldier during peacetime. After a short spell at the outbreak of war, he was made Sergeant. He was very surprised after a year or two to be called up for further promotion, but saw at the same time that commissions were being handed out to regulars.

He repeated that on his return to base, he would recommend that Doug and I should be rewarded for our time working up here in these conditions. Looking down into the valley below, we saw that most of the jungle was covered by mist.

We were still in the monsoon time, and in the last few days torrential rain had fallen. The air was very close and oppressive, and a heavy mist was forming, making movement difficult to say the least. It was unbearable having sweat forming at every exertion.

During a lull in the rain, we decided to stroll half a mile into the village and make ourselves known to the natives – though I could see by their fixed stares that they still felt suspicious. We stopped at various huts, and it was quite interesting to watch the women weaving the local cloth. From it they made the skirt or *poen*, all in different dyes, which they got from coloured berries.

We paid a visit to the observation post. Four Pathans were on duty, leaving five to take over for the night. They made us most welcome, making chapattis and coffee. They were surprised to see an army Captain with us. What could he want? They promised to contact Chittagong when possible to give them our position and obtain instructions; but by then, we'd be on our way again. It would at least let them know we were still around.

The rain started again, making the trail very slippery. We had to look out for snakes as we made our way back to the village. They seemed to like the rain, slithering under leaves, and when trodden on they reared their heads and struck quickly.

All four of us had stout walking sticks, and lashed out at the least movement underfoot; we must have killed dozens.

Making our way along the top of the ridge, we glanced down into the valley at the jungle below and wondered what its inhabitants were doing.

We arrived back at our basha before dusk, worn out and fit to drop. After a wash and clean clothes we felt much better – now for a meal and a good rest.

4th July, 1944

Last night Captain Wade suggested we should move back down the ridge towards Rangamati. He had intended to make it as far as Ijal, but decided against it, as we were tired and footsore. Besides, we had bouts of malaria which seemed to be with us all the time and were the main cause of our fatigue.

If I'd had any mepacrine tablets left, they would have kept it away, but they'd all been used. I should have signalled for a supply at the last post.

I felt a bit shaky, but tried to hold it off. It was no good giving in – I'd have a tot of rum, and rest.

It was decided that we would start off again in the morning. I sent a sepoy off to the observation post, instructing them to signal Chittagong about our location – if contact was made.

All day we were busy in packing for the getaway in the morning. The two Pathan IOC sepoys would carry the bulk of the load, while Captain Wade and I would take the rest.

We sat out on the verandah plotting our journey till late last night. We'd not had a bad stay here – if it wasn't for the terrible stink and the mosquitoes.

I still felt a bit shaky; it would take some time to get the fever out of my system. I felt so weak all the time. I stretched out on my charpoy and finally dropped off.

It must have been about six when I awoke to the sounds of the dawn chorus. The air was filled with birdsongs and shrill cries from the jungle down below from all the wildlife – what a din!

I could hear the sepoys moving about in the lean-to kitchen, and smelled the coffee aroma drifting through. It was time for me to get up. Looking across at the bulk of Captain Wade, I could see he was still fast asleep.

The sepoy brought in the coffee and shook him to announce the new morning, saying, 'Coffee, Sahib!' After a light breakfast, it was soon time to get ready to push off.

By about ten we were ready. After making our farewells to the chief and all his entourage, we moved off along the top of the ridge, followed by scores of screaming children, all laughing and dancing around us. They were our escort till the trail reached the end of the ridge. Then, when we started to descend down the steep trail, they stood back to wave and made shrill cries in farewell.

On reaching the edge of the jungle, we looked up to the ridge to see the children still waving to us. We hadn't realised they felt any affection – it was nice to know.

We entered and made our way through deep undergrowth. So many times have we had this experience, that we had our dahs ready to chop down and hack branches that might get in our way. We tried to avoid leeches that might be clinging on the leaves.

We made steady progress; it was obvious that we'd have to make camp tonight. We pushed on, and a suitable clearing was finally reached. It was not quite to our liking, the ground being a bit rough, but as the daylight was fading, it would have to do.

The sepoys in no time had the ground cleared of clumps and bamboo shoots, their sharp dahs making short work of it. Soon a tripod was erected, fire lit, and water boiled for coffee, while suitable spaces were cleared for us to relax in.

By this time, daylight had gone. It was not exactly dark, as the blue sky above gave enough light for us not to bump into each other; our fire also gave enough surrounding light.

As we were having our meal of rice and coffee, movement could be heard in the undergrowth. It could be animals or humans – it might be local natives having a nose, or some heavy animal. We stacked more wood on the fire and hoped for the best.

It was decided to stop up as late as possible and before turning in, we drew lots for the guard duty. We'd have two hours each, and as we were four, it would take us past eight o'clock. My duty was from four to six.

I was awakened by a sepoy whispering the news that the Captain had been on duty earlier, and was now fast asleep again. The fire was stoked up, and there had been no incidents during the night – so far!

It was a most memorable experience – the dawn was approaching and shafts of light were slanting through the tree tops: another day was dawning.

In a short time, the air was filled with a crescendo of song. Birds and fowl were competing at the highest pitch, together with squeals and grunts from marauding animals. I hastily stoked up the fire!

The sepoys were the first to awake, and by the time the coffee was ready, Captain Wade stirred and muttered, 'Morning!' After a snack of rice and biscuits, our first job was to clear up the campsite, brush away all signs of our stay by using branches, and leave them scattered around.

Off we started on the last lap. The sepoys reckoned it would be about four miles to Rangamati, we should reach there by evening. It was after about three hours along the trail that a suitable clearing was reached; so far, the terrain had been passable. There had been a few stumbles and curses as we tried to keep our packs in position.

I believe Captain Wade twisted his ankle; he didn't complain, but he was limping badly. I asked if he was all right, and he answered in the gruff voice, 'Yes!'

We were now rounding the brow of the hill, and coming out of the undergrowth. This gave us a clear view of the scene below; I suppose we were about a thousand feet up, and as the sky was quite clear, we could pick out Rangamati down below. Approaching the outskirts, we were met by four IOC sepoys running towards us, waving their arms in greeting – we had arrived!

Rangamati

6th July, 1944

After helping to carry our loads, they escorted us to the outskirts of the village, though I must say that it had grown into a town since we passed through on our way on the outward journey.

As we made our way up a steep incline, I remembered the trail we were following, even though more bamboo bashas had been built recently on either side.

Looking down, I saw that Rangamati itself had enlarged. What was once deep undergrowth, around the perimeter was now rows of bamboo huts – quite a township.

Now that we were on the last leg, we all felt relieved, and looked forward to a rest; I knew Captain Wade needed one. He was still limping; his ankle must have hurt, but there was not a word of any pain.

Arriving at the observation post, a sergeant of the IOC stepped forward to salute and welcome us, at the same time giving orders for all our kit to be taken up to the dāk bungalow. In the meantime, he asked if would we like to rest awhile to have coffee.

I could see Captain Wade wanted to make for the bungalow, but I must say he gave in and flopped down in a bamboo chair at the Sergeant's basha.

Apart from the coffee, we were given a large chapatti, which in itself was a meal, so by the time we had reached the dāk bungalow, we were ready to rest.

I recognised the bungalow at once; it was quite a well-built building; I suppose it was put up for the use of hunting parties during the Raj. As I mentioned before, these dāks were built at intervals on the trail stretching for miles through the jungle.

The interior of the bungalow was just as we had left it. Apparently, no other party had cause to stop there, as it was such an isolated spot.

To have more privacy, Captain Wade and I decided to billet the sepoys in an adjacent basha; perhaps they would rather be on their own anyway.

On hearing we were on our way there, the Sergeant in command had had our bungalow cleaned and swept out – the whole place smelt of carbolic.

We both had a good wash, and kitted ourselves in the last of our clean clothes; the *dhobi* wallah would have a busy few days washing all our dirty linen.

A bobijee had been sent up from the village. His appearance seemed favourable. He wore a clean shirt and *poen*, and had the usual grin covering his face. He looked like a Lushai, but it was difficult to say; in Rangamati they all looked about the same.

On entering our small dining room, I found Captain Wade sitting with his right foot immersed in a bowl of cold water. Looking at it, I could see it was terribly swollen. I asked at once, 'How the devil did you walk?' He said he didn't want to make a fuss!

7th July, 1944

I wondered how Captain Wade had slept last night. I couldn't rest, my legs ached and the sweat poured off me. I had the shakes – it was the bloody malaria again. I found my way to the lean-to, and eventually after searching various boxes, discovered a few mepacrine.

I swallowed two and returned to my charpoy, hoping they would do the trick. I found a towel, wiped the sweat off, and lay down under the mosquito net. I must have slept a little, for the sun shone through the shutters when I awoke. I could hear movement nearby, and later the bobijee put his head round the door, saying, 'Cha, Sahib?'

He told me that I had slept late. It was now nine o'clock, and the Captain Sahib was up. He'd had breakfast, and gone down into the village. It was when I managed to get off my charpoy and tried to stand up that I realised how weak I was.

The shaking had stopped; I just felt so weak. I needed to pull myself together. I staggered out to the lean-to, had a good sluice down with cold water, and felt much better.

The air was close and oppressive; the monsoon was still with us, and now and again sheets of rain came cascading down – torrential downpours. I asked myself how the bamboo built roof could stand the strain.

I wondered if Captain Wade had managed to avoid the rain. He hadn't returned yet; his ankle must be feeling stronger for him to walk about.

The rain eased off. Perhaps he had taken shelter. I'd soon know. In fact, he arrived back looking a bit weary, and said the weather was all right when he started, but soon the heavens had opened up.

His ankle felt much better, and he asked about my fever. After telling him I felt a bit weak, he remarked what a couple of soldiers we were.

In the afternoon, I made my way up the gradient to the observation post, to check the working, and to enquire if any messages had been received referring to our movement.

A signal had been received. When deciphered, it instructed Captain Wade and myself to make our way as soon as possible to the post at Howlong, where they were having trouble with the generator.

I told the Sergeant in command to signal back as soon as possible informing them of our state of health, and saying that we would start off as soon as we felt fit.

Back at the bungalow, Wade was in a bad mood – his ankle had started to hurt again. It was decided that I would go ahead to Howlong, taking two sepoys, and the tools we'd need for repairs.

The monsoon had eased off, leaving a thick mist hanging at low altitudes, which made the trail leading into the undergrowth quite ghostly.

We both sat up late. He was furious that his ankle was giving pain, as he would have liked to have gone to Howlong with me. He would have to follow later.

8th July, 1944

Last evening, I paid a visit to the Sergeant's basha to detail two Pathan sepoys to accompany me on my trip to Howlong. They had to be ready at dawn carrying Sten guns and rations.

I had a fairly good night's sleep. My fever had slowly lessened; the shivering had almost gone, and I felt stronger. I hoped to work it off by taking the trail easy.

It was precisely at the break of dawn, when I was awakened by one of my sepoys, cheerfully announcing the new day and offering me a mug of coffee. I was soon ready, as I had packed the necessary food and tools last night. Wade was still asleep; there was no point in waking him up, as we had planned our action last night.

The other sepoy appeared, kitted out in smart uniform – they were both a credit to their regiment. They carried large packs and Sten guns: I was well escorted.

As we started down the trail, making sure of our footholds, we found the recent monsoon rains had washed away most of the tracks. This made the going most unsteady; I had many a stumble trying to keep upright.

Then, as we entered the undergrowth, there was cover, and the trail had some dry stretches, in which we became more steady. Soon, on finding a clear space, I said we'd rest for a while.

A bundle of wood was quickly collected, and with the billycan soon boiling, a welcome mug of coffee was made. We had picked up a few leeches; I lit a cigarette to burn off about five from the shoulders of the sepoys. I had two clinging to my collar, which were soon destroyed.

As we sat there, packs of rhesus monkeys formed in large numbers, screaming and swinging from bough to bough. If any give-away of our position was needed, this was it.

Together with the monkeys, loud squeals and grunts could be heard all around. The sepoys kept up a chatter, sometimes with loud laughter, to stop them from getting closer.

While drinking our coffee, we could hear drums. When we were making our farewells to the chief, he did say signals by the beating of drums would be passed from village to village, giving our position, and that we would be watched all the way.

We had no sight of any natives at any time. They must have had impregnable lookout points hidden in the undergrowth – I was glad and thankful that they were there for our safety.

The sepoys maintained during conversation that we had covered at least six miles. I thought we must have done well; we seemed to get quite used to the rough terrain. At one time, we picked our way; now we pushed on, slipping and cursing as we negotiated the trail.

As we pushed on, I recognised certain points in the trail from when we came that way before.

Rounding a bend on the trail, I called a halt to rest awhile. It was mid-afternoon, and the sun rested a quarter of the way up in the west giving us about four hours' daylight: we had time for coffee.

Waiting for the water to boil for the coffee, one of the sepoys ventured further along the trail to see what was ahead, and came hurrying back with the news that Howlong could be seen on the brow of the next range of hills.

We quickly finished our coffee and set off, determined to reach our goal before darkness fell, now that we had sighted it. My legs ached like the devil; I didn't dare look at my feet, there must be horrible blisters – I hoped they wouldn't burst before we reached our destination.

My sepoy escort seemed cheered up by the knowledge that it wouldn't be long now before we reached the observation post. The light was beginning to fade, and the trail was still a bit slippery. The monsoon wasn't over yet, and the air was very humid; sweat poured over my body, and I expected a few rashes when I came to off my shirt.

Howlong

9th July, 1944

By the time we had reached the observation post it was quite dark, but we were heartened by four IOC sepoys running to greet us. With some laughter, they told us that we were under observation for most of our trip; from their post, they were able to detect most of our movements.

What a relief it was on arrival at the dāk bungalow to find a cheerful bobijee in charge – all thanks to the IOC Sergeant in command. He had had the bungalow swept and cleaned out, and a meal of chicken curry with a bowl of rice wine laid out for our return. The bobijee was my old friend, Cyril Sirren.

He joined me at the meal, narrating all the incidents that had occurred. He said that they had felt isolated, having no means of communication; the generator just went dead. I promised to look at it first thing in the morning.

Soon after the meal, my companion asked if there was anything more I required, and left me to get down on my charpoy and try to rest. My feet felt a bit raw, so the blisters must have broken; I'd have to leave them till morning.

I must have slept well, for it was daylight when I woke up. The sun was streaming through the slits in the bamboo and the air was filled with the sounds and song of animals and birds. I wondered what the time was.

A head appeared round the door asking if I wanted cha. It was a Bengali sepoy, and when the coffee came, I asked where Cyril Sirren was. It appeared he had been on the rice beer last night.

10th July, 1944

After a light breakfast of rice and coffee, I asked Cyril to show me where the jenny was placed. In most cases the practice was to set the unit in a deep burrow, where the exhaust sounds were muffled, making detection less obvious.

On locating it, I had the generator lifted out and cleaned, ready for me to strip down and find the trouble. I did this and the trouble was clear – the brushes were worn down, leaving the commutator with segments clearly corroded.

Within two hours, I had the armature reassembled complete with new brushes, fitted in the casing, and ready to test. When we started the jenny, a steady output of five amperes was given; now to get the heavy duty batteries connected and off we go.

The Sergeant in charge was overjoyed, now we could signal Chittagong tonight. The batteries would by tonight have been charged up, enough to signal that we were in operation.

I hadn't heard a word from Captain Wade; he must have been on his way, he was nearly ready as I came away. He said, 'I won't be far behind you.' I hoped all was well.

I had intended to start for Rangamati today, but would have to wait for him; he might have had further orders.

Now that this post was in operation, it seemed best to wait here till Wade showed up. I was being well looked after, and would arrange a meal for him on his arrival.

Sepoy Sirren obtained a nice cockerel from the village; he didn't say the price – I bet he stole it – anyway, it would make a nice meal for Wade on his arrival.

It was after a lunch of rice and eggs that we had news that Wade was located on the trail not far away. He had been spotted by a hunting party from the village, but they hadn't made contact.

In the meantime, Cyril and the second bobijee were busy preparing his room in the bungalow by sweeping out and polishing.

Sitting out on the verandah, and looking down into the dense jungle undergrowth, it was difficult to pick out any movement, but at last in an opening I picked out four figures moving slowly towards us.

It was another hour before they entered the village, and as they came up to the bungalow, it was obvious that Wade was a bit shaky. He was limping badly, and perspiring profusely.

I could see he was pleased to see me – he even shook my hand – he must be human after all!

After he had showered and put clean clothes on, he was his old self, apologising for the state he arrived in and at the same time admitting the quest for a suitable route was wasted. It was midnight and lots of gin later when we retired.

11th July, 1944

At breakfast, we discussed our next move. Wade's original plan had been to push up to Ijal, a town which boasted of being a centre of all communications. However, we both had little to offer, being on our knees and worn out.

No reports of any Jap movements in the area, and certainly no drums were being sounded, sending their telegraph of warning; perhaps they had given up coming this far.

In the evening we went down to the post and tried to contact Chittagong to inform them of our position; it seemed to us that we had been forgotten.

During our watch we sent coded signals out, but received none in reply. After a lengthy wait, we gave up, and delegated two sepoys to take the night shift, to make sure a signal wasn't missed.

I think Wade's intention now was to make his way down to Rangamati to report to 14th Army HQ. All was quiet down here; I didn't think hostilities would come this far.

I had a restless night. Where the leeches had been removed by cigarettes and salt, open sores were left. I had applied cream, but they were still irritating. I'd have to dust them with powder and dispense with a shirt for the day.

The usual dawn chorus filled the air, together with grunts and squeals from the undergrowth; it all seemed so far away from civilisation.

Sepoy Sirren came in with coffee, and told me that the Captain had risen early and gone for a stroll. At the sight of my sores he became concerned, and hoped they would clear soon.

Later, Wade came in to say his ankle felt much better; in fact, he wanted to make preparations to move on, perhaps tomorrow. There was no reason for him to stay – he had examined all the routes and trails and in his opinion there wouldn't be a push down as far as this; they had their hands full around Kohima.

The day was spent in collecting Wade's belongings, and packing them in boxes and kitbags. During his stay, he had collected all sorts of memorable objects, such as small statues carved out of animal tusks, together with all the warlike weapons the headhunters carried.

He said that on returning to base, he would try to relate his experiences to fellow officers, and certainly tell them of the two RAF sergeants on wireless observation post maintenance, how the posts were based miles apart, and the conditions we had to live under.

He would make for Rangamati, taking one sepoy and recruiting two local natives from the village – headhunters, preferably!

I told the bobijee and Sirren to prepare a super meal for Captain Wade's farewell dinner this evening; he wasn't aware that it was being prepared.

12th July, 1944

It was a rather hilarious farewell party. The IOC Sergeant arrived with two sepoys, as did the chief of the village, accompanied by two of the elders – all suitably dressed in feathers and bamboo decorations. If only I could have taken their photo!

The meal consisted of wildfowl, boar, and a pot full of wild vegetables – *kolebeha* (potatoes) together with edible root greens.

During the meal, grunts and belching were the order of the day. Captain Wade sat there in his haunches thoroughly enjoying it all, nodding and gesticulating at the chief to make his point clear.

The night was as usual very humid. There was no fresh air, and the mosquitoes filled the air in large packs, making dive-bombing attacks. We were swatting the blasted things all the time; I anticipated swollen lumps in the morning.

We sat out on the verandah till past midnight, drinking the local rice beer. By this time, the Sergeant and sepoys had retired to their beds, leaving me with Wade and the chief's party – they didn't seem to want to stir.

Although Captain Wade had made up his mind to move on in the morning, I could gather by his manner that he was feeling sorry to leave. After all, he had made many contacts among the different tribes, and they all respected his authority.

After a night tossing and turning, I was awakened by the babble of voices, and came to the conclusion that it must be Captain Wade's party making ready to move off.

It was a fine morning with a clear sky; the air was a bit humid, and the best time to start on the trail was before the sun rose to its midday peak.

By six all was ready. Captain Wade set off together with an IOC sepoy armed with a Sten gun slung over his shoulder, and two tall headhunter-type natives, loaded up with bamboo spears and carrying wicked looking knives.

I never thought the time would come when we were to part. After handshakes, and mutual hopes of meeting again, he was off. I watched as he and his party made their way down the hill trail to disappear into the undergrowth leading to the jungle.

I made my way back to the bungalow feeling very lonely. I was on my own now; at times I had wished the old bugger many hurtful things, but now he had at last gone, the good times came flooding back.

I entered Wade's quarters to see if he had left anything, but the room was bare – swept, and all clean.

I had from now on Cyril Sirren and two IOC sepoys to take care of my needs, so it wouldn't be so bad. He joined me on the verandah to ask if there was anything I wanted, and to say he had acquired a chicken to make a meal for today.

I had a small lunch of curry, and flopped down on my charpoy to rest. I must have dropped off, for on awakening, I found Cyril with the exciting news that a native out hunting had seen Doug's party on the trail making their way towards us. They would be about three miles distant.

It would take Doug at least another half day to reach here, so in the meantime we had time to prepare his room – what good news!

With Cyril to help make the room more comfortable, we soon had the chairs and table in place, and his charpoy all ready with a mosquito net over it.

It did make me wonder why he was coming up here; I should be making the journey to him.

The sun was on the wane at about five, when I heard shouting accompanied by chanting from the trail down below. Soon Doug was seen leading a small party of two sepoys and two Lushai bearers, carrying loads on their backs.

It was good to see him again, but I noticed straightaway how thin he had become. After many exchanges about each other's travels, he disappeared to have a cold shower and to put on clean clothes.

During the meal, he said he was getting fed up with Ramiaitui as there was nothing to occupy his time. There were plenty of IOC personnel on duty at all times; all he did was check the gear, and that could easily be done by a senior and experienced sepoy.

The living quarters were quite good; he had a sepoy to wait on him, but there was nothing to look forward to. All went smoothly.

He had received the signal that Captain Wade was on the trail making his way down, but during his way on the trail up here, Doug hadn't heard of or seen him; knowing Wade, I bet he had wandered off course when hearing of a village nearby – whether it was dangerous or not!

It was like old times. We were together again, and swapping tales – I believe he was glad to get away from the crowds. We had both have acquired a way of working alone; we organised and conducted our duties in conditions tending to this.

Before retiring, I did feel a bit shaky. I hoped it wasn't another dose of malaria. I took a couple of mepacrines in case.

I spent a restless night, perspiring and shivering like the devil. My charpoy was soaked in sweat. I'd have to stick it out till the dawn when Cyril could bring more tablets.

Through the slits in the shutters, the dawn light was arriving. Soon the sun would rise above the valley below. It was about five; I guessed someone would be stirring soon.

It was the Lushai cook who was first to arrive. I banged on the wall to attract his attention, and he was soon at my bedside, scurrying off to find fresh sheets, and returning to wipe the sweat off.

He then fetched Doug from the next room, and from then on I had all their attention in helping to lower my temperature.

14th July, 1944

One of the Lushai bearers with Doug seemed to know how to treat malaria. I drank a filthy fluid, and for a time I must have dozed off. I woke up feeling much stronger; the shivering had almost stopped.

This attack had taken the strength out of me. I must have lost quite a lot of weight and I felt quite feeble.

Outside, the weather was quite rough – high winds, with rain pouring down. I was thankful that we were in a strongly built bungalow – often it was a bamboo shelter.

As I lay there my thoughts were of home, and how Audrey was managing. I wondered what she would say if she could only see me in this stinking hole!

I intended to write a long letter and try to give a graphic description of our living conditions. I'd have to get a runner to take it down to Rangamati.

Doug came in to have a chat, during which it was decided that when my bout of fever abated, we'd try to contact Chittagong to get some clues as to what they had in mind regarding our movements.

He had spent all last night up in the post, glued to the receiver in the hope that a signal would be sent, but had no luck. In the meantime, the rain was still torrential. It was lashing down in buckets. The danger was that it would wash away parts of the trail, making it precarious in places, especially when it was narrow on the steep khud-side.

I felt stronger this morning; the shivering had eased off, but I was very weak. I staggered out to the verandah – perhaps a breath of fresh air would help. The Lushai cook brought out some rice and coffee; I should attempt to eat something.

Sitting here at the highest point of the ridge enabled me to gaze down on endless miles of hills and valleys stretching as far as the eye could see. At the same time I wondered what life was like in the jungle below.

I could faintly hear the beating of drums, and asked myself if any messages were bring transmitted from village to village, and if any Jap patrols had been located.

The rain abated a little, leaving the air humid and close. The sweat was pouring out over my skin. I hoped it wouldn't start up the dormant rashes.

Hearing a commotion at the entrance to the front of the bungalow, I looked out to see the chief of Howlong approaching, together with four ferocious looking guards, all carrying primitive weapons of defence.

From the expression on the chief's face, it was obvious it was a friendly visit. He came forward to meet me with his hand outstretched, a custom he had acquired from the hunting parties in the days of the Raj.

Using Cyril as the interpreter, the chief said he had just heard of my bout of malaria, and brought me a few bottles of medicine used by them to combat the high temperature. I explained to the chief that the worst was over and the high temperature had come down. The shivering had gone, so all I had to do now was build myself up again.

They stayed for quite a while, during which time the bobijee supplied bowls of rice and chapattis, washed down by ample rice beer measures. I thought he would never go, but at last he signalled that he would leave, after expressing his pleasure at our company.

After they had gone, we both agreed it was the most unusual company we'd ever had a meal with – the chief, wearing little else but feathers and ornaments, together with his ferocious looking headhunters.

We sat out on the verandah, drinking mugs of rice beer, discussing our future movements. We would have to contact Chittagong for further instructions; perhaps they had new personnel who had no knowledge of us.

The rain had eased off, leaving the air close and humid, and the mosquitoes were building up in large droves. We'd have to rub in plenty of cream before crawling under our nets; it would be a battle to get sleep.

Doug came into my room saying he couldn't sleep, and suggested making our way up to the post to try to contact Chittagong.

It was a mad idea, but at least we'd be moving away from stagnant air. Going up to the post might be much cooler, as we would be climbing all the time.

We arrived at the post to find a sepoy at the top of the ladder waving to us. I asked him how the devil he knew we were coming, and he said a native had seen us; we hadn't met a soul on the trail.

In the small observation hut, we were made welcome with coffee and chapattis, but found what news they had was very little. There was no signal for us – they were mostly undecipherable.

The dawn light was just rising above the forest below when we made our farewells to the two sepoys on duty. I think our visit helped to pass the night's duty.

By the time we had returned to our bungalow, I felt very shaky; the walk there and back had taken the energy out of me. I'd certainly have to build my strength up.

16th July, 1944

The bobijee had prepared a breakfast of fried eggs. I ate one and washed it down with a bowlful of the local beer. By the time Doug and I had spoken of further plans, we both felt it was time to lie down for a while.

Before resting, I had to remember to write to Mother; it would be her birthday on the sixth. I'd get a runner to take it down to base.

I decided to write to Mother then and there. If I left it till the morning there would be other jobs to do. It was nearly dawn by the time I had finished and could take a few hours' sleep.

I also wrote to Audrey, and had the usual things to say: how I missed her, and was wondering and dreaming of how she was coping; though I knew well that when the going was tough, she would battle on and come through.

I had to arrange for a runner as soon as possible in the morning to take the letters down to Lunglei – a distance of about thirty miles; it would cost me a few rupees.

The chief soon found a trustworthy native to take my letters down. While in conversation, he told me no word had been received of any Jap patrols in the area; the villages within twenty miles had kept their drums silent, so no signals had been sent.

I still had a touch of fever. I was very shaky, and feeling weak. I took some more mepacrine and hoped to get stronger; I wouldn't let it get me down. Doug came in to say he was going to take a walk down the trail. I said he had better take a sepoy and Sten gun, just in case any Jap patrols had gone off course; it was very difficult to detect then in the undergrowth.

I had Cyril Sirren and the bobijee, while many natives from the village would be up here like a shot in the event of any trouble. Making a bed on the floor of the verandah, I settled down to a few hours' rest.

I must have dozed off, for I woke up to find Doug bringing me a mug of tea, with Cyril jabbering away in his high-pitched voice. After drinking the tea, I realised that I felt much better. The shivering had stopped, and on standing up I felt less shaky.

Doug said he only went along the trail for about a mile, and the sun was beginning to sink beyond the Chin Hills below, so he decided to turn back.

We sat out on the verandah to have our meal of boiled eggs and rice. It was not bad when washed down with mugs of rice beer. This was very strong, and burned one's stomach on settling down.

At about midnight, Doug said he would go up to the observation post and enquire if any signals had been received. He took with him Cyril and a Sten gun. Off he went, saying he would see me in the morning, leaving me with the bobijee as guard.

After checking all shutters, I eventually crept under my mosquito net to attempt to sleep, and dropped off after hours listening to the mosquitoes trying to get through the mesh.

It must have been only a couple of hours before I woke up again with sweat pouring off me. My mattress was saturated, and I was feeling weak. I rolled off the charpoy in an attempt to stand up, with the result that I fell on the floor – that was where the bobijee found me later.

Before getting me back on to the charpoy, he had to put a dry blanket down, as my own was wet through with sweat. What a fool I felt!

17th July, 1944

When I woke up, I found the morning sun streaming through the slits in the bamboo walls, while all around could be heard the morning chorus of birds and creatures of the jungle far below.

Soon I saw the grinning face of the bobijee. He was holding a mug of coffee and saying, '*Tekai*, Sahib?' He asked how I felt and said I must rest.

Slipping off the charpoy, I still felt a bit wobbly, but I was determined to pull myself together.

Pulling on shorts and a shirt, I decided to walk round the bungalow. In doing so, I noticed how much the vegetation had shot up; in some places it had nearly covered the surrounding line of the path.

I was surprised to find a sepoy on duty. When I asked if it was necessary, he replied that his Sergeant had heard rumours that Jap patrols were in the area, given to them by villagers nearby.

Sure enough, as we were talking drums could be heard in the far distance, sending signals to be passed on up the trail. Who needed the wireless post?

I stayed chatting with him for about half an hour, then proceeded to resume my stroll. Noting how the vegetation had grown, I came across young banana plants showing fruit at its early stages; I'd have to mark their position.

On returning to my room, I lay on my charpoy for a while, though I must admit I felt much better. I felt less shaky, and had the idea of a mug of rum. On going through to the outside kitchen, I met Doug who said he was on his way to see me. When I mentioned a tot of rum, he was all for it.

Returning to the verandah, he said he had been down to the village and managed to purchase some eggs. I did notice he was beginning to look a bit thin in the face. On my asking if he felt all right, he did say he felt a bit weak. 'Come on,' I said, 'Let's have a few mugs of rum, it might make us both feel better.'

The rum certainly did the trick. We both passed out after a light lunch of rice and chapattis, and it was about five when the bobijee came into the room to enquire if I was all right. Anyway, I did feel much stronger – it must have been the rum!

Sitting out on the verandah watching the sun slowly sinking below the range of hills, we decided to have another session up in the post that night. There was a very clear sky, filled with stars. I could clearly see the plough, but that's as far as my astrology went.

Later, the bobijee announced that our evening meal was ready. It was a good thing Doug had obtained the eggs, they went down well with rice and chapattis. Afterwards, we both got ready to move up to the post.

By now the light was failing and it was nearly dark. I suggested taking Cyril, complete with Sten gun, just in case there might be an inquisitive native around, half cut on the local beer. Cyril was only too pleased to come along.

18th July, 1944

We followed the same routine, making ourselves as comfortable as possible on the bamboo stools with our headphones on. We attempted to decipher the codes of hundreds of signals being sent over the waves, hoping ours was one of them.

Then Doug waved his arm to attract our attention, and indicated he had intercepted and decoded a signal from Chittagong.

It appeared they had almost given us up. Tales of our movements had reached them from other units, but when they investigated these, they lost us again.

Now we were once again in contact, Doug sent a signal to the effect that we'd both had enough. We had established and serviced seven posts covering hundreds of miles – some deep in the jungle amongst various tribes, of whom a few were not so friendly, but were still headhunters and difficult to negotiate with.

The fact that we had a government bobijee with a fluent knowledge of all the local dialects in itself made our roving job less difficult.

The weather was still very depressing. We were still in the monsoon season, and the sudden heavy downpours of rain made the trails very slippery – not forgetting the leeches that slipped off the overhanging boughs.

I still felt weak, and Doug would have to build up his strength before any attempt at moving. It will be quite two to three days before we started to prepare for our departure.

Sitting out on the verandah, we both felt better in the knowledge that our roughing it in these hills was coming to an end. From all accounts, it appeared the Japs had no further plans to push this way. Natives filtering through the hills carried reports of heavy fighting around Kohima.

We decided not to tell our sepoys yet, but carry on as we were as long as possible. Knowledge of our departure might give the natives other ideas, like looting our stores.

During a lunch of eggs and rice, Doug said he would lie down for the afternoon, while I opted to go down into the village. This could be very interesting; those who had picked up a little English would tell me of anything that might be of help concerning the movements of any strangers – people working undercover for the Japs.

In the village, I wandered around between the bamboo huts, sometimes stopping to admire the handiwork of the women as they weaved the skeins of fibre picked from cotton trees that grew in profusion in the undergrowth. Their looms consisted of a bamboo structure secured to the bamboo wall of the basha. The operators worked away at producing the skirt worn by men and women called a *poen*.

Now they had got accustomed to seeing me around, their greetings were quite friendly. They often offered me tea, but on looking at the earthen mugs in which the liquid was held, I often made signs indicating I was full up!

Passing through the village, I decided to have a stroll towards the undergrowth, following a narrow worn trail which obviously hadn't been used lately. On approaching it, I was halted by a loud shout. I turned round, and a tall native came running towards me, waving his arms as though telling me to stop.

On reaching me, and pointing towards the undergrowth, it was obvious that he didn't want me to go in alone – he would come along too in case of danger.

After a lot of gesticulating and trying to understand each other, it became clear he was sent by the village to safeguard me on my mad ramble.

Leading the way, and looking back to make sure I was following, he made steady progress. As we followed the trail into the jungle, it became more dense, with the overhanging foliage closing in on the trail.

By now my guide was hacking away at the branches with a wicked looking dah or hunting knife, all the time chanting a village war song.

We had only covered about half a mile when I made signs that it was far enough. He immediately burst out laughing and clasped his hands together in agreement, making signs that it was getting too dense.

On emerging out of the undergrowth, we found quite a crowd from the village waiting – especially the children, who let out shrieks of laughter as they made a ring around us.

Turning to my guide, I shook his hand. At this he seemed a bit flustered and passed it off by grinning broadly from ear to ear. Cyril Sirren came to join the crowd, asking what all the fuss was. On being told, he informed me that the trail was noted for its treacherous snakes!

On returning to our bungalow, I found Doug still resting. On awakening, he learnt of my afternoon stroll and expressed his relief that I'd come through all right.

After a coffee, he suggested he would like to see this path I had taken, so through the village we went and on to the trail again. Seeing the overgrown entrance, he said I must have been mad.

We went a few feet along the trail, just to see the conditions, when we were confronted by three natives barring our way. I could see at once that they weren't of this village, as their dress was different. They just stood there staring.

Luckily, the stand-off was broken by the arrival of a crowd of our villagers, who quickly told the intruders to clear off, leaving us both feeling better.

Returning to our bungalow, we flopped down on our charpoys to rest for a while after our encounter.

During a meal of chapattis and rice, we discussed our plans to make our way down to the nearest point where we could join the Karnaphuli River, at a place where it would not be too dangerous.

20th July, 1944

We sat up late into the night making plans for the move and the packing of our belongings into strong crates. What to pack, and what to make into packs for the porter corps to carry would all take some time to sort out.

It was difficult for us to accept that after all our travels in these hills and our living amongst these primitive tribes – a life we'd both got accustomed to – would eventually become distant memories.

We'd have to allow about a month in which to reach Chittagong. The three hundred mile journey could only be made by negotiating with different native chiefs for help and guides; not to mention the fast-flowing Karnaphuli River. It would be most difficult steering our *kistis* and canoes in the strong current over underwater boulders, not to mention the sudden falls!

We flopped down on our charpoys in the early hours, both keenly anticipating our adventures to come. At least, we'd have new challenges to meet.

In the morning, the humidity lifted slowly. The air was much fresher, making movement easier. The monsoons were slowly abating; down in the valleys, life was awakening, witnessed by the chorus of animals and birds.

Over a breakfast of rice and hard biscuits, Doug and I planned our day. I would make my way down into the village to seek out the chief and inform him of our move. I didn't think he would be pleased, as he thought that our presence here kept the Japs away; when I told him the post would still be manned by nine Pathan sepoys, he'd feel much better.

Taking the Lushai cook as interpreter, I made my way down to the village, passing through the sprawling maze of bamboo huts. In most cases, the women would be sat at each entrance, working at crude bamboo weaving frames, and gave us a slight bow and a smile.

Approaching the large basha situated in the centre, I realised that we were expected. A small group of elders were standing on the verandah at the top of the entrance ladder, waiting for us to climb up.

On entering the main opening, I found the chief with his hand outstretched in greeting. He made signs for us to squat on the floor.

Using the cook as interpreter, I informed him of our future plans and said that in a few days' time we would be leaving. He shook his head, and we could see he was sorry. In the meantime, women came forward with bowls of rice beer, together with trays on which large chapattis were offered.

During our exchange regarding the matter of porters, he offered us six strong natives to act as guards and porters – men he could trust.

As we would be packing personal loads, they wouldn't be all that heavy. All the loads we arrived with consisted of equipment to put in place in the observation posts. The chief did say that no news of any Jap movements had been received from villages within a radius of twenty miles; he would keep in touch.

I spent about two hours at the chief's basha; he seemed to be more talkative now he realised we were going. I suppose our presence at the village gave him a sense of security.

On returning to the bungalow, I told Doug of my visit, and said that the chief would provide porters and help us in our move.

In a way I was a little sorry to leave. Though the conditions were very crude and basic, we had both become accustomed to the free and easy way of life – no clocks, no traffic, just rise at sunrise and rest at sunset.

Though disease was rampant, they seemed to get all the medicines they needed from plants and the bark of trees; I remembered the awful liquid I had to swallow when suffering with dysentery.

The jungle also provided all their fruit and vegetables – not to mention the tobacco plants. I had some drying on the roof; all I had to do was roll the leaf and bind it with fine bamboo twine.

Just outside the village, growing on the hillside, were sugar canes. I often used to see natives clambering up carrying loads of these, bent forward under the weight.

For meat, they hunted for wild boar, fowl, and even snakes and monkeys.

Down below there were herds of buffalo, but I didn't hear of any being killed; there was enough game up here to hunt.

Elephants, too, were to be seen moving about. They were smaller than the African type, but could be dangerous if provoked. In our travels, our guides used to lead us downwind, away from the herds. We'd often glance in their direction as we moved away, but so far they hadn't detected us.

We didn't get much done today, apart from the visit to the chief. We both had a rest before making an inventory of all our needs; there was a lot to list. We contacted the Pathan Sergeant informing him of our departure. He was surprised, and sorry that our friendship would be broken.

He promised that the posts would be well looked after by a constant nine man crew.

Looking round the bungalow, we saw there was only our personal belongings to pack away. All the odd pieces of furniture that the natives had made, such as the small tables and the stool, we would have to leave behind.

We both agreed that it was about time we made a move towards HQ in Chittagong. We both needed medical attention, especially Doug, who still complained of stomach pains, while I had touches of malaria. Doug was looking much thinner, and had a job to keep his food down.

We'd both had to rough it, and had eaten jungle vegetables raw, not knowing whether they were poisonous or not. If the natives ate them, why not us?

We decided to pay the post a visit after the evening meal and see if there was a signal for us; but at two in the morning, we gave up and returned to our bungalow.

22nd July, 1944

While we were having breakfast, a sepoy from the night duty at the post came down with a chit stating they had received a signal. In effect, it was to order Doug to return to Chittagong via Lunglei for hospital treatment. We had to make arrangements to have plenty of backing for the journey, and they would signal everyone to give him help.

The signal shook us – we were about to be parted. We talked all the morning about what precautions we should make. He would have to muster a small porter corps to reach Lunglei. From then on, the District Commissioner would make the arrangements for Doug to travel the three hundred miles via twisting trails and the fast-flowing Karnaphuli River.

The afternoon was spent in writing to Audrey and Mother. Doug would take the letters down to Chittagong on his journey – at least I'd know they would be delivered.

In the next few days we would have to have a meeting with the chief to ask him to detail three reliable porters for the journey. Doug would ask the DC on arrival for payment to the porters.

We at last collected all Doug's bits and pieces to make a small pile in his bedroom; we were not far out – three loads of about fifty pounds was our estimate.

Meanwhile, the air became very close. The sweat was running off us, while our friends the mosquitoes were forming packs, dive-bombing to enable a few to get a foothold on our skin.

We chatted away on different topics, but our parting was foremost in our thoughts: to have a fellow Brit to talk and argue with – and we often did that! – was a luxury.

Just before we started our evening meal, a runner arrived from Lunglei with mail and a note from the DC wishing us well, and asking when we'd meet again.

I wrote a short note to say Doug would probably leave here in a couple of days' time; we had organised porters and a guard. Would he do the same for the Lunglei–Demagri stint?

In my letter to Audrey, I told her that by the time my letter reached her, there would be a fifty-pound cheque waiting for collection at her bank; I thought it might help.

The war seemed to be going our way. On the grapevine, we'd had news that we were amassing a huge build-up, so perhaps there was something in the offing.

Doug and I packed all his small boxes of personal things, ready to be slung on the backs of the porters. We had done our best to limit the weight to fifty pounds each. He would be carrying a shoulder pack containing his bedroll and a few essential toiletries.

We learned that the chief had organised a farewell feast and booze-up in Doug's honour for his last night. We'd have to go and put up with the stink of all the cows and swine that made up the party.

We decided to take our Lushai cook with us. He would be able to translate. A little English was spoken, but it was when they jabbered away, at the same time staring a little ferociously at us, that we were worried. Perhaps they thought we'd make a nice meal!

On entering the chief's basha, we were shown to special spaces on either side of the chief, and sat cross-legged on the sagging floor.

Earthenware mugs of *Zophan* rice beer were brought to us by his women, and at the same time we were presented with a *poen* or coloured cotton skirt as a gift for our wives.

The basha was quite large – about thirty feet in circumference, built with bamboo tree trunks with interwoven branches, making it as near waterproof as possible. Where the poles were lashed together at the top, a five foot hole was left to allow the smoke from the fire on the middle of the floor to escape.

There we were, trying to express our appreciation at the feast in our honour, enjoying the meal: chicken curry, wild boar roast, and some items we would rather not attempt, all washed down with rice beer.

During the meal, the chief – conversing with our cook – had his attention on us all the time. I wondered what they were saying; but then our Lushai was very faithful. He would protect the sahibs who have the money.

At the other end of the basha, a small party began to chant to music supplied by some home-made bamboo instrument. Some of them were twirling round and round, and the thin bamboo floor sagged dangerously under the weight.

Our Lushai made it plain to us that the chief was very sad that we were going. As I said before, he regarded us as a guard against raids from other tribes.

Soon the party was well away. The din from the screeching instruments combined with the babble of high-pitched tongues. Doug and I were well in and accepted by all, though some of the glances in our direction were a bit off.

All the time we both were trying to understand the gestures and languages. Our Lushai was interpreting as fast as he could; it all became very confusing, as we were knocking back the rice beer.

It must have been past midnight when we decided to make a move back to our bungalow. Of course, the chief made signs that there was plenty of time, but after many handshakes and bowing, we eventually left.

He insisted on giving orders to two stalwart natives to see us home safely – he maintained that there might be one or two villagers roaming about full of rice beer who might revert to their old headhunting ways.

It was a relief to reach our bungalow. It was pitch-dark, all around beasts of the night could be heard grunting and squealing. With a cheery wave, our guards disappeared into the undergrowth.

24th July, 1944

Next morning my head throbbed like hell. Standing up made it worse; it was only after a couple of coffees that it became easier. We must have drunk far too much rice beer.

I could hear Doug moving about and hoped his stomach was all right. He said this was the morning in which to move off. On entering his room, I found him quite cheerful. I asked how he felt, and his answer was that he was perfect. When I told him how I felt, he said I was knocking it back last night.

He said he might as well make a move. All his kit was ready and his porters were outside. The morning mist had lifted, leaving a clear sky with a slight breeze – just the job.

It was about eight when he was ready to leave, making for Rangamati, a distance of about ten miles. We both hoped it would go well, and no obstacles would be met, like inquisitive natives, who liked to ask questions about who you were; but then, the Lushai porters would see them off.

After shaking hands and wishing each other all the best, we both made a vow to meet again. The memory of the bond made in our travels can't be forgotten.

I stood on the verandah watching as the small party made its way down the trail slowly towards the village. I watched intently as they emerged out in the clearing, leaving the village behind, making their way towards deep undergrowth.

Before entering, they stopped to wave, and I acknowledged by waving a towel; little did I realise it was to be the last time we had contact with each other for many weeks.

On entering the bungalow, the sudden emptiness struck me. Then the faithful Lushai came in with some coffee, a huge grin covering his face, as much as to say, I'll look after you.

After coffee, I walked through the village and found my way up to the observation post to check that all was well, and collect any messages.

It was evident that my approach had been seen, for as I drew near the ladder leading up to the hut, two sepoys were waiting outside waving a welcome.

On entering the post, I found a sepoy on duty busily concentrating on deciphering signals, determined not to miss ours when it was sent.

In the corner, a sepoy was occupied, preparing chapattis over a camp stove, while the third was showing me round the small room. The whole structure of the hut was very sound. Thick bamboo logs were the main support, and it was wedged between the tree trunk and the main boughs, camouflaged by large leaves.

In a small space, all the equipment that was required was fitted in such a way as to make it easily operational. The team were helped by having a lookout from which the valleys and jungles could be seen stretching far in the distance. The posts holding the installations were well hidden from below by the surrounding trees.

24th July, 1944

I checked the jenny and all the installations, and found them all in good condition. The Pathan Sergeant had his sepoys well under control; they seemed to be a happy unit.

When on duty, I asked them to signal that Doug was on his way down, and asked for confirmation of his safety as soon as possible.

I stayed with them till past midnight, and was given a meal of chapattis and rice together with a mug of rum. During the meal, questions were being asked about England, London, and other cities.

During the conversation, I did think what a ludicrous situation we were in – sitting here in a hut built high up in the fork of a tree; while in this small space we had all the modern equipment needed to communicate with personnel in almost every corner of the world.

At the first light of dawn I was roused out of being half asleep by a sepoy offering a mug of coffee, with the usual grin and, 'Morning, Sahib!'

Looking out through the small gap in the bamboo wall, I gazed down far below over the mist covered valley, to the range of hills that form the Chin and Naga chains, wondering who was down there, and if any Jap patrols had got this far.

Meanwhile, the sepoys had cooked a breakfast for me of fried eggs and rice, cheerfully hoping I would like it. After the meal, I thanked them for their help and looking after me. After shaking hands and waving farewell, I made my way down the hill towards the village.

The village was wide awake; women were busy sweeping out their huts, or sitting down at their looms to start another day's work making cloth to form garments. There were few men about; they would have formed hunting parties and would probably be away till sunset.

As I passed through, most of the women made signs of welcome, while some just glared. I didn't like to think of their antipathy – I didn't know how to approach them.

Arriving back at the bungalow, I found the cook had prepared a chicken curry and huge chapattis. I had to eat some; I daren't tell him I had just eaten the same at dawn.

All the time, I was wondering how far Doug had got on the trail, knowing he wasn't all that strong. However, his porters were aware of his condition, and would stand by him in all emergencies.

Sitting out on the verandah, it was obvious to me that a storm was building. The air was heavy and humid, dark clouds were forming, and as the monsoon season was still with us, sudden bursts of torrential rain were to be expected.

The mosquitoes were beginning to form into packs, hovering about, and waiting to swoop down on any uncovered flesh.

25th July, 1944

I had just begun to drop off to sleep, when the heavens opened. There was lightning and thunder, together with torrential rain making a terrible din on the corrugated tin roof of the lean-to.

As sleep was impossible, I sat out on the verandah watching the storm as it opened up above. Sheets of lightning lit up the whole valley below, with the loud thunder claps shaking the earth, making the bungalow walls tremble with the strain.

Luckily, the building was situated amongst sturdy trees, which served as a strong shield against the high winds. At times these were quite frightening.

Sitting out there, my thoughts were of Doug. I hoped he had reached shelter; his porters would have seen the storm coming. They would have experienced these conditions many times before and made for the nearest village.

The storm was still raging – forked lightning illuminated the jungle far below, while the heavy rain was surely causing many bamboo huts and trails to be washed away.

Returning to my bedroom, I lay on my charpoy under the mosquito net, but sleep was impossible. What with the heat and the mosquitoes trying to penetrate the mesh, together with their consistent droning in flight, I prayed for the dawn to break.

I must have dozed off, for the next thing I heard was the voice of the cook saying, 'Coffee, Sahib.' He told me of all the damage the storm had done. Many huts had been swept away, together with most of the main trails; it would take many days to clear the debris.

Added to all this, snakes were everywhere, slithering over the ground, having been dislodged from their lairs under the bracken or leaves.

The torrential rain was still pouring down. I looked out to see what damage had been done. The lean-to kitchen had disappeared and its corrugated roof could be seen wedged between the branches of a tree about thirty yards away; there was no sign of all the utensils.

After a breakfast of eggs and rice, I ventured out to see what further damage had been done. It was obvious that a lot of work lay ahead. New tracks had to be made between what was left of the bamboo huts.

The natives were standing about in groups, looking round and trying to decide where to start. It was all rather pathetic; still, there was plenty of bamboo and wood all around, so it wouldn't take them long to rebuild the village.

Returning to the bungalow, I walked around the verandah to check for any roof leaks. After a thorough search, I found no water had come through. When these government dāk lodges were built, money and labour was plentiful.

We had to do all the cooking in Doug's room, until the lean-to kitchen was rebuilt.

26th July, 1944

My main concern was the post. Had it stood up to the force of the gale? After all, it would receive the wind's full force, being built at the highest point without much protection.

After a light snack, I made my way through the debris, picking out the trail leading up to the observation post and climbing over fallen trees uprooted by the force of the storm.

At last the post could be seen, with the small hut still intact wedged high up in the fork. It must have been well constructed to have withheld such an onslaught. As I approached, two Pathan sepoys could be seen waving, and shouting a welcome. I climbed the ladder to find two more sepoys on duty at the transmitters, trying to connect with Chittagong.

They were very pleased to see me and asked all sorts of questions, at the same time preparing chapattis and rice. In the middle of all this, one of the sepoys on duty reported that he had received a signal to the effect that a Captain Sanford was on his way up here with a small platoon of Gurkhas.

On returning to the bungalow, and with the aid of the cook, we cleaned up Doug's old room and cleared out all the cooking utensils. We'd have to repair the lean-to this afternoon. The cook hurried down to the village to recruit natives able to do the job, and within an hour they were busy erecting the small kitchen.

While the work was carried out, I had a sepoy scanning the jungle trail below to sight the party's approach. It was about two o'clock when the lookout shouted that the party could be seen making their way along the trail, about two miles distant.

At last he arrived. He was bent forward and on his knees, but he still managed a smile and handshake, before flopping down in a chair on the verandah. His small platoon of Gurkhas would be taken care of by the Sergeant in charge at the basha at the base of the observation tower. I must say the morale shown by the Gurkhas was a credit to them. Their concern was for their Captain. Only when he was attended to did they leave for their quarters.

After a meal, when the Captain had retired to his room, I made my way to a small clearing at the rear of our bungalow. Here the Gurkhas had already erected two bell tents, with fires below tripods holding the cooking pots.

On my approach they all stood up, but when I waved my hand to explain it wasn't my right, smiles broke out and many hands were outstretched.

The Sergeant in charge stated that they had spent a few weeks at Demagri and had been briefed about our mission up here. Tomorrow I would take him up to the post.

27th July, 1944

Starting from Chittagong, Captain Sanford and his small patrol had braved the swirling Karnaphuli, with all its dangerous falls, sometimes having to unload and carry boats and stores over treacherous ground to bypass them.

The journey had been made much worse by the arrival of the monsoon. At times they took shelter in friendly villages, or, like us, were fortunate enough to find a dāk bungalow.

During breakfast, he discussed sending a signal affirming HQ of his safety and whereabouts. Would I accompany him and introduce him to the Sergeant in charge? As we made our way on the trail up to the post, he expressed his surprise at my being up here on my own.

During our conversation, I told him that up till a few days ago I had a companion called Doug, a wireless operator, conversant with all aspects of decoding and reading signals. Unfortunately he had been struck down with a stomach bug. He had been suffering for many months, and was now making a slow return to base.

Now I had a small contingent of IOC sepoys, led by a sergeant. Previously, Doug and I had been responsible at all hours of the day.

The Captain seemed quite interested as I recalled our living rough at different tribal villages, especially as most had been, and some still were, headhunters.

Our main asset was the government bobijee assigned to us, a most loyal chap speaking many languages, who had been with us up to a few weeks ago, but had to return to his village to attend to family matters. He had promised to come back to us as soon as possible.

In the meantime, we had recruited the present cook as a replacement. He was quite good but not as likeable.

Payment was made by a chit made out by me for them to present for payment at the District Commissioner's office at Lunglei, at a distance by jungle trail of about twenty miles.

The more I detailed our life up here to the Captain, the clearer it became that he was most interested. He said he would certainly report about us to HQ on his return.

On his arrival up here, he had huge blisters on his feet; after treatment with the native medicine, they all healed up. He wanted to know what it was, and I told him it was the juice from the bark of a certain tree.

He too was a liaison officer, sent up here to find and map out routes and main trails that might be of use in an emergency. However, he believed the Japs had been halted around Kohima.

I told him that Doug and I were sent up here with wireless transmitters and equipment to set up observation posts along the Lushai and Chin Hills close to the Burmese border. The Indian Observer Corps were to maintain them.

The sepoys on duty at the post managed to contact Chittagong with the news that Captain Sanford would like further instructions and would await them here.

Before returning to our bungalow, we called in on the Gurkhas at their camp, to find they had it all under control – two bell tents, with cooking arrangements between. While the Captain inspected the camp, I had a chat with the Sergeant, a very polite chap. He obviously didn't know how to address me, but once we'd shaken hands, he became more at ease.

We stayed at the Gurkhas' camp for quite a while, during which time we were given tea and portions of their home-made cake. It tasted like hard shortcake, but it went down – after much chewing!

On our return to our bungalow, we found the cook had prepared a huge curry of wild boar. It appeared that while we were away the chief had sent this meat up as a gesture to Captain Sanford.

It certainly tasted all right, helped by a mug or two of the local rice beer. We sat out on the verandah with the oil lamp set low so as not to attract the mosquitoes; while at the same time we could enjoy the perfect stillness and the cool of the evening.

During our conversation, Sanford said he would like to push on towards Ijal at some time in the morning; he had briefed his Sergeant to be ready. At the same time, he expressed his gratitude for my help, especially regarding the routes of main trails connecting villages.

He was still amazed to find an RAF technician in such a godforsaken hole, living in these conditions, amongst barbaric tribes who still practised headhunting and indulged in warlike chanting around their fires late into the night.

It was past midnight when we finally retired. He remarked that this meeting would be in his memory for all time, and he would certainly report his experiences with me to his HQ on his return.

28th July, 1944

The following morning I had a word with the Gurkha Sergeant and asked him to arrange to have a strong light stretcher made for the Captain, but not to let him see it. I felt his feet might give trouble at some time on the way.

It was during Sanford's final preparations for starting that a runner arrived from Lunglei with news that Jap patrols were heading this way. I immediately contacted the chief at his basha with the news, and asked him to spread the news by way of drums from village to village covering the northern Lushai range.

Within an hour, we could hear drums making their warning at far distant villages. I wondered if the Japs were aware that they were being stalked at every move by invisible headhunters, who hid in the undergrowth, and knew all the hidden trails.

Sanford was amazed at the tribal telegraph, and was thankful he hadn't started. He had to tell his platoon of the delay. Of course, the Gurkhas would have looked forward to an encounter with the Japs. Perhaps they would meet them later.

Last night, Sanford and I ventured up to the post to warn the Sergeant of the Jap patrol. Perhaps they wouldn't come up this far; but we asked him to contact Chittagong to delay the food drop till it was all clear.

I had intended to arrange for natives to make a clearing for the drop, but that would have to wait till the Japs left the area.

Later this morning, native scouts returned to the village with the good news that the Jap patrol had turned back. Obviously they'd found empty villages, with not a soul to be seen. Little did they know that every move they made was being watched.

As the danger had lifted, Sanford said that he would make a start. His Gurkha platoon was packed and ready, and he was taking one of the native scouts to go ahead for the first few miles on the trail to Ijal. They would be moving away from where the Japs were located, unless of course other Japs were patrolling north of us.

I went down to the clearing which had been the Gurkhas' camp to find them all ready to move off. The camp had been cleaned up, and not a scrap of paper or refuse could be seen. The patrol was ready and waiting for Sanford to take control.

I shook hands with the Sergeant and we both expressed enjoyment at our meeting. Perhaps – who knows? – we would have the pleasure of meeting up again.

I stood on the verandah looking down on Sanford's small troop as they assembled prior to starting off. As they got into line, they all turned to wave, before covering the short distance to the undergrowth.

About five hundred yards farther along the trail, I could see another clearing; watching intently, I had to wait quite a long time before they emerged into view. They were too far away to see well by now; also, mist had started to form.

I waved, and wondered if they could see me up here; the mist was obscuring our vision by now. As I looked, I was quite sure they waved; then they were out of sight. I shall never forget our brief but close friendship.

I often wondered how Doug was. I hadn't heard a word from him, or received any signals. I hoped he had got down to Chittagong safely: no news is good news, they say.

I decided to remain here for a few days, in case the post received a signal concerning my movements. Maybe they had forgotten of my existence; in any case, the IOC Sergeant would inform me at once.

It all seemed very quiet around me now. I had only the Lushai cook as company – he was a good fellow, truly loyal; he was never far away.

I walked round the bungalow on the rickety bamboo verandah, carefully avoiding the weaker patches. My intention was to see if there were any broken places which an intruder could squeeze through. Now that I was on my own, it might give ideas to some of the natives; I would check all round.

31st July, 1944

I stopped to look down into the jungle far away – flickering lights from village fires could be seen, stretching far into the distance. I wondered if any Jap patrols were down there.

All the shutters seemed secure, so I decided to turn in. The cook met me to say he had cooked a chicken curry – was there anything else? He seemed to appreciate my loneliness, for he said he would sleep on the verandah.

I crawled under my mosquito net at about midnight. As the air was rather humid, there were plenty of mosquitoes. I dropped off at last, listening to them trying to penetrate the net.

I had a fairly good night, waking up a few times to listen to different calls of the night prowlers. When dawn arrived, it came with a clear sky. It was still humid, which warned me not to overdo any work. I was soon perspiring, and decided to have a cold wash down in our little lean-to at the rear.

During the morning a runner arrived from Rangamati with the news that a Captain Searl was on his way up here, and would be about six miles away at this moment.

I immediately sent the runner back on the trail to inform Captain Searl that he would have to bypass me, as I was out of food and living on jungle produce. It would be impossible to feed his platoon of Punjabis. I hoped he received my reply in time to take another trail.

I had to make my way up to the post to ask the Sergeant to send a signal to Chittagong to delay the ration drop, as Jap patrols were still in the vicinity. I hoped contact could be made.

On my way up, I could hear distinctly the village drums relaying the warning farther up the trail. The Japs would put it down to local festivities; little did they realise their every move was monitored.

Arriving at the post, I was greeted with many expressions of welcome. They asked me how I was managing on my own, at the same time offering coffee and a chapatti.

It was about midnight when the sepoy on duty contacted Chittagong and was able to get my signal off – 'Message received, will go off the air and will try to contact tomorrow.'

Walking back to the bungalow at this time of night could be a bit scary, and it was a great relief when the Sergeant detailed two sepoys to see me safely back to the bungalow.

The faithful cook was still up, sitting out on the verandah waiting for me. When I said he should be in bed, he just grinned, displaying all his broken teeth, and said he was glad I was back. A meal of eggs and rice was being kept hot – would I like it now? I couldn't refuse.

1st August, 1944

I had quite a good night. I must have been tired, for I couldn't remember crawling under my mosquito net. It had been a long time since I'd dropped off straightaway.

During breakfast on the verandah, with the sun rising above the range of hills below, the morning cries of all the wildlife making a din to welcome the day, I felt it all seemed so far away from the overpopulation and traffic congestion of my homeland; but I guessed that living up here would become monotonous too – I would crave for company.

I decided to have the IOC Sergeant signal my intentions to pack up and make my way down to Chittagong. There was nothing up here for me now; the posts were all well maintained, permitting full observation over thousands of miles and giving cover and stability to all villages.

I must say we couldn't have carried out our signal operation without the co-operation of all the various villages, who gave us all the different ways and means in communications.

During the morning, I decided to return to the post and instruct them to signal my intentions; perhaps they had forgotten my existence. My WOU might have been moved.

The Sergeant promised to contact Chittagong as soon as possible; he'd let me know if any contact was made. Arriving back at the bungalow, I decided to go down into the village to inform the chief of my plans about leaving, taking my Lushai cook as interpreter.

When I got to the chief's basha, it was obvious that they had sighted my approach, for on the verandah stood a few warriors at the opening of the main shutter.

After climbing the rickety ladder, we were ushered into the main building, to be greeted by the chief sitting on the rather large bamboo chair which acted as his throne.

Waving his arm for us to be seated, he indicated to his women to bring forward rice and chapattis, together with earthenware mugs of rice beer. It was evident he was pleased to meet me again, but when my Lushai cook explained that I would be leaving in a few days time, by the look on his face he seemed sad at my departure.

He regarded my presence at the post as being a safeguard against the Japs; but when it was explained that there would be a platoon of IOC there permanently, his relief was clearly shown.

I promised that before my departure I would pay the chief a final visit; after all, he had been a great help in many ways.

In the meantime, he promised to have a couple of trusted natives on standby to accompany me and my Lushai bobijee for the first few miles on the trail.

By the time I had to leave, what with the rice beer and chapattis, I felt quite squiffy. Fortunately, my Lushai cook was there to see me back all right.

In my signal of intentions sent to HQ I had said as I was on my way down. The plan to make the provisions drop would have to be put off, and I hoped the cancellation would be acted upon in time, as I'd had no signal confirming a drop.

The time now was past midnight, and I felt I'd had quite a good day, organising most of my plans for my push down the trail. The cook put his head round the corner to announce that he had prepared a chapatti, so I'd have to eat it, just to please him; though I would suffer in trying to get off to sleep.

2nd August, 1944

Much to my surprise, I had quite a good night, and woke up with natives chattering just outside my room. Their high-pitched voices making a noisy babble as they all put their point over, mingled with shrieks of laughter; it was a nice start to the day's work.

After a breakfast of rice and eggs, I resumed my search of each room for any articles I might have missed. I found a nice pair of sandals; Doug must have left them behind. As mine had worn out a long time ago, they would come in very useful.

Lately, I hadn't worn anything on my feet, and the soles had become quite tough as long as I walked on beaten trails with no broken stubble, I was able to move about freely.

I decided to make my final departure in two or three days time; it would give me plenty of time to check around for pieces of equipment I might have left. The IOC Sergeant gave orders to his sepoys to help in any way possible.

In the meantime, the chief posted scouts around the perimeter of the neighbouring villages, covering a radius of about twenty miles. From there, scouts in settlements miles away would be on the alert. I couldn't see how the Japs could possibly infiltrate without being spotted.

After a light lunch I wandered down into the village, making my way between bamboo shelters that were crudely constructed, but at the same time solidly built to withstand the monsoon storms.

No men were to be seen; they would be out in the jungle on hunting parties. The women were squatting at the entrance to their huts, working at the looms making the cotton *poens*.

Children came running to me, laughing while I tried to find something to say. The only word of greeting I'd learnt so far was '*Collome*' – which was generally accepted.

Some of the children, during their constant jabbering, were trying to show me models of animals they had carved out of bamboo; all were neatly done.

After being escorted back to my bungalow by all the children, I watched the sun sinking down over the forest down below. Daylight was fading fast as I checked all the shutters and doors before settling down for the evening.

My bobijee prepared a nice curry, after which I sat out on the verandah and gazed down at the flickering lights from village fires covering miles across various boundaries. It must have been past midnight when I decided to crawl on to my charpoy; my friends the mosquitoes were well in attendance, but not one penetrated my net.

3rd August, 1944

The usual crescendo from all the inhabitants of the jungle woke me at dawn. Looking through the shutters, I could see the sun rising above the jungle far below; soon it would clear the morning mist and bring another scorching day.

After a light breakfast, I decided to visit the chief again just to make sure he had organised my porters. On arrival at his basha, I found him chairing a small gathering of elders. When he saw me, he left them to greet me, ordering one of the women to bring us some coffee.

We sat on bamboo stools. He said he was glad I had come, as he had organised a farewell party in my honour for the evening. I could bring my Lushai cook as interpreter – there would be dancing round the bonfire, and plenty to eat and drink. He had asked the Sergeant and sepoys to attend as well.

Leaving the chief's basha, I made my way up the trail towards the observation post to enquire if any messages for me had been received, and to say I hoped the Sergeant would be able to turn up for the farewell party tonight.

They must have seen me approaching, for when I had reached the post, they had coffee ready. But there were no messages; in fact, no signals had been sent either way.

The Sergeant said he was surprised at the news of my departure. The feeling that he had a friend in whom he could confide, always helped to solve some problems. He said if there was anything he could do to help, let him know. He would detail an escort for part of my journey.

As no signals had been received regarding my departure, I guessed they thought that by now I would have organised my own move. Before leaving the post, I strolled around the small compound, imprinting in my mind the surroundings so that in future years they would still be there.

After having their assurance that they'd be at the party tonight, I made my way back to the bungalow, to find the bobijee had prepared a chicken curry.

He said the news that I was moving on had spread through the village. The fact that many natives had grown accustomed to seeing me about the place would make my absence seem strange.

4th August, 1944

Last evening I strolled down to the village to see how the event was progressing, to find a huge fire had been built in the centre. A circular bench seat had been erected to allow the dignitaries to have the best view of the proceedings.

In my conversations with the chief earlier, he said the territory had been well searched for any Japs. The fire would be taken as any ordinary village fire; in any case, there would be his scouts stationed at various points covering many miles.

The Havildar, Ali Hassan, arrived together with two sepoys, and were soon mingling in with the natives, showing their appreciation at being invited – though I expect the sepoys would be all for the girls and rice beer.

Soon the party was in full swing. Villagers were singing and chanting while dancing a circle around the fire – what a sight they were to behold, their scantily clad bodies covered in sweat, as they bent forward and linked together to form the circle.

Children too were having their own celebrations, forming small parties in which they danced round and round, laughing and shrieking in their excitement, while a short distance away their mothers were keeping an eye on them.

The local *Zophan* beer was being passed round for all to drink, together with bowls of rice and chapattis; there was plenty to eat and drink. I noticed some of the young braves were getting a bit boisterous, and were watched over by their elders, hoping to keep them in check.

As the night wore on, the dancing and chanting became more frenzied. The ring of dancers were prancing more wildly, throwing their arms high in the air, with their voices droning out the same monotonous tune over and over again – it's still in my memory now.

I quite enjoyed it all, squatting by the side of the chief's chair, puffing at my home-made cigar. This was a tobacco leaf picked from the jungle, bound with bamboo twine; it was all very pleasant.

Towards midnight I began to feel quite squiffy. I had drunk quite a lot of the rice beer and I noticed the chief glanced in my direction with a wave of his hand. Perhaps I ought to make a move back to the bungalow.

By now the party had become less crowded. Most of the children had been packed off to bed, and those left were mainly young warriors, prancing around and showing off their prowess in various activities.

After bidding goodnight to the chief, and promising to see him before I finally went, I was about to start back when the IOC Sergeant detailed two sepoys to escort me back to the bungalow, saying there might be a few natives still high on drink plying their old trade as headhunters.

As it was easily a ten minute walk to my bungalow, I was very grateful for the escort.

Before crawling under my mosquito net to stretch out on my charpoy, I sat out on the verandah to take in my last sight of the wonderful show of lights flickering from villages stretching over hundred of miles; it will be imprinted in my memory for ever.

I awoke early. It must have been about five, for as I gazed through the gaps in the bamboo walls, I could see the sun rising to send shafts of light through the jungle treetops. It all looked so peaceful.

As I got out of my charpoy, my head started to throb like the devil – the result of my drinking too much rice beer. I'd have to take things easy this morning; perhaps a dose of cold water under the tap would help.

The bobijee put his head round the door to enquire how I felt and tell me breakfast was ready – would I eat any? After dipping my head in a bucket of water, the throbbing seemed to ease off, allowing me to have coffee and hard biscuits.

All my packing for the move was done. The bobijee had stacked the different sized rolls against the wall of the bungalow all ready for the porters. It would be about an hour before we started off.

As I promised, I went down to the village to say farewell to the chief. I approached his basha and found him sitting out on the verandah in the company of others. On seeing me he came to meet me, extending his hand in friendship, using the greeting he had acquired from the days of the British Raj.

Making signs for me to wait awhile, he entered his basha and returned holding a bamboo walking stick. It had a nicely shaped handle and was just the right height. Grinning from ear to ear, he duly presented it to me.

Smiling, and waving in different ways, we finally parted. I looked back as I made my way up the trail and he still stood there waiting until I moved out of sight, as he made his last farewell wave.

On my walk back to the bungalow, I noted different places of interest that will always be imprinted in my memory. From the trail, one could gaze down on the jungle stretching as far as one could see, giving cover to the many villages of different tribes.

Arriving at the bungalow, I found my three porters sitting on their haunches beside various loads all packed and ready for the journey.

The Lushai bobijee insisted that I gave the bungalow a check over. He then locked all doors, saying he would keep the key and await instructions from Lunglei.

It was about eleven when I had finally checked out and said farewell to a blissful spell amongst a people who looked ferocious, but in close contact proved most friendly and trustworthy. I knew that at all times they had safeguarded every walkabout I made.

6th August 1944

About a mile from the village, at a branch in the trail, I met my friend the IOC Sergeant together with two sepoys, both kitted out in full. They carried rifles, and had wicked looking kukris hanging at their sides.

I thanked him for the escort, and said I hoped we'd meet again in the near future. Then we shook hands, before making our way along different trails.

One of the sepoys was leading, together with two porters. I and the bobijee went in the centre, and the remaining porter and sepoy brought up the rear. As the trail was quite narrow, it was obvious that we had to move in single file.

The main village we were heading for was Ramiaitui, approximately twenty-five miles away. It would mean camping along the trail, or perhaps in a friendly village.

As we made our way along the trail, overhead in the treetops packs of rhesus monkeys were screaming and chattering in defiance at us, not to mention the fact that anyone in the vicinity would know of our position. I was hoping no Jap patrols had come down this far.

In the distance drums could be heard, transmitting any news that might be useful. No doubt they had us closely watched; we didn't see any scouts, but they were there, darting from cover to cover and impossible to detect.

By now the sun was directly overhead and perspiration was pouring off our bodies. We would very soon have to find a clearing to rest; we were all getting a little unsteady, stumbling, and cursing the uneven trail. Finally we found a clearing that would require some work to give us room for a fire and rest space.

Soon we got organised. The porters cleared the space and had a fire going, with the rice pots fixed on tripods above. Meanwhile, they sang and laughed as they worked.

The two sepoys busied themselves making a clearing in the bracken to provide spaces for us to rest. In no time we were all sitting round the fire enjoying chapattis and rice.

The Lushai said there was a village about three miles farther on, so after our meal we soon had the camp cleared of any signs of habitation. The ground was covered over with dead branches to disguise our short stop, and we got ready to push on.

I must say I was glad for the rest. My feet had become very sore, with painful blisters. As I started off again, I could hardly stand, but after a while the pain eased and became bearable.

With the two sepoys leading, we steadily pushed on. Our escort of monkeys still chattered away high up in the treetops. Now and again, one of them would dare to dash screaming towards us in defiance, then sheer off chattering abuse.

Making our way steadily along the trail, we were all in good spirits. The rest had helped; now we had to try to reach the village before dusk.

Suddenly, one of the porters held his arm up for us to stop, at the same time indicating and making signs that someone was approaching. Sure enough, two tall natives came walking towards us, adorned in the usual way by having their ears and noses and lips pierced to display large ornaments.

They wore little clothing, just an animal skin to cover their loins. Round their waists were thick leather bands to carry knives, and a pouch in which arrows were kept, while a large bow was slung over their shoulders.

They stood still as we got nearer. Their eyes were glued to our sepoys holding the Sten guns. Both were very wary about the next move. They were magnificent warriors – both well over six feet tall.

It was our Lushai bobijee who made the first move, going up to them with hand held high and speaking in the local language, and after a while the tension became much less. They even were showing smiles all round, while glancing in our direction and looking less ferocious.

In a short time, they resumed their approach towards us. All the time their eyes were fixed on the two sepoys and Sten guns. Passing them without incident, they came to where I was standing. Both clasped their hands, bowed forward in a salute and moved on. I dread to think what would have happened if I'd been alone.

In their chat with the Lushai, they said that at no time had they heard of any Jap patrols in the district. In their hunt for food they invariably left the main trail for the dense undergrowth.

As we moved along the trail, our porters were chanting a monotonous tune, repeating the same notes over and over again – mainly to keep large animals away and to keep their morale up.

It must have been after at least two hours at a steady pace that we decided to look for a suitable clearing for coffee and a rest. Then, rounding the next bend, we could see a cluster of huts on the hillside not far away on the next ridge.

Our trail now was leading us down to the valley below. From there we'd have to climb to the village we had sighted, hoping it was a friendly one.

On reaching the outskirts of the village, we found the whole place deserted. There wasn't a native in sight. The only creatures making their presence known were a school of monkeys, gibbering and making horrible guttural sounds as they sprang from branch to branch.

My bobijee stood in the centre of the village and shouted out loud that he wanted to speak to someone. Eventually, a tall native emerged from the main building.

At the same time, heads appeared from behind shutters, eyes bulging with curiosity. It was only when the two in the centre began to laugh and shake hands that the village became alive. The children were first; they came running to us dancing circles around, obviously excited at the sight of strangers.

Very soon we were surrounded by various families all gawking at us. I would say they hadn't seen a white man since the old elephant hunts of the Raj.

Our bobijee was kept busy explaining to them who we were – that we were friends and that we were here to stop them being overrun by the Japs.

Eventually, the tension eased and natives came nearer. Some began to speak to us in their dialect, at the same time giggling at our efforts, and hoping we understood; but I'm afraid we couldn't pick out a single Urdu word.

Our bobijee seemed to get on very well with them, which was very fortunate. We were very grateful to have such a talented companion. He negotiated for a decent hut in which we could spend the night. In the meantime, he asked if I would like to meet the chief.

His basha was built in the centre. It was larger than the others, complete with the usual balcony or verandah supported by sturdy tree trunks.

As we approached, it was evident we were expected, for a small party of dignitaries was assembled at the main entrance on the verandah. In front sat a rather stout figure, adorned in a lion's skin, complete with feathers from various wild birds, and bangles of ivory hanging from his nose, ears and lips.

As we got nearer, one of the chief's party came forward to meet us, at the same time making signs and speaking some sort of lingo. Stepping forward our bobijee replied and explained our mission.

Waving to us to sit down, the chief ordered earthenware mugs to be brought forward containing the local rice beer. At least this loosened their tongues, for soon our bobijee was finding it difficult to answer all the questions. He told me that while we were talking to the chief, a hut was being prepared for us.

Our bobijee then asked if we would have a meal with the chief? 'Very glad to,' I said. Soon we were squatting down on the bamboo floor, while women arranged places for the cooking pots.

The interior of the main room in which we were sitting was similar to others I had visited. There was a cone shaped roof with a hole in top to let out the smoke, while around the walls, on ledges, shrunken heads were displayed – trophies of past headhunter wars.

The time passed quickly, and after the meal, we were shown to our hut. It was quite a large basha with plenty of room; charpoys had been placed at different angles. There would be five of us, while the porters bedded down in the open.

As the porters were sleeping outside, we felt quite safe, and soon settled down.

9th August, 1944

I had a disturbing night, what with the awful stench and the rats squeaking as they scampered around. I don't know if the other chaps heard them, but I was glad when the dawn slowly came.

The two sepoys were up and moving about, both chattering and laughing. The bobijee had made a small fire, and was patiently waiting for the water to boil for the coffee.

I staggered out of the hut to get a breath of fresh air. It wasn't a good night's sleep, and I was glad when the dawn came. I thought the other members of my party would be glad to get moving from here.

When we'd had coffee and biscuits and cleared up inside the hut, I made my way, together with the bobijee, to seek out the chief and thank him for his hospitality in letting us stop for the night, even though it was an ordeal.

Climbing up the short ladder to reach the verandah, we were greeted by a regal figure – a tall warrior with all the trimmings of authority on display in the form of bamboo and ivory bangles.

The bobijee explained that we were here to say farewell, as we would be continuing on our journey towards Lunglei. At this we were told that the chief was away at the next village and wouldn't be back till sunset. The elder would explain our departure and wished us a safe trek.

Returning to our stopover camp, we met up with the other members of my party and found them all waiting to move on. Their packs were all ready, so soon we were away again through the village to find our trail.

On reaching the well worn trail, I thought the surroundings seemed familiar; we must have come this way on the outward journey. Now the foliage had partly grown over, making us go in single file.

As we moved along at a steady pace, the porters chanting a tribal song, while at the same time easing their loads to a less painful part of their shoulders, we made fairly good going.

After a time, I remarked to the bobijee that we must have covered about five miles, and should look out for a suitable clearing in which to camp for the night.

We came to our clearing at last. It was just the job – open ground, giving us a clear sighting all round.

In no time the tripod was erected for the coffee pot over the fire. While we waited, the bobijee was busy making chapattis, with the porters clearing the ground and making suitable hollows in which one could get comfortable for the night.

We did our usual two-hour watch rota. During my stint, apart from all the weird calls from the jungle, the time passed without incident. One of the sepoys took over at about four; it gave me a couple of hours' rest before dawn.

10th August, 1944

At dawn, coffee and biscuits was the order of the day; we wanted to get moving early while the air was cool. We would appreciate a rest when the heat became unbearable, and the sweat poured off us.

Before moving off, the usual camouflage job was done to the site. When we had finished, it would take a close look to detect any suspicion of its use. During the clearing up, I became aware of my legs feeling very painful. It was cramp from lying in a awkward position. I would have to keep going and wear it off.

We were now moving along in single file, the Lushai leading, with one of the sepoys by his side. They started the usual chanting, making jokes and laughing. The danger of Jap patrols had receded, since contacts with village scouts confirmed that they had moved out of this area.

We were now beginning to perspire. It was about midday and the heat was most oppressive. The sweat was pouring off, and the danger was that through lack of salt in our system, the sweat would irritate the skin and bring out sores.

At about four, a suitable clearing was reached in which we could bed down for the night. Soon we had a fire with the cooking utensils over it. While the water was heating up, the bobijee was preparing the chapattis, working to a procedure followed so many times before.

The night passed quietly, apart from queer animal cries. Some were screeching in turn, trying to outdo each other. There was occasionally an adventurous animal who got near our camp, but in most cases they just squealed and grunted before moving away.

I was awakened by the bobijee offering me a mug of coffee. The morning was quite clear; usually a heavy mist hung around. It must be getting drier.

It didn't take long to restore the site to how we found it, then we were off again. I reckoned it would take at least two days to reach Lunglei.

As our rations were very low, we'd have to rely on the wild fruit and vegetables that grew in abundance around us. We certainly wouldn't starve.

The trail we were on wound up and down in the undergrowth. Sometimes a clearing was reached, enabling us to stand to view ranges of hills stretching for miles out of sight. Down below us was Lunglei, on the crest of one of the ranges.

We met a native hunting party, all wearing the usual adornments of brightly coloured feathers, with bones hanging from any excess skin, not to mention the huge bows slung over their shoulders. During their conversation with our bobijee, he learnt that they hadn't heard of any Jap patrols in this area; they must be moving up towards Ijal and Kohima.

We made another stop. I'd thought perhaps we would make Lunglei today, but we were all feeling tired. Our limbs were getting very stiff. We would all be glad to have a good wash and rest; by the time the coffee and rice were ready, we were glad to bed down for the night.

Lunglei

11th August, 1944

From where we were standing, it seemed we'd have to make our way down the steep hillside into the jungle to find the trail leading to Lunglei, so the sooner we started the better.

The porters and sepoys were much more cheerful after sighting Lunglei. As we pushed on, chanting began and jokes were exchanged, with the faithful bobijee starting the chanting.

It was decided that we wouldn't stop for a rest. After sighting Lunglei, it would be better to get the journey over, then have a good rest.

Approaching Lunglei, I recognised various locations on the way. It was all so different up there; all the adjoining plots of land were cultivated, with corn or maize. Sometimes a green tobacco field stood out among them.

On arriving at our destination, we made for the dāk bungalow, and found smoke issuing from the chimney pots. As we drew near the verandah ladder, a couple of smartly dressed natives came forward to greet us.

We were informed that our party had been under observation for the last day or two. Scouts had tracked our progress most of the way, though we certainly hadn't seen a soul.

Inside the bungalow, everything was spotless – it was all swept clean, with the bamboo furniture shining with polish. Coming from the kitchen was an aroma of cooking; after all our sleeping rough and snatching what food we could, this was a complete turnaround.

I decided to rest for a while before reporting to the DC. The two sepoys, after a night's rest, would make their way back to Rangamati to report at their post at IOC and to my helpful Sergeant.

The porters would present their pay chits at the DC's and when paid would return to their villages, no doubt to tell their families of their travels through the Chin Hills.

After sorting out my belongings, I felt a bit groggy. I hoped it wasn't a touch of malaria. I took a dose of mepacrine and lay down for a while, feeling a bit shivery.

I must have dozed off for quite a while, for when I awoke it was half-light, and the sun had nearly sunk beyond the range of hills. I eased myself off the charpoy and had to steady myself by holding on to the bed rail.

I noticed there were plenty of mosquitoes buzzing round. I'd get the bobijee to spray the room. Staggering out to the verandah, I called out for him to bring coffee. Immediately, his head appeared from behind the kitchen shutter, to enquire about my health and to offer me coffee straightaway.

When the coffee arrived, the bobijee volunteered to go up to the DC's office to tell them of my fever. If there were any important messages to discuss, they'd have to come down here.

12th August, 1944

Last night, I went round to the bobijee's quarters to check that he had settled in. It appeared he was quite happy; he had all his belongings put away neatly in boxes, and was about to start cooking for the evening meal.

He could see I was sweating like the devil and shaking, and advised me to go back. He said he would come up later to see if I was all right, at the same time presenting me with a bottle of the local rice beer.

Returning to the dāk bungalow, I managed to find a clean shirt and shorts. After a cold water rub down, I felt a little better – especially with a few mugs of rice beer inside me. By the time I was ready for bed, the rice beer had taken over; what with a touch of the shakes as well, I was glad to creep under the mosquito net.

I had a rough night, with the sweat pouring off me. I was glad to see the light of dawn arriving. I slid off my charpoy and staggered on to the verandah to cool down. I still felt very weak, but then again, I was getting used to these bouts of fever.

Soon the bobijee came in with a mug of coffee and a cheerful, '*Tekai*, Sahib.' He wished me a good morning and asked about my health; he also made a nice chapatti, which went down very well.

After the meal, I dressed in shorts and shirt and presented myself at the DC's office to enquire about supplies for my next push down to the next stop at Demagri. I wondered if any of my old associates would still be there.

It was about ten when I arrived at the supply depot, only to find the DC was away on his rounds. The last time I was up here I had missed him, but I found the same Jemadar in charge, and he was pleased to see me again. He laughingly remarked that I looked a bit wacked!

During our conversation, he remarked that it was only a few days ago that Doug had been able to resume his journey down to base, as he had been held up here with his stomach trouble. Luckily it had eased off enough to allow him to resume his trek. I only wished I could have seen him, but I was out of luck.

I gave the Jemadar a list of my provisions, and after glancing through it he said they would be ready in the morning. I said, 'There's no hurry for a couple of days. I'll have to get rid of my weakness before I get moving on.'

He said what I wanted was a good dose of wallop, and produced two bottles of Rosa rum and a bottle of whisky. He told me he'd come down to the dāk bungalow to check on my health now and again.

So it was decided that I would have to rest for a while. The Jemadar said it would be foolish of me to attempt to stagger on; he would see that my porters were paid and given provisions for their journey back to their villages.

On my way back to the bungalow, I met a small unit of Gurkhas setting up camp, and to my surprise they were my friends from my previous stopover. They were all very pleased to see me again.

13th August, 1944

I had another rotten night, sweating and shivering. I'd have to lie low for the day, and rely on the bobijee. Lord knows what I'd have done without him; perhaps my Gurkha friends would enquire, as I wouldn't be passing through on my way out of the camp.

I remained on my charpoy most of the day; by late afternoon, I felt much stronger and decided to make a start in the morning if my recovery kept up. After all, this malaria would be in my system for quite a long time.

When I told the bobijee of my plans, he suggested I rested for another day; but as I felt stronger, I told him to arrange for the porters to report here with their loads at dawn ready to move on.

In the morning I found the porters all packed and ready to continue. By the time the bobijee and I had collected our kit it was about ten, so finally we made for the trail leading to Ridge Camp, where there was a dāk bungalow about eight miles away.

The two sepoys attached to us down here reported to HQ and were detailed to other duties. The reason was that the trail from here would be less dangerous, and the villages we encountered would be friendly.

The trail we were following was well used, for all the fallen branches and bracken had been piled on either side, giving travellers free movement. Hitherto in our travels we had to stumble and crouch to avoid the undergrowth.

As we were making good progress, we aimed to reach Ridge Camp by sunset. We plodded on in single file, one of the porters leading, me next, with the bobijee and porter bringing up the rear.

Before starting on this trail, we were warned of bamboo traps set by the locals against inquisitive and troublesome neighbours. These traps consisted of bamboo branches laid so that if trodden on they released a strung arrow directed at the spot of interference – with such force that it would be fatal.

The leading porter stopped at three places to point down on the trail to where these traps were visible – at the same time we gave the location a wide berth!

We made good progress, so I called a halt to rest and make coffee. By now it was midday and the sun was at its height. Down in the undergrowth the heat was oppressive, and the sweat was beginning to pour off us. The danger was that it might irritate the skin to form rashes.

It was about four when we finally reached Ridge Camp; I recognised the layout, as we had passed through it on the way up. The dāk bungalow could be seen overlooking the camp high on the hillside.

As we approached the bungalow, one or two figures could be seen coming to welcome us. I was pleased to meet some sepoys of the IOC who after initial greetings offered to help with the packs on the way up to the bungalow.

14th August, 1944

As we walked, the sepoys told me that the CO, Captain Bossack, had taken over one room in the bungalow, but as there was plenty of space, there was no need to get in each other's way.

On meeting the Captain, I found him quite a likeable chap. We shook hands, and he expressed pleasure in meeting me; he had heard about my work and seemed eager to hear my report at first hand.

After seeing my porters to their quarters, and the bobijee installed in a lean-to by the kitchen, I was shown to my room. My first joy was to have a cold shower and put on clean clothes.

To my surprise, on entering the small sitting-cum-dining room, I found a table laid out in the centre in readiness for the evening meal. Captain Bossack came forward to say he had arranged with his cook to prepare a chicken curry, and in the meantime, would I have a whisky?

During the meal we chatted about our travels. I told him about Doug and that I was waiting for a signal telling me who to report to on arrival back at Chittagong.

My host explained that he only obtained his commission because of his knowledge of most of the local languages – an asset which came in very useful. He mentioned too that he had under his command a small detachment of IOCs who were camped not far away from the dāk bungalow. If we had time, a visit to the Sergeant in charge would be most helpful.

By the time a few bottles had been emptied, we were well away, and it was past midnight when we eventually crawled under our mosquito nets and flopped on to our charpoys.

I dropped off and was wakened by the chatter of the IOC platoon getting ready to move on. The Captain hadn't mentioned it before to me; perhaps he thought that I already knew.

Before moving off, the Captain came to my room to say farewell. He'd thoroughly enjoyed our drinking session. He said he was making for Kohima. This was quite a distance away – about three hundred miles. After shaking hands, I wished him the best of luck.

I stood on the verandah to see them off. What did the future hold for them? Reports from natives who had visited the north said the conditions were very tough. The Japs were digging in and had foxholes everywhere; they'd have to be smoked out.

Looking down, I followed the soldiers as they wound their way along the trail. They sometimes went out of vision as the foliage became dense, then they emerged in a clearing. Soon the platoon was hardly visible. Turning back into the bungalow, I wondered if we'd ever meet again.

The bobijee came in from the kitchen to say the midday meal was ready – chapattis and rice. Afterwards I would rest while the heat of the day was at its worst, then I'd check some of the provisions later.

15th August, 1944

I was up late last night, collecting my pieces from various rooms to make a heap near the entrance. There wasn't much – enough for one porter; much of what I put aside would have to be left behind.

I was woken by the chattering of natives outside, and the cheerful face of the bobijee, who said he had coffee and rice ready.

After a shave and wash, and a mouthful of rice, the next job was to check how the porters were sorting out the loads. From the sounds of much jabbering and arguing, it was apparent that the small loads were being fought over.

At last we were ready. The village I was making for was called Thurchaudia. I believed there was a dāk bungalow there, though the village itself was quite small.

A small crowd of natives from Ridge Camp came to see us off. As we made for the undergrowth, we constantly waved back to them till they were out of sight. Then we entered the trail in single file, walking under thick foliage.

It soon became evident from the moisture dropping on to the trail that we were in for a slippery time. The porters were cursing as they tried to steady themselves by grasping branches, often breaking them off.

To add to our burdens, a school of small monkeys had gathered high up in the trees and began to issue guttural abuse down at us, spitting and squealing. The danger was that for any Jap patrols in the vicinity, they would be a give-away of our position.

As we pushed forward, the foliage became less dense. Gaps appeared to allow sunshine to dry up parts of the trail, making it much easier to gain footholds. The porters began chanting as they bent forward carrying their loads.

After about two hours I called a halt at a good clearing, and the porters nodded in agreement. I think they'd hoped I would stop soon; the slippery trail had been a struggle, and their legs must be painful.

Soon the fire was made, with the tripod and water pot over it. In the meantime, we all sprawled on the ground, resting. At the same time we hoped no nasty little insect would creep over us.

Overhead, a school of small baboons were making their presence known by loud shrieking and coarse grunts. As I lay on my back looking up at them, I became aware of how close they were to each other. Their heads were continually swivelling round in different directions, noting the movements of the others.

We didn't stop long as I wanted to push on to the next village. Signs of our brief stop were thoroughly removed, and the site left as we found it. Fallen branches covered any signs of habitation.

Thurchaudia

16th August, 1944

After about two hours along the trail, up ahead we could see an opening in the overhead foliage, through which the blue sky and sunshine gleamed. The porters shouted with delight, and on reaching the clearing, we were rewarded with the view of a range of hills that stretched away out of sight below us.

Smoke from village fires could be seen, making a haze over the foliage; they were hundreds of miles away. I wondered what tribes lived down there. Heartened by the sight of habitation, the porters began their chanting, at the same time moving on with sure steps. We were now following a trail that wound down the hillside, and would take at least two hours to reach level ground.

After much grunting and cursing, we eventually reached even ground. The Lushai said the village of Thurchaudia would take us another two hours to reach, and rather than stop for coffee, we decided to press on.

On approaching the village, we could see the dāk bungalow clearly. It was built on high ground, again having the advantage of clear views of visitors when they came near.

As we got close, figures could be seen running down to meet us. The first was Doug! The sight took me completely by surprise – I thought he would be miles away. After shaking hands and trying to find words to express our delight, it was all a bit emotional.

When I had at last seen the porters safely billeted, I entered the dāk bungalow with Doug, to find every possible detail had been worked on. My bedroom was spotless, and there were clean sheets and blankets on the charpoy. In the small dining room the table was set for the meal.

I said to Doug, 'How did you know I was coming?' He'd known a week ago; the jungle telegraph had my movements tracked from my first start – and I thought we were under threat from inquisitive raiders!

I must say Doug was much thinner; he would have to build himself up before thinking of moving on down. He insisted he felt well, but the sight of the chap said it all.

After a wild boar curry we both felt much better. There was so much to tell about our travels, though in Doug's case, it wasn't the distance covered, but the tribes he had encountered that mattered. At one village they had seemed a bit hostile; they could see he was sick, with only two porters as security. He must have felt helpless at times, but managed to avoid any nasty incidents.

We sat up late, planning our journey down the Karnaphuli River. We would be travelling down with the current. Sometimes this was very dangerous, as the river contained shallow stretches over rocky beds, making manoeuvring most difficult. It would be quite different from our battle coming up against the stream at the start of our venture.

17th August, 1944

In the morning, I could tell by Doug's appearance that he was in no state to travel. He looked awful, with a thin gaunt face, and a frail figure – not the old Doug he used to be when we first met.

I decided to put off our return for a few days. Doug maintained that he was strong enough, but I persuaded him to get stronger before setting off; after all, we were free agents.

The Lushai cook would be leaving us in the morning to return to his native village, so we'd have to manage for ourselves, unless the IOC could spare a sepoy to do for us.

This village was quite small, about a dozen bamboo huts scattered in a circle surrounding a much larger basha, which was obviously the headman's or chief's – I had yet to meet him.

After we'd had a snack of rice and biscuits, we were resting on our charpoys when a native came with the news that the chief, with a small party of elders, was on his way to meet us.

As Doug and I sat out on the verandah awaiting their arrival, we both wondered what to expect. We had quite a surprise when they came into view – the two leading natives wore army issue trousers, complete with shirts! Their black hair tresses were plaited to form a high bun, making the wearer look much taller, and they had the usual display of bone and ivory bangles hanging from every spare overlap of skin.

After exchanging handshakes and bowings, we invited them into the bungalow. The two in charge of the party seemed quite used to being invited into the white man's home, but the four others seemed a bit suspicious; their eyes darted from one object to another.

Eventually they got accustomed to the surroundings and settled down to listen to their leaders in conversation. They said they had heard of Doug's illness and had brought with them a potent drug that they used themselves to cure stomach pains.

I could see Doug was a bit dubious, but he did thank them for the thought, and said he would try some after a meal. I reminded him of the potion that cured my dysentery.

The broken English they used was barely recognisable, but considering the language problem, I think the conversation went off very well. They invited us to come down to the village at any time; we would always be welcome. During the conversation they said a lot of English sahibs came down as far as this to hunt.

As we tried by gestures and signs to give our interpretation of events, our guests were becoming more and more demonstrative, waving their arms, and making faces to prove their point.

Eventually, after a few mugs of the local brew and much bowing and toothless grins, they made their departure.

They had just departed when a runner arrived from Demagri. He had a note from Captain Scott asking us both to have tiffin at his basha, to form a small party and let our hair down.

I'm afraid I had to return a note to explain Doug's condition, hoping Captain Scott would understand; perhaps later, when Doug's condition was better, we could look forward to a get-together.

The rest of the day was spent in packing non-essentials, they would be taken down the trail by the IOC sepoys to the stores at Demagri to await our collection later.

I did wonder how Captain Scott knew of our whereabouts, but then the jungle drums were beating all the time. I did at one time ask myself why the establishing of a WOU was needed!

A sepoy arrived to say he was sent up here to cook and do for us during our stay; I expect Captain Scott had realised we could do with some help. By the evening Doug seemed a little better. Colour was getting back to his cheeks, and his movements were firmer.

I still reckoned it would take two days before he was able to walk steadily, so it was decided that we would just rest to enable him to regain his strength. We both spent the evening sitting out on the verandah, from where the range of hills could be seen stretching far out of sight down below; it was so quiet up there.

All we heard was the sound of animals making various weird calls trying to outdo each other. It became monotonous at times; when the loudest cries seemed to be just outside, we wondered if something was trying to find a way through the high fencing.

Our sepoy came to say he had built a fire some yards from the main gate; it would deter large animals from attempting to jump over or force their way in.

We both wondered what awaited us on finally reaching Chittagong. I knew we'd need medical attention, but was there a medical unit there now? Perhaps our liaison friends would have the answers.

Soon it was almost time to turn in. Clouds of mosquitoes were gathering, making a low droning sound as they moved around. Our sepoy had already put our nets around the charpoys – I hoped he hadn't trapped some inside!

We had quite an evening, chatting about our travels. We were looking forward to when we eventually reached base, and could rest and enjoy decent food. But we weren't looking forward to the journey down the fast-flowing Karnaphuli, with its deep waterfalls. It was bad enough struggling against it on the way up.

It was past midnight, and neither of us felt like turning in. We were quite comfortable in our bamboo chairs; the clouds of mosquitoes seemed to concentrate in one end of the building. At last we decided to turn in. I think Doug was feeling more settled.

18th August, 1944

I was awakened by the cheerful voice of the sepoy saying, 'Morning, Sahib,' as he set down a large mug of coffee. Looking out, I could see the cloudless sky heralding another hot day. After coffee I'd have to see how Doug was. I was hoping he'd had a restful night.

I found Doug sitting up drinking his coffee when I entered his room. He said he had slept quite well and felt much better, and would get up later to test his legs. Yesterday he couldn't stand for any length of time.

We both decided that it would be unwise to attempt to start off down the trail before he was much stronger. After all, nobody seemed to care where we were, so we could take our time.

In the afternoon, a runner arrived from Demagri, which was a mile or two away, and presented a note from Captain Scott inviting us to dinner for the following night. Doug insisted he could manage it, so I gladly accepted by a return note. I stated that Doug was still very weak, but was determined not to miss such an invitation.

So now he'd have to try to build his strength up for the mile or two stroll down to Demagri, but in our favour was the fact that most of the trail was well used and mostly even.

The rest of the day was been spent checking our inventory of belongings, choosing what to throw away and what to keep. I guessed the village natives would be up here scavenging all that we threw out.

During the sorting out of all the surplus clothing and utensils, our sepoy acquired quite a number of articles; in fact, I didn't think there would be much left for the natives.

I don't know how Captain Scott knew we had arrived up here, but then the natives had all our movements under close surveillance at all times. Their scouts were positioned at most strategic corners.

The light was fading by the time we had sorted all our bits and pieces and stacked them in different heaps. It was when the sepoy came to say he had a meal ready that we realised we'd done enough for the day.

During our meal of chapattis and rice, Doug seemed much better. He ate well and was quite talkative about our trip down to Demagri. He was sure that by tomorrow he'd have gained enough strength for the walk.

As we sat out on the verandah, I thought what an unusual situation we were in, surrounded by jungle and listening to the cries of numerous animals that filled the night air. Some were quite blood-curdling, but we had got quite accustomed to the din, so we both accepted it.

Our sepoy help finished clearing up and said goodnight before retiring to his room at the back. His gun was at his bedside ready for any emergency, so we felt fairly safe.

19th August, 1944

This morning we were up at dawn. The sepoy was singing away as he prepared a breakfast of fried eggs – it was quick, anyway.

Doug said he felt much better – a bit weak in the legs, but hoped they would get their circulation back as we progressed along the trail. By ten we were both ready to stagger down the hillside. We decided to leave the sepoy to look after the bungalow; I guessed it would be dusk before we arrived back.

As we set off, a few natives stood by watching us. I expect they were curious about where we were going. They hadn't seen us together before, and it was a surprise to see Doug out and about.

By now the sun had risen overhead. Although there was some cover provided by overhanging foliage, we were beginning to sweat. Doug said he was all right; he certainly looked better.

It wasn't long before Demagri came in sight, with the dāk bungalow clearly visible on the approach. In a short time we were at the steps leading up to the verandah.

There seemed to be a large encampment nearby, judging from the sound of a babble of many voices, and going round the back we discovered a large encampment of military personnel.

On making enquiries, we learned that they were a platoon of IOCs on their way to Ijal under the command of a Major Clarke.

It was mid-morning when the Major arrived at our bungalow. He was a tall man, looking every bit the soldier who had seen many postings. Dressed in shorts and an open shirt, with fair hair and sporting a moustache, he came forward to greet us both quite informally, and said that he had heard of the two BORs doing a good job in maintaining observer posts in northern Lushai.

After showing him his room and the rest of the bungalow we sat down with him to a meal of chapattis and rice, during which he told us of the difficult times they had experienced in battling against the strong flowing waters of the Karnaphuli River. It had taken them nearly three weeks, sleeping rough on the river banks, to do the journey.

We told him we'd been through the same experience – an exhausting battle against the elements.

We all retired to our charpoys for the afternoon; by now the sun was at its hottest, making us all perspire. The sweat saturated our clothes.

After we'd had a rest and wash, we decided to have an evening meal together, inviting Captain Scott – perhaps he could bring a bottle of whisky.

It was such a relief to stretch out on our charpoys; the heat was becoming unbearable. We hoped to cool off before our get-together tonight.

20th August, 1944

We had a grand party last night. Four IOC liaison officers arrived, including Scott, a couple of Sikhs and Pathan officers.

We had plenty of drinks. During the introductions and swapping of information about what one's job involved, they wondered what the hell two BORs were doing up in this region.

It was past midnight when the party split up; the Rosa rum and whisky had loosened all barriers of rank. Being stuck up here in this godforsaken jungle we all thought it was great to converse in English.

Doug didn't drink much, which was quite sensible – he felt a bit tottery even without it. I thought Major Clarke might have gone easy on the drink, as he was off again first thing in the morning, but I suppose he could take it; he must have been well used to these parties. All was quiet, but within a short time there would be the babble of the IOC packing their gear to move on towards Ijal.

Just as dawn was breaking, the shrill voices of the sepoys as they were assembling to move off woke me. I scrambled off the charpoy to watch their departure from the verandah and caught a wave from Major Clarke as he led the platoon down the trail and slowly out of sight.

As I stood there, Doug came out of his room to join me. He spoke quite cheerfully, saying he felt much better and was ready for a good meal. After breakfast, we decided to check our supplies prior to loading them into the canoes in the morning – assuming Doug was fit enough to travel.

In the afternoon Captain Scott came up to say farewell, and to wish us a safe journey, at the same time knocking back a large rum. He seemed quite fit after last night's binge.

I made a chit out to give to our Lushai cook so that he could collect his pay from the DC at Lunglei. I expect he went up there like a shot!

Neither of us was looking forward to negotiating the swirling Karnaphuli River. There were so many boulders on the river bed, some breaking the surface, that we'd have to keep a sharp eye ahead as we rode with the fast current.

We checked all our gear, and every room in case we had left any of our belongings. As we went from room to room, memories came back of different incidents that had occurred during our stay, and we were sorry to leave in a way.

It was our last evening at this dāk bungalow. It had provided us with the rest we both needed, especially Doug, who seemed his old self. We were all ready to move off in the morning, to leave these hills and jungles that had given us many experiences, some in our favour, but many detrimental to our mission up here.

The bobijee had prepared a good meal for our last supper – a large chapatti, together with portions of chicken, and of course, a bottle of the local beer!

21st August, 1944

This was the day. I woke up early to find the morning sun streaming through the woven laps of the bamboo walls. We thanked our lucky stars the monsoons were over.

We had a breakfast of coffee and biscuits, and then went down to check the canoes. These were tethered in an inlet away from the river. On arrival, we found a little *chiko* sitting on the bank, cheerfully waving his arm and saying, '*Tekai*, Sahib!' as if to say, 'I've looked after them!'

By this time, quite a crowd had gathered to see us off; most of the village were jabbering away, making jokes and laughing, while Doug and I checked the loading.

In the first canoe was our guide and companion. I came second, taking a rear seat behind a cheerful Lushai boatman who had travelled up and down the Karnaphuli River for many years. He knew all the lanes in which to steer, for clearing the boulders and negotiating the waterfalls.

Doug brought up the rear; he had to have an experienced boatman with him. Before setting off, it was agreed that we would keep as close a possible, keeping a sharp watch on each other's canoes, to help in case of trouble.

All was ready at about ten. When we were in position, we waved to all the villagers and pushed off from the bank making our way out of the inlet into the mainstream.

As we neared the river we could hear the roar of the fast-flowing waters. We could also see thick mist rising halfway up the surrounding trees. For a while we had a quiet progress, just paddling along, admiring the colours of all the different trees that overhung us – not to mention the hordes of monkeys following our movements and scrambling quite close to us.

Soon we came to the main river. We had arranged beforehand that we would all keep as close to the bank as possible, thus trying to avoid the strength of the centre.

The main difficulty was keeping clear of the huge boulders lying near the surface. We were twisting and turning, and my Lushai boatman was at all times straining and doing his utmost to keep us afloat.

Sometimes, I lost sight of the leading canoe – the spray and mist obscured our vision. Looking back, I could just see the outline of Doug's boat; he too was covered in the heavy spray.

Before we started off, we had decided that a village called Chawlong would be our first stop, where we could rest and check our equipment. We were told that a bungalow overlooked the village.

We must have travelled in this dangerous current for at least two hours, so we were nearing Chawlong. In the leading canoe, the native suddenly waved his paddle and pointed towards the bank to signify we were nearly there.

22nd August, 1944

By the time we had reached the village, we were whacked. On the banks of the inlet were crowds of inquisitive people, while at the landing place was a group of stalwart natives ready to help.

After helping us ashore, they transferred our loads to the bank, amid chattering and laughter from children, who were quite taken by the sight of white strangers; they were darting about trying to help in any way they could.

When the natives had allocated loads to suit each other, we set off to climb the steep bank leading to the village, which we had to pass through to reach the dāk bungalow.

As we trudged through the village, many enquiring faces were turned in our direction, some friendly, others looking quite ferocious, depending on what experience they had of foreigners. Arriving at the bungalow, we found our Lushai cook had bought or pinched a nice cockerel; judging by its smell while cooking, it would be the basis of a nice curry.

The rooms were the same as in other bungalows. I would say they were all built to the same design, with an outside lean-to for a kitchen, and set well above the ground. Three foot sturdy logs giving enough clearance to deny any inquisitive animals access.

All the rooms were spotlessly clean, so after a nice chicken curry and a mug or two of the rice beer, we were soon stretched out on our charpoys under our protective mosquito nets. We'd previously arranged with the chief to provide two trustworthy guards to keep an eye on our kit.

The chatter and shrieks of children heralded the dawn. On awaking, I felt very stiff all over. I stretched and did a few exercises, but the effort seemed to aggravate the stiffness. I would have to take things easy – time would tell.

Doug came into my room to say he'd had a good night, and he asked how I felt. After telling him I felt as stiff as a poker, he too said his joints were terribly painful; perhaps as we got moving the stiffness would ease off.

After a light breakfast, we made preparations to get started again. We checked all the rooms, in case we'd left anything behind, shook the hands of our native helpers, and made our way down to the inlet where our transport should be waiting.

On arrival at the river bank, we were surprised to find no canoes, but two kistis waiting. At least we would now travel in comfort with plenty of room.

Both boats were loaded with our equipment, waiting for us to arrange who was to take the first. After a short discussion, Doug said, 'You go.' As I stepped into the *kisti*, I met the grinning face of the native who had the responsibility of guiding and propelling the boat down the fast and dangerous river.

His job was to steer the boat by means of a long pole, at the same time running backwards and forward on the roof which covered the *kisti*.

23rd August, 1944

Inside the *kisti* I had plenty of room; most of our equipment was distributed out to make the weight even. I had plenty of space to stretch out, and layers of blankets had been put down to make the journey as comfortable as possible. A Primus stove and cooking utensils were arranged on a marble base.

It would take at least four days to reach Chittagong, making stops when possible on the river bank, or if we were lucky at a friendly village.

I had a touch of the shakes and shivers at that moment, and took a mepacrine tablet, hoping it would bring the fever down.

We were progressing quite nicely, keeping to the centre, thus avoiding the boulders that jutted out from the bank; they could easily tear a hole in the bamboo built *kisti*.

Doug's *kisti* was doing well, keeping just behind us. As the natives ran backwards and forwards on the bamboo roofs, they called out to each other, making remarks and laughing. So far the journey was without incident.

As we made our way along, schools of small monkeys followed us, leaping from bough to bough at each side of the river. Their shrill chatter disturbed all the birds and other inhabitants of the jungle.

After some time my boatman began looking for a suitable inlet to pull into. The sun was high above, so it was about midday; the heat was oppressive, and sweat was pouring down our bodies. We'd have to rub in cream to avoid getting rashes.

Ahead we could see quite a large gathering of natives. As we got closer, it was apparent that they were expecting us; on the bank, numbers of them had collected in small groups, jabbering away and pointing in our direction.

As we got near, it became evident that they were friendly – they were all smiling and laughing, with the children dancing round and round. Warriors waded waist-high to pull our kistis in to the bank.

On land, while the boatmen were explaining our needs to the elders, the children became most interested in us, staring up at us. I suppose they didn't see many white people; I must say they all seemed quite friendly.

Our boatmen explained that the village had been warned of our coming a couple of days ago, so they'd had plenty of time to prepare.

After unloading our kit on to the bank, the crew made the kistis secure under a clump of trees, out of sight, while natives began to sort out who should carry what to the village.

About half a mile along a narrow track we came to a cluster of bamboo huts forming a circle around a large basha – the usual layout in all the villages. I suppose it enabled the chief to stand out on his verandah and survey all, keeping an eye those who tended to make trouble.

24th August, 1944

On reaching the chief's basha, we were met by a small gathering of the elders, all attired in their different ornaments of office, with huge rings of ivory hanging from ears, nose, lips, and any surplus flesh.

These, and all the coloured painting on their bodies, made them all look very awesome when first seen and approached; but once you were accepted, you had a friend for life.

Inside the basha, like others, the light was very dim. You had to peer deeply into the half-light to get used to it. There was the usual seating arranged at one end, while those of no importance had to squat down on the sagging bamboo floor.

Having got used to the dim light, we could see that there were many elders seated, all displaying rings and ornaments according to their rank. At the centre sat the chief. He too was adorned with impressive rings and plumage. As we approached, his hand was extended, and he bade us a hearty welcome in clear English! We learnt later that a little English was used when hunting parties came this way.

As Doug and I got accustomed to the light, we saw shrunken heads displayed on small ledges at about four feet off the ground. These relics of headhunting no longer caused us any bother – even though the looks of some warriors suggested it was still carried on!

Sitting by the side of the chief, we could see he would be about thirtyish. I suppose he would have been the late chief's son; anyway, he seemed quite friendly, giving a smile in our direction while chatting to his advisers.

Meanwhile, women began to bring in huge earthenware pots of curry and rice, together with vegetables and roasted wildfowl. Although I still felt a bit shaky, I had to eat some.

I managed to eat a little portion of rice and jungle chicken, but still felt a bit queasy – the babble of the natives and the heat made me feel ill. Doug could see the effect it was having on me, and he made signs that we'd both had a good evening, but as I felt a bit ill, we would like to retire to the basha the chief had provided for the night.

Two warriors escorted us along the trail to our basha, which was quite a sturdy bamboo hut. When they had seen us inside they made bowing signs, holding their hands together, and melted away into the darkness.

As we entered, the dim light from an oil lamp gave us a hint of all the mod cons: an old worn mesh straw mat lay on the floor, covered in filth, while side by side were two charpoys with the webbing torn and sagging.

Our kit had been deposited in a heap in the corner, so all we had to do was sort out some clothing to put on the charpoys, to make them as comfortable as possible.

As we tried to cover the charpoys with different articles of clothing, it became evident that there was a horrible stench everywhere; we couldn't sleep in this.

As I wondered how to get rid of the stink, I had the brainwave of using the smoke from my home-made cigars. Doug didn't smoke, so I had to sit on the edge of my charpoy and puff away till the stink was less.

At last we managed to drop off to sleep, only to be woken by a number of rats scurrying over the bamboo floor, shrieking amongst the stench as they searched for food.

Jumping out of our charpoys, we grabbed whatever we could lay our hands on and proceeded to chase the blasted rats out, taking quite a time to get rid of the last. Now we knew where the awful stench came from.

We both were exhausted by the time the hut was clear – the whole episode must have taken some time. It was no good getting back on our charpoys as we could see the light of dawn rising above the ranges of hills below. The quicker we got out of this stink the better.

25th August, 1944

By the time we had repacked our bags the sun was beginning to rise. A few natives passed by on their way down to the village, grunting a morning's greetings. I wondered what conditions they slept in…

Making our way down to the village, our first thought was to get coffee and something to eat.

On arrival at the chief's basha, we found quite a lot of natives about, and by signs and waving our hands we conveyed to them that we wanted coffee and chapatti or rice.

While we were trying to make them understand, a tall native came forward and in broken English suggested that he understood and that we should follow him. It became apparent he was an authority in his own right, for natives bowed as he passed; perhaps our luck had changed.

As he led us towards his basha, in halting English he explained how long ago he helped the hunting parties of the Raj to flush out tigers, and the exciting events that followed. 'They were good times, Sahib!' he said.

When we reached his basha, it was evident that he must have held quite a good position. His home was in a large compound set aside from the maze of small huts. It looked like and could have been built on the same pattern as our dāk government bungalows.

As we approached, the main door opened to reveal young women waving to our new friend. Laughing, he responded and turned to us to explain that they were his sisters.

Climbing the few steps to the verandah, we were ushered into quite a large room. The bamboo mesh floor was spotlessly clean and was covered by the skins of different animals. Tables and chairs of bamboo were placed at different positions, making the whole place look inviting.

Three smiling young women came forward, giggling, at the same time casting enquiring looks at their brother, who introduced them one by one; but as he did so, it was very difficult for us to understand his words.

Indicating that we should sit down, the young women fetched bowls of fruit, together with rice and chapattis, placing them on the table before us.

During the meal we tried to make our new friend understand what a terrible night we'd had, with the stink and rats. After much gesticulating and waving of hands, we got our message across and understood he would tell the chief.

By this time, the sun was overhead. It was midday, and with no cloud, the heat was becoming oppressive and intense. The only answer was to rest in the shade and take things easy.

It was evident that we couldn't move from the village till morning, so after enquiring from our friend where to find a night's lodging, we were immediately offered a large room at the rear of his basha.

Thanking him, we made our way to the chief's basha to inform him of our plans, and found him sitting outside on the verandah. He seemed quite pleased to see us, clapping his hands for the women to bring coffee and chapattis.

We didn't mention the terrible night's episode. We thought it best to keep quiet; the quicker we got away the better. During coffee, we made him understand that we would be off at dawn.

We were now on the last lap of our mission, and were only a day or two from Chittagong. We wondered what reception would be waiting there at the jetty.

We sat out on the verandah at our friend's basha for the rest of the afternoon, making plans for our last few days travelling on the Karnaphuli River. At least we'd be going with the tide, not battling against it.

After coffee and fruit, we decided to make our way down to the jetty which we would be starting from in the morning. On arrival, we found the *kisti* by a small inlet, with two natives busily checking it over.

By making signs, we made them understand that we were the two sahibs they were to look after, as well as maintaining the kistis, while we made the trip to Chittagong.

Bowing, and grinning all the time, they helped us aboard and showed us the space set aside under the bamboo roof. They had laid out matting, and had left plenty of room for blankets on which we could rest or sleep.

In the centre an earthenware base was laid in which a stove could be lit to do the cooking; it was all very cosy, and spacious.

Making them understand that we would arrive at dawn to start off, we bade them farewell and made our way back to our friend's basha.

27th August, 1944

On arrival at the basha, we were greeted with all the attention possible. A table was laid out with numerous dishes of fruit and cooked pastries – chapattis and small bran cakes.

I remarked, what a difference it was to the reception we had received at our arrival last night! If only we had made the acquaintance of this chap, we could have made this stop on the river bank much more pleasurable.

During the meal we tried to converse in English; the girls were in fits of laughter at our attempts to speak their language, though I must say their English was quite passable. Like their brother, they had learned from hunting parties in the past.

Our host got quite excitable when speaking of those days. He said everybody seemed happy then. There was plenty of food, fires were lit at dusk and dances were held, with the chanting of native ditties going on throughout the night.

Now it was a tight security zone, with scouts posted to keep an eye on Jap movements; though, as he said, none of them had been reported in this area.

They were grateful that our observation posts were in action, spread over their part of Lushai. Many believed that the presence of these posts kept keep the Japs away! Little did they know the truth.

We told our friend that although we were moving back to Chittagong, we had left behind members of the Indian

Observer Corps (IOC) in charge, who would do their utmost to help the villagers in any way.

On hearing this, our friend was reassured, and said he would spread the news among surrounding villages.

We spent quite an enjoyable evening, and our host made us both welcome. What a difference from our previous night's ordeal! It was quite late when the time came to get some rest, and we were shown to our room at the rear of the basha.

A bamboo lean-to, it was quite roomy, with the flooring covered by bamboo matting. There were two charpoys placed at each end, leaving plenty of room to move.

Doug and I were most impressed. Everything was spotless – at last we would have a good night's rest. It was past midnight when we at last crawled under our mosquito nets, and we were soon asleep.

We were woken at dawn by a native bringing in coffee. He wore a cheerful grin and was muttering some welcome we couldn't understand, but he meant well. He also placed a large bowl of water and a towel on one of the tables.

After a wash and shave, we wandered round to the front of the basha to explore and meet people, only to find most of the natives were up and moving about.

On looking up to the verandah we saw our friend beckoning us to come up and have breakfast. Soon we were tucking into fried eggs and rice.

28th August, 1944

During breakfast our friend said he'd had all our kit taken down to the jetty where our *kisti* waited. All we had to do was say goodbye and get down there.

We both found it hard to express our thanks for all he had done; without his help we would have been lost. In reply, he said it was all he could do to repay all the good treatment he had received from the sahibs for helping in the hunting parties.

They were the good days, he said, they were all paid well, and looked after – not like now, with the Japs patrolling and pillaging their villages. That was why the villagers were grateful for our lookout posts, and glad that they would still be in operation when we returned to HQ.

Now it was time to make our farewells. We shook hands with all our new friends, while the children were dancing and laughing around. We both came to the conclusion that this was a most memorable moment that would stay with us for quite a time.

Stepping into the *kisti*, we looked back at all the villagers waving – a very nice gesture from people who until recently were a headhunting tribe.

At last we were moving. The chap on the bamboo roof propelled the *kisti* by means of a long bamboo pole, running backwards and forwards the length of the boat, finding a suitable place on the river bed from which to push and guide the craft.

We were now moving to the centre of the river where the strong current would carry us with it – not the battle we had against it on our outward trip.

Doug and I made ourselves comfortable, arranging the blankets at either end of the deck space, leaving plenty of room in the centre for meals or stretching out.

We seemed to be moving quite smoothly. As both ends of the boat were open, we could watch the jungle foliage slipping by, sometimes harbouring schools of monkeys screaming and chattering as they followed us.

At noon we pulled into the bank to give the boatmen a rest and to have a meal. We collected firewood, and soon had a fire going complete with the pot over for the tea.

While drinking it, rice was being cooked for our midday meal.

After the meal, the heat and lush soft grass made us feel drowsy, and it must have been quite an hour before we stirred ourselves to proceed on our journey.

As we climbed into the *kisti*, the talk was that it would be only about another day or so before the jetty at Chittagong was reached.

Chittagong

29th August, 1944

As we were being carried by the fast current in the centre of the river, it became evident that we'd only have to stop for one other night before reaching Chittagong. I wondered if there would be anybody expecting us.

Dusk was falling as we put the *kisti* against a jetty to spend our last night on the river. Now that our journey was nearly over, memories of incidents in our travels came to mind – of the ferocious headhunters we had encountered and of the filthy conditions we had to endure.

We went through the same procedure. We collected wood for the fire, and soon had the rice and coffee on. We made suitable hollows in the grass in which to lay our blankets down, while the boatmen made plans to keep watch during the night.

The light was going fast; soon we were relying on the firelight to move about. We squatted round the fire, scooping up the rice with our fingers and trying to break the issue biscuits.

One of the boatmen strummed a weird monotonous Indian tune on a instrument that looked hand-made – still, the tunes seemed to go with it. What with the swarms of mosquitoes, the howling of wild dogs, and the deep-throated croak of the bullfrogs, we just covered ourselves up and tried to sleep.

During the night I woke up and peered about. The fire was well away and the flames lit up quite a large area. It was being attended by one of the boatmen, who was crouched down nearby. Watching him, it was difficult to make out whether he was awake or asleep.

Dawn arrived with the chorus of birds and cries from the nearby jungle. Doug was awake and moving about. I asked him if he'd slept all right, and received the reply that he'd had a good night.

Coffee and rice over, we soon had our gear packed into the *kisti*, and our campsite cleaned. All was now ready for our last river journey to Chittagong.

At last, as we rounded a bend in the river, the jetty came in sight. Figures could be seen waving to us, and as we pulled in we were welcomed by a sergeant and corporal, who made remarks about our appearance – all in good humour.

They had orders to take us straight to a field hospital. Before starting, I asked the Sergeant to give the boatmen directions as to where they could collect their pay. He said that it had been arranged; so after bidding them farewell, we set off for the field hospital.

On arrival at the hospital, we were separated and taken to different wings. I found myself put in a tent apart from the main building. It was quite a large one, containing four beds; one was prepared and it was for me.

I was shown the toilets and the washing area, and told to clean myself before having a meal. A fresh set of clothing was on its way.

After a soaking in the bath, and putting on clean clothes, I returned to my tent.

30th August, 1944

Later I was taken to the dining hall and given my first good meal for many months, during which time I met up with Doug. He had gone through the same treatment as myself. We exchanged notes and hoped to meet again in the morning.

Returning to my tent, I was surprised to find a set of headphones by the bed. When I put them on, I was listening to *London Calling*!

I lay there for hours, soaking up the voices and music – the orderly came to check if I was all right. It must have been midnight when I eventually disconnected the headphones.

The next morning, on putting on the headphones, I heard the announcement that Paris had been liberated. The whole hospital was excited; those who were off duty were glued to the wireless, hanging on to every word.

After breakfast, I was taken to the MO for an examination. I weighed eight and a half stone! My bones were sticking through in many places. I was asked how many times I had doses of malaria, and the amazement on their faces when being told about a dozen was obvious.

I told them of my dose of dysentery and how I'd been wasting away, with blood and matter pouring out of my rear. I told how the chief, on hearing of my sickness, came up to my basha to see if he could help at nearly midnight, and immediately fetched another native to go with him down into the jungle. I said they were looking for the bark of a tree that when soaked, emitted a fluid that stopped my insides bleeding.

They were all most interested, asking if I knew the name of the tree; but of course, at the time I was too far gone to take any notes.

trying to sell their wares, cheerfully retiring when no sale was made.

As would take about six hours to complete the journey, I reckoned there would be many more stops. By now the air had become much cooler, and we were beginning to pass through light wisps of cloud as we wound our way up the narrow track, round and round the hillside.

Before reaching Darjeeling, we made three more stops at small platforms, to be greeted by cha wallahs trying to sell their wares and light refreshments.

We could see the station as the track levelled out, and there were no other trains in sight. I wondered if ours was the only train in operation. By the time we had stopped, we'd both pulled on our jerseys – there was a vast difference in temperature.

A jeep was parked nearby, from which a corporal driver stepped out to greet us. He stowed our kit in the rear, at the same time asking numerous questions. He had heard from different sources of the two BORs coming up here after living rough.

He explained that we were to be billeted at a nice hotel – we'd soon get there, with the jeep negotiating the narrow streets, scattering pedestrians out of the way.

Arriving at the hotel, we were welcomed by the proprietor, who seemed quite a nice chap. He was grinning from ear to ear, at the same time giving orders to a porter to carry our kit in.

We were allocated adjoining bedrooms, which was quite a relief, as I couldn't see us cramped together. From my window I had marvellous views of distant mountains and valleys. Our hotel seemed to have been built on the hillside before the others.

Tea plantations could be seen stretching over the hillside far out of sight. We would have to ask for transport to enable us to explore.

Meanwhile, our main aim is to gain strength. We were still both a bit shaky; it would take a few days to regain our will to exert ourselves. However, I must say we both felt much stronger after our rest.

One morning I woke early, and on looking out to the mountains, could see quite clearly the top of Everest, the tip visible far above the clouds. The sighting only lasted a few minutes before clouds obscured the view.

On another day, while wandering through the bazaar, we came across some donkeys for hire. Soon we were riding down narrow tracks through the plantations, hanging on for dear life, swaying and bumping as the donkeys trotted along.

By the time we'd had our money's worth, we both felt shaken up. We'd have to rest to regain strength.

After twelve days we received a message to report to the MO for a check-up. The result was that we were both assessed fit to travel. I was being posted to Karachi to a CRO (Civilian Repair Organisation) while Doug was to report back at Chittagong Hospital.

I wrote to Audrey and packed my kit ready to go down to Chittagong with Doug. There we would part – I believe he had to undergo further examinations of his stomach.

1st October, 1944

On returning to Chittagong, I went with Doug to the hospital to make our farewells. We both wanted to make sure we'd meet again and we exchanged addresses. I stood there and watched as he disappeared into the main entrance – and that was that.

Making my way to the station, I was fortunate in only waiting an hour before a train en route to Karachi arrived. It took all three days for the journey; we stopped at nearly every station, but it did enable me to stretch my legs and get something to eat.

Arriving at Karachi station, I left my kitbag in charge of a porter, and enquired where the CRO in the town was. The chap in the ticket office was most helpful; he phoned my destination, telling them I had arrived.

Very soon a jeep drew up, with the driver saying I was expected, and I was to be taken to my billet. On the way, he said the large house we were making for was situated on the foreshore. There were only four others there, with plenty of room, and a cha wallah to look after us.

What a house! It was more like a palace. There were huge windowless rooms, and the charpoys were spaced well apart with mosquito nets over them.

During conversation with the other inmates, it became evident that we were all prey to tropical illnesses, mainly malaria – and this was a camp in which to rest until a place could be found for us en route for home.

While waiting for the next move, we often sat on the beach, whiling away the time. We used to chase shore crabs, which are visible at a distance, but bury themselves out of sight in the sand when approached.

One day I was taken into Karachi to report to CRO and the CO. On meeting us, he said this would be only a stop for us while we waited for a ship home.

The depot was quite roomy. There were about half a dozen lifts, all in use, operated by mechanics of the Indian Air Force. They were all doing a good job and all seemed very busy.

As I was waiting for further movement, no responsibility was given me. I went about the workshop discovering each mechanic's talents and discussing movements.

After about a fortnight, the CO called me up to his office to inform me that he had received a signal to release me for embarkation. I would go to Bombay and board a hospital ship.

I wrote to Audrey saying I was on my way home, and didn't know how long it would take, but would keep in touch.

The big day arrived. I was told to make my way to Bombay and report to a hospital ship en route for home. We passed through the Suez Canal and eventually docked at Southampton. I was told to report to Northallerton for further hospital treatment and I spent a fortnight having some more tests. Then I was discharged, and made my way home at last.